The Canadian Remote Sensing Contribution to Understanding Global Change

The Canadian Remote Sensing Contribution to Understanding Global Change

edited by
Ellsworth LeDrew, Murray Strome, Frank Hegyi

1995

Department of Geography Publication Series, No. 38,
University of Waterloo

Publication Sponsored by the Institute for Space and Terrestrial Science

Department of Geography Publication Series

Series Editor   Bruce Mitchell
Editorial Assistant   Kate Evans
Cover Design   Ellsworth LeDrew
Printing   Graphic Services
                         University of Waterloo

ISBN # 0-921083-45-9

Canadian Cataloguing in Publication Data

Main entry under title:

The Canadian remote sensing contribution to
  understanding global change

(Department of Geography publication series ; 38)
Includes bibliographical references.
ISBN 0-921083-45-9

1. Environmental monitoring - Remote sensing.
2. Remote sensing - Canada. I. LeDrew, Ellsworth
Frank. II. Hegyi, F. (Frank). III. Strome, M.M.
(Murray M.). IV. University of Waterloo, Department
of Geography. V. Title. VI. Series.

TD193.C3C3 1992   363.7'063'028   C92-095533-9

 Printed on Recycled Paper

Cover Images

The cover images are colour coded mappings of the changes of sea ice concentration and snow water equivalent for the Northern Hemisphere from February (typically the month of maximum ice extent) to September (typically the month of minimum ice extent). The sea ice is coded in colours representing ice concentration from zero (blue) to 100% (red) using the AES/ISTS sea ice algorithm provided by Dr. I. Rubenstein. The snow water equivalent algorithm was developed and provided by Dr. B. Goodison and Ms. A. Walker of the Atmospheric Environment Service of Environment Canada and values are represented in shades of grey. The data are derived from the passive microwave signals received by the Special Sensor Microwave Imager (SSM/I) on the Defence Meteorological Satellite Program satellite and provided by the National Snow and Ice Data Centre at the University of Colorado.

ACKNOWLEDGMENTS

The concept for this book arose out of discussions by the Global Change Committee of the Canadian Advisory Council on Remote Sensing (CACRS). The members of that Committee share in the contribution towards the final product. They are:

Dr. H. French, Department of Geography, University of Ottawa
Dr. B. Goodison, Canadian Climate Centre, Atmospheric Environment Service
Mr. F. Hegyi, Ferrihill Technologies Ltd.
Dr. E. LeDrew, Department of Geography, University of Waterloo
Dr. T. Raab, Canadian Astronautics Ltd.
Dr. A. Royer, CARTEL, University of Sherbrooke
Dr. M. Strome, Forestry Canada, Petawawa National Forestry Institute
Ms. D. Thompson, Intera Technologies Ltd.
Mr. A. Turner, Canadian Wildlife Service, Environment Canada
Mr. J. Whiting, Saskatchewan Research Council, Environment Branch

Some of the chapters were invited presentations at the International Society for Photogrammetry and Remote Sensing (ISPRS), Commission 7, Symposium on Global And Environmental Monitoring held at Victoria, B.C. in September of 1990. It was chaired by Mr. F. Hegyi. This book is in many ways a development from that symposium.

We wish to acknowledge with gratitude the following who have contributed to the technical editing of this book: Kathleen Lamothe, Karen Beasely, Lisa Webber and Greg McDermid.

Financial support for the publication of this book has been provided by the Environmental Change Theme of the Institute for Space and Terrestrial Science, funded by the Province of Ontario through the Centre of Excellence Program.

Additional acknowledgements for individual chapters are as follows:

Chapter 2
The provision of Figure 2.1 by NASA is gratefully acknowledged.

Chapter 3
Funding for the research projects outlined in this paper have been provided by the Ontario Ministry of the Environment. Surface water quality parameters have been obtained from that ministry as well as the Ontario Ministry of Natural Resources. None of the statements expressed here are attributable to or necessarily reflect the views of those ministries. We would particularly like to express our appreciation to the assistance provided us by W. (Bill) Keller, Sudbury, M.O.E.

Chapter 4
The research for this chapter was supported by the Institute for Space and Terrestrial Science and by NSERC. The provision of the colour coded sea ice images by D. Cavalieri is gratefully acknowledged.

Chapter 7
I would like to acknowledge the inputs of my colleagues at CCRS who helped to put this chapter together including critically reviewing the manuscript, supplying some of the illustrative material, and preparing the final text. In particular, I would like to acknowledge the efforts of B. Brisco, J. Cihlar, C. Prevost, M. Trindade, C. Langham, and C. Neveu.

Chapter 8
The authors wish to acknowledge the constructive comments of a

number of colleagues. These include Drs. F. Ahern, J. Cihlar and K. Raney and Mr. C. Prevost of CCRS, and Mr. A.M. Turner of Environment Canada.

Chapter 9
The constructive comments of Mr. Gerry Lee of the Canadian Wildlife Service have aided the accuracy and clarity of this document and are greatly appreciated.

Chapter 11
This paper is based on the preliminary Experiment Plan and input from two workshops held in 1988 (New Hampshire) and 1990 (Ottawa). All the attending scientists contributed material and ideas. Revisions of the plan and preparation of the document was carried out by the BOREAS Science Steering Committee (SSC): Piers Sellers (Chairman and Editor), Josef Cihlar, Michael Apps, Barry Goodison, Bob Harriss, Don Leckie, Ellsworth LeDrew, Pam Matson and Steve Running. Significant contributions were also made by Forrest Hall, Barry Rock, Don Strebel and Diane Wickland.

Chapter 14
The authors acknowledge the assistance of DonnaLee Desaulniers who wrote the section on WINDII, and the help and encouragement of CAL, CCRS, CSA and Spar Aerospace.

Chapter 16
The authors would like to express their thanks to Mr. Russell Koffler of NOAA and Dr. Vince Solmonson of NASA for their assistance in obtaining the latest available information on the Eos Program and EosDIS in particular. They would also like to thank Dr. Josef Cihlar for providing information on the International Geosphere-Biosphere Data and Information System.

TABLE OF CONTENTS

CHAPTER 11   237
BOREAS (BOREAL ECOSYSTEMS-ATMOSPHERE STUDY): GLOBAL CHANGE AND BIOSPHERE INTERACTIONS IN THE BOREAL FOREST
BOREAS Science Steering Committee

CHAPTER 12   259
REMOTE SENSING AND GEOGRAPHIC INFORMATION SYSTEMS (GIS) APPLICATIONS FOR MULTI-RESOURCE INVENTORIES IN CANADA
F. Hegyi

LIST OF AUTHORS

G. Boer
Canada Climate Centre
Climate Research Branch
University of Victoria
P.O. Box 1700
Victoria, BC   V8W 2Y2

R. Brown
Research Scientist
Applications Development Branch
Canada Centre for Remote Sensing
588 Booth St.
Ottawa, ON   K1A 0Y7

I.K. Crain
The Orbis Institute
P.O. Box 4115, Station C
Ottawa, ON   K1Y 4P3

H. Epp
Northwest Territories Centre for Remote
          Sensing
7th Floor, Scotia Centre
Yellowknife, NWT X1A 1L9

W.F.J. Evans
Professor
Environmental Resource Studies
Trent University
Peterborough, ON   K9J 7B8

E.A. Gallie
Department of Geography
Laurentian University
Ramsey Lake Road
Sudbury,, ON   P3E 2C6

D. Goodenough
Forestry Canada
Pacific Forestry Centre
506 West Bumside Road
Victoria, BC   V8Z 1M5

J.F.R. Gower
Institute of Ocean Sciences
Fisheries and Oceans
P.O. Box 6000
9860 West Saanich Road
Sidney, BC   V8L 4B2

J.R. Harris
Continental Geoscience Division
Geological Survey of Canada
1 Observatory Crescent,
Ottawa, ON   K1A 0Y3

F. Hegyi
Ferihill Technologies Ltd.
Suite 702 - 1483 Douglas Street
Victoria, BC   V8W 3K4

J.D. Heyland
Science Institute of Northwest Territories
P.O. Box 1617
Yellowknife, NWT X1A 2P2

J.K. Hornsby
RADARSAT International
3951 Shell Road
Richmond, BC,   V6X 2W2

E. LeDrew
Department of Geography and the
Institute for Space and Terrestrial Science
University of Waterloo
Waterloo, ON   N2L 3G1

C.-P. Lo
University of Georgia
Athens, Georgia
U.S.A.

D.I.R. Low
Radarsat International Inc.
Suite 600, 1525 Carling Ave.
Ottawa, ON   K1Z 8R9

H. MacKay
Intera Information Technologies Ltd.
2 Gurdwara Rd.
Suite 200
Nepean, ON   K2E 1A2

N. McFarlane
Canadian Climate Centre
Climate Research Branch
University of Victoria
Box 1700
Victoria, B.C.   V8W 2Y2

R. Pitblado
Department of Geography
Laurentian University
Sudbury, ON   P3E 2C6

K. Raney
RADARSAT Project Office
Canada Centre for Remote Sensing
2464 Sheffield Rd.
Ottawa, ON   K1B 4E5

R.A. Ryerson
Energy, Mines and Resources
Canada Centre for Remote Sensing
588 Booth Street, 3rd Floor
Ottawa, ON   K1A 0Y7

M. Strome
Forestry Canada
Petawawa National Forestry Institute
Chalk River, ON   K0J 1J0

P. Teillet
Energy, Mines and Resources
Canada Centre for Remote Sensing
588 Booth Street, 3rd Floor
Ottawa, ON   K1A 0Y7

D. Thompson
Intera Information Technologies Canad Ltd
2500-101 6th Avenue South West
Calgary, AB   T2P 3P4

S.M. Till
Energy, Mines and Resources
Canada Centre for Remote Sensing
588 Booth Street, 3rd Floor
Ottawa, ON   K1A 0Y7

R. Trenholm
College of Geographic Sciences
Nova Scotia Land Survey Institute
P.O. Box 10
Lawrencetown, N.S. B0S 1M0

A. Turner
Research Officer
Integrated Ecosystems Monitoring & Analysis
        Div.
State of the Environment Reporting
Environment Canada
Place Vincent Massey, 10th Floor
351 St. Joseph Blvd.
Hull, Québec   K1A 0H3

J. Whiting
Saskatchewan Research Council
15 Innovation Boulevard
Saskatoon, Saskatchewan   S7N 2X8

BOREAS Science Steering Committee

P. Sellers
923 NASA/GSFC
Greenbelt, MD 20771

J. Cihlar,
Energy, Mines and Resources
Canada Centre for Remote Sensing
588 Booth Street, 3rd Floor
Ottawa, ON   K1A 0Y7

M. Apps
Forestry Canada
5320-122 Street
Edmonton, AB T6H 3S5

B. Goodison
Climate Research Branch (CCRD)
Climate & Atmospheric Research
        Directorate
Atmospheric Environment Service
Downsview, ON   M3H 5T4

F. G. Hall
NASA/Goddard Space Flight Center
Code 923
Greenbelt, MD   20771

R. Harriss
University of New Hampshire
Institute for the Study of Earth
Science & Eng. Research Bldg
Durham, NH   038243525

D. Leckie
Forestry Canada
Petawawa National Forestry Institute
Chalk River, ON   K0J 1J0

E. LeDrew
Department of Geography
University of Waterloo
Waterloo, ON   N2L 3G1

P. A. Matson
ESPM: Soil Science
University of California, Berkeley
Berkeley, CA   94720

S. W. Running
University of Montana
School of Forestry
Missoula, MT   59812

PREFACE

Environmental risks are seen as primary threats to the future of our planet and its people. It is becoming increasingly clear that the combined effects of unprecedented levels of population growth, industrialization and urbanization exacerbated by the wasteful and profligate use of natural resources in the industrialized countries and massive poverty in developing countries are producing large-scale environmental and natural resource degradation that is approaching critical thresholds. And all the damage that has been done to date to vital life-support systems, the atmosphere, waters and plant and animal life has occurred at levels of population and human activity which are bound to grow even further in the period ahead.

All this would point to a future that is very bleak indeed as we are about to end this millennium and to begin a new one.

However, there are also sound reasons for hope as we view the future of our planet. Risks to the global environment are now receiving wide public attention. Concern for the environment is moving to center stage, to the top of the political agenda both nationally and internationally. Fundamental issues as to the relationship of our environmental future to our economic life have been the subject of the United Nations Conference on Environment and Development which met in Brazil in June 1992. The decisions taken by the nations of the world at this conference have been enlightened by rapidly advancing knowledge as to the sources, causes and effects of environmental change and the basis for solutions to the problems they create.

This has been made possible because of the vastly increased knowledge base, resulting from dramatic improvements in monitoring and assessment capabilities during the past two decades. Amongst these improvements, none is more important or promising than space-based remote sensing. Remote sensing techniques provide a unique and unprecedented means of analyzing and understanding changes taking place in the environment and resource endowment of our planet. They provide the knowledge base required to guide the policies and actions through which human activities' impact on the earth's environment and resources and enable us to monitor and evaluate these impacts.

Remote sensing is thus in a very real sense an instrument of hope. It facilitates the planning and implementation of development policies and practices required to achieve a sustainable balance between our economic aspirations and environmental imperative. No technology offers more promise of helping to ensure that human activities remain within boundaries which will provide the future viability and security of our planet as a hospitable home for human and other forms of life.

Canada has been in the vanguard of leadership in the development of remote sensing and its application to the management and stewardship of natural resources and the environment. The Geographical Information Systems it has developed have made a seminal contribution to the processes of understanding and guiding global change. This book documents the Canadian experience as a unique and important chapter in the efforts of the human community to avoid the risks and realize the hopes that are the key to our common future.

Maurice F. Strong
Chairman
Ontario Hydro.
Formerly, Secretary-General
United Nations Conference on
Environment and Development

INTRODUCTION

Ellsworth F. LeDrew, Murray Strome, Frank Hegyi

We do not inherit the earth from our parents,
We borrow it from our children.
Anonymous

Canada has developed an enviable international reputation in remote sensing. We have made substantial technological contributions in sensor design, satellite development, satellite data receiving and processing systems, and have been at the leading edge of algorithm and procedure development for applications. Our vast territory and wealth of natural resources have challenged us to be at the leading edge of the science.

We are also being challenged by the concerns of Global Change. As a nation with a significant Arctic land mass, our decisions that may affect snow and ice cover through our use of Arctic resources will have global consequences through the important role that these surfaces have as part of the planetary heat engine. Our enormous tract of Boreal forest and wetlands has similar global implications through carbon cycling and methane production. We have an important responsibility to manage our heritage - that which we receive from our predecessors and that which we pass on to our successors. Canada's use of her resources will have an impact in the global arena.

Canada will also be affected by the consequences of Global Change. In many regions, the climate is marginal. In the Arctic and sub-Arctic, the structure of ecosystems and trophic relationships are both relatively simple and specialized. The physical environment exacts a strange control. A few favourable years can result in establishment of a species which can be eradicated in a single harsh year. On the prairies, our specialized agriculture is vulnerable to both the amount and timing of precipitation. Our forest industry is at the mercy of drought and thunderstorms. Permafrost adds considerable expense to mining and engineering operations. It is evident that anticipation of and planning for all aspects of Global Change must be an integral part of managing our natural resources.

The concept of Global Change has many different interpretations, depending upon the perspective of the analyst or scientist. It is worth quoting from the Joint Communiques of the Economic Summit of Paris France, July, 1989:

"There is growing awareness throughout the world of the necessity to preserve better the global ecological balance.

This includes serious threats to the atmosphere, which could lead to future climate changes. We note with great concern the growing pollution of air, lakes, rivers, oceans and seas; acid rain, dangerous substances; and the rapid desertification and deforestation. Such environmental degradation endangers species and undermines the well-being of individuals and societies.

"Decisive action is urgently needed to understand and protect the Earth's ecological balance. We will work together to achieve the common goals of preserving a healthy and balanced global environment in order to meet shared economic and social objectives and to carry out obligations to future generations.

"We urge all countries to give further impetus to scientific research on environmental issues, to develop necessary technologies and to make clear evaluations of the economic costs and benefits of environmental policies."

It is clear that any definition would be counter-productive in its self-limitation. It is essential to understand the pervasive linkages between all components of the planet system: physical, social, biological, economic and political. The importance and force lie in its universality.

One program designed to address issues of Global Change is the International Geosphere-Biosphere Program (IGBP), whose stated objective is: "A study of Global Change is to describe and understand the interactive physical, chemical and biological processes that regulate the total Earth system, the unique environment that it provides for life, the changes that are occurring in this system and the manner in which they are influenced by human activities" (ICSU, 1989, pp. 2). Some specific questions are:

-How is the chemistry of the global atmosphere regulated and what is the role of terrestrial processes producing and consuming trace gases?

-How do ocean biogeochemical processes influence and respond to climate change?

-How does vegetation interact with physical processes and the hydrological cycle?

-How will climate change affect terrestrial ecosystems? (*ibid*)

To this admittedly physical orientation must be added the Human Dimensions of Global Change, a companion program with the following objectives:

-To improve scientific understanding and increase awareness of the complex dynamics governing human interaction with the total earth system;

-To strengthen efforts to study, explore, and anticipate social change affecting the global environment;

-To identify broad social strategies to prevent or mitigate undesirable impacts of global change, or to adopt to changes that are already unavoidable

-To analyze policy options for dealing with global environmental change and promoting the goal of sustainable development. (IFIAS, 1988, pp. 4.)

Several events encourage the study of Global Change from these perspectives, and make such studies feasible. There is unequivocal evidence that a variety of components of the planet's system are changing now. This is a real phenomena coming at a time when population pressures are mounting rapidly. It also comes at a time when we have the computer capability to model integrated and complex systems in an effort to understand the causes and processes of change. We can manage the enormous data volumes that must be brought to bear on these models. It is also the time when we can monitor the entire planet from space in a consistent manner. From remotely sensed data we can derive parameters to drive the models for regions where previous data of any type were not available. We can compare images from an historical archive of almost two decades and map regions of change. We can measure the rate of change and identify spatial patterns that may provide clues as to the causes. We can target areas where mitigating action is a priority. An early IGBP document highlighted the critical role that remote sensing must play in our study of Global Change (Rasool, 1987). A recent report of the Canadian Global Change Program (Chilar et al, 1989) identified some uniquely Canadian remote sensing issues as a discussion document for the development of the Canadian Global Change research agenda.

We are at a decisive point in the study of Global Change. The policy analysts are responding to public pressure and asking the scientists for credible answers. The scientists are responding by planning interdisciplinary and international programs of considerable magnitude to provide those answers. The scientific cry in the wilderness has become a powerful voice.

It is imperative that Canada assess its very real strengths in remote sensing and make a substantive contribution to the science of Global Change. We must convince the politicians and the Canadian public of our skills and play a role in the international research agenda with a level of funding that will ensure success. This is a task of educating the policy analysts and instilling a pride in the Canadian accomplishments.

Hence this volume. The Global Change Working Group of the Canadian Advisory Council on Remote Sensing (CACRS) has been working with the Technical Committee of the International Society of Photogrammetry and Remote Sensing (ISPRS) Commission VII Mid-Term Symposium on Global and Environmental Monitoring. We saw the Symposium held in 1990 as an opportunity to synthesize and emphasize Canadian achievements in remote sensing that may be brought to bear on the issues of Global Change. Accordingly, we invited experts to write chapters describing the state-of-the-art of their particular sub-disciplines. What follows is not all-inclusive. What must result from this volume is a call for public action, and a research agenda for the next two decades.

CHAPTER 1

CLIMATE MODELLING AND GLOBAL CHANGE

G.J. Boer and N. McFarlane

INTRODUCTION

General circulation models (GCM) are the accepted tool for studies of potential global change because they are global in extent, are based on the laws of physics and behave in a manner similar to the real system. These models provide the only currently available method for simulating the three-dimensional distribution of potential climate change due to, for instance, the increase of greenhouse gases.

Climate models are validated primarily by the success with which they simulate the current climate and this success, or lack thereof, is particularly important in assessing the confidence which may be placed in simulated climate change results.

Satellite observations are particularly suited to obtaining information about the global distributions of radiative and other parameters which may be essentially unavailable in other ways. These data are important for describing the current climate, which is known only to modest accuracy, and one of the primary goals of remote sensing should be to improve this situation. Moisture related quantities such as atmospheric specific humidity, cloud, precipitation, evaporation, soil moisture, snow and sea-ice, are particularly poorly known.

Changes and trends in global climatological quantities are important for detecting climate change. Climate model results suggest the patterns or "fingerprints" of potential change which are sought in the observations. Suitable satellite data can provide the observational evidence.

The production of greenhouse gases and their accumulation in the atmosphere means that we are carrying out a global experiment, the

1

expected result of which is to change the climate. The nature, magnitude and distribution of this climate change is the question at issue.

In what follows, a brief description of the Canadian Climate Centre (CCC) GCM is provided together with some of the results of its simulation of the current climate and the changed climate due to doubled carbon dioxide (CO_2). For this greenhouse gas climate change experiment our three-dimensional atmospheric general circulation model is coupled to a simple "slab" ocean and thermodynamic ice model.

FEATURES OF THE SIMULATION

A new version of the CCC GCM (hereinafter GCMII) is used for the climate simulations discussed here. The general form of the new model is similar in many respects to the earlier one described in Boer et al. (1984a). Both utilize the spectral formulation in which prognostic variables are represented as truncated series of spherical harmonics with coefficients that vary temporally and in the vertical direction. Calculations of non-linear dynamical terms and contributions of physical effects are carried out on an appropriate transform grid. The new model has the same vertical resolution as the earlier version (10 layers in the vertical from the surface to the 10mb level). However the horizontal resolution has been increased from a triangular 20 wave (T20) spectral representation to one with 30 waves (T30). The associated grid has 96 equally spaced points in longitude and 48 in latitude giving a grid square of 3.75 degrees on a side. The new model also has an improved treatment of the vertical variation of the prognostic variables.

Both versions of the model include full diurnal and annual cycles and a complete representation of the hydrological cycle. The new model has modified treatments for various physical processes. These include: (1) a more sophisticated treatment of radiative transfer and a fully interactive parameterization of cloud cover and cloud water content; (2) a modified treatment of land surface processes which includes more sophisticated treatments of the surface energy balance and soil hydrology; and, (3) a treatment of the ocean mixed layer and sea ice which includes a specification of oceanic heat transports that permits realistic simulation of the ocean surface temperature distribution and ice boundaries.

SIMULATION OF THE CURRENT CLIMATE

The current climate is simulated by running the model through several annual cycles until a statistical equilibrium state is achieved. The results from the last ten simulated years are pooled together to form monthly and seasonal climate statistics that can be compared with the corresponding observation-based quantities.

The model simulates the climate for the whole globe in considerable detail. As noted above, the available observations do not in general provide as much detail. Some aspects of the current climate are better known than others. Temperatures and winds throughout the troposphere and surface pressures are best known. Model results can be tested quantitatively against observation-based climatologies for these fields. Quantities related to the hydrological cycle, such as specific humidity, cloudiness, precipitation, evaporation, soil moisture, snow and sea ice mass are not well known on a global basis. Although ground-based observations of precipitation and cloud cover are available, they do not have sufficient spatial resolution globally to provide reliable quantitative estimates of the climatology of these features. Only qualitative comparisons between model and observation-based climatologies for these features can be made.

The results of a simulation of the current climate made with GCMII are discussed in some detail in McFarlane et al. (1991) and compared with observation-based climatologies for winter and summer seasons. Here, a few results for the annual average climate are presented to illustrate the utility of general circulation models for climate simulation and to demonstrate as well the value of remotely sensed data, particularly satellite observations, in evaluating their performance.

Surface pressure and temperature

Figure 1.1 displays the annually averaged mean sea level pressure from observations and as simulated by the model. The main features of the field are realistically represented, both as to location and magnitude. In general, mean sea-level pressure is simulated very realistically by the model in all seasons of the year.

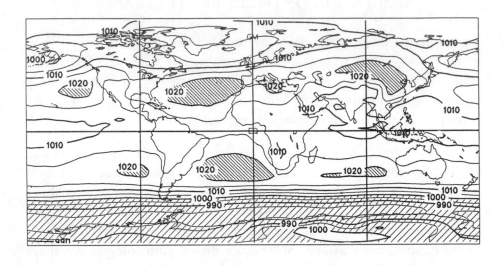

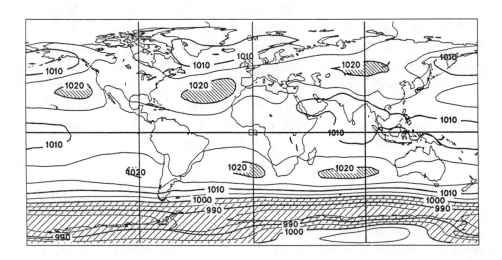

Figure 1.1: Annually averaged mean sea level pressure (a) simulated (b) observed. Units mb.

Although the model reproduces the climatological features of the atmosphere near the surface in a realistic manner, there are some differences. This is illustrated in Figure 1.2 which displays the annually averaged screen level temperature as observed and simulated by the model. It is quite apparent that the main features of the climatological field are realistically reproduced, although simulated temperatures are somewhat too cold over land surfaces. The largest differences from observation-based climatology are found in mountainous regions. The reliability of the observation-based climatology in these areas is uncertain, however.

Temperatures and zonal winds in the free atmosphere

The zonally averaged annual mean temperature fields, as simulated by the model and as obtained from observations, are shown in Figure 1.3. Although there is good agreement between these two fields in general, the simulated temperatures are too cold at high latitudes in the upper troposphere and lower stratosphere, particularly in the southern hemisphere. Simulated temperatures are also slightly too warm in the lower troposphere at high northern latitudes.

The development of cold anomalies at high latitudes in the upper levels is a common deficiency of general circulation models (Boer et. al. 1991a). These cold anomalies are most pronounced in the polar night during winter, particularly in the southern hemisphere.

Synoptic and larger scale wind and temperature fields in middle and high latitudes are nearly in gradient balance, both in nature and as simulated. Thus the high latitude cold anomaly in the simulated zonally averaged temperature field is reflected in zonal winds being somewhat too strong in the upper troposphere in middle latitudes. This is illustrated in Figure 1.4 which displays the annual mean, zonally averaged zonal wind field as simulated and observed. The broad features of the observed wind fields are simulated reasonably well.

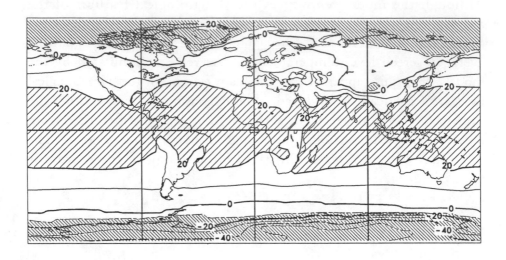

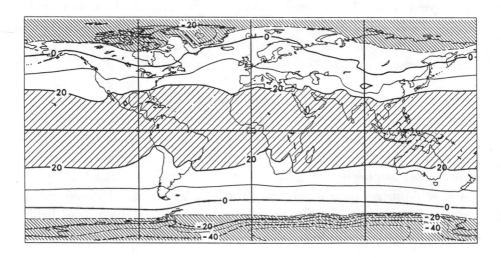

Figure 1.2: Annually averaged screen temperature (a) simulated, (b) observed. Units °C.

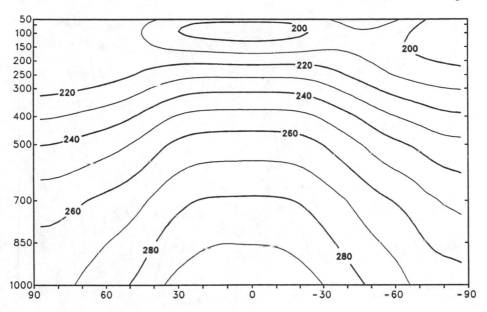

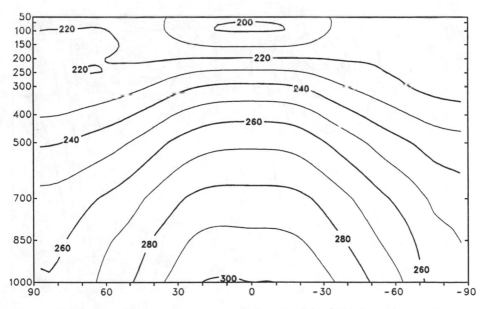

Figure 1.3: Zonally averaged annual mean temperature (a) simulated, (b) observed. Units °K.

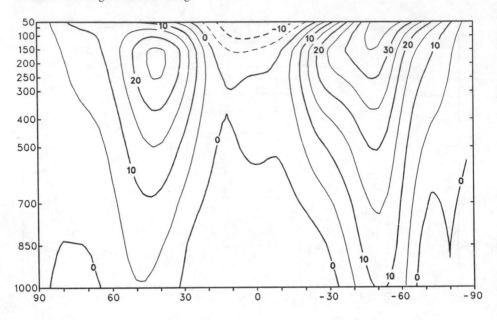

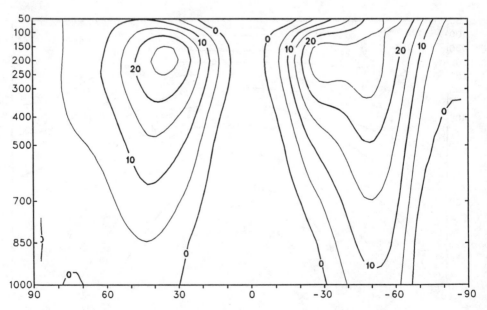

Figure 1.4: Zonally averaged annual mean zonal wind (a) simulated, (b) observed. Units ms^{-1}.

Precipitation

Precipitation, as simulated by the model and in nature, is a much less smooth field than temperature or surface pressure. The occurrence of precipitation on small spatial and temporal scales makes the task of observing it more difficult. Thus, estimates of the observation-based climatology of precipitation are less reliable than for temperature and surface pressure. However, the broad features of the climatological precipitation field are sufficiently well known to permit comparison with the simulated field. The annual mean climatological precipitation field, as estimated by Jaeger (1976), is displayed in Figure 1.5 along with the simulated field. Although differing in detail, there is very good general agreement between simulated and observed climatological precipitation patterns.

Clouds and radiation

The role of simulated clouds in the model is to account for the effect of cloudiness on the radiation budget of the earth. Unfortunately, the spatial distribution of clouds and their optical properties is not well known on a global basis. However, satellite-based observations provide basic information on the radiation balance. Data from this source are now available with sufficient temporal and spatial resolution to permit estimation of the climatological features of various components of the radiation budget of the earth. A useful review of radiation budget studies that are based on theses data is provided by Hartmann et. al. (1986).

Comparison of simulated and observed components of the radiation budget provides information on the realism of the simulated distribution of clouds and their optical properties. For example, the coincidence of relative maxima in cloudiness with minima in out-going terrestrial radiation is a feature of the radiation budget in the tropics that is well documented from satellite observations. This correspondence between cloudiness and out-going terrestrial radiation is due to the presence of high clouds, most of which are associated with deep moist convection in the tropics. Since most of the precipitation in the tropics also originates from moist convection, the spatial structure of the out-going terrestrial

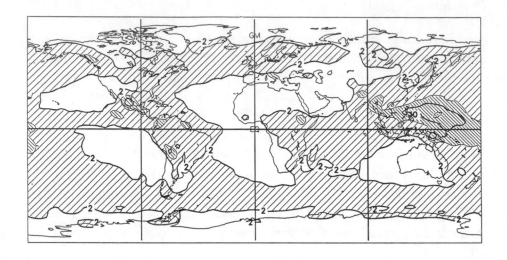

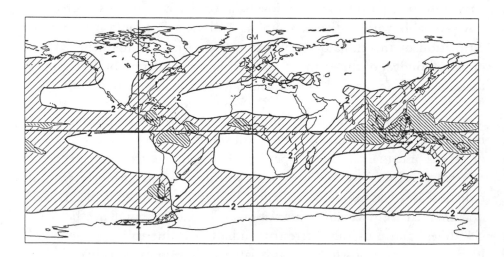

Figure 1.5: Annually averaged precipitation (a) simulated, (b) observed. Units mm/day

radiation field also provides an indication of the spatial distribution of precipitation.

Figure 1.6 displays the simulated field of annual mean total cloudiness which takes into account the cloud over-lapping assumptions that are used in the model. The out-going terrestrial radiation simulated in the model and the climatological distribution of out-going terrestrial radiation, as estimated from NIMBUS 7 observations, are shown in Figure 1.7. Although this estimated climatology lacks some of the spatial detail that is apparent in the simulated field, there is good general agreement between the simulated and observed distributions of out-going terrestrial radiation. The coincidence of relative maxima in cloudiness with minima in the out-going terrestrial radiation is clearly seen in the Indian and South-east Asian monsoon regions and the inter-tropical convergence regions over Central Africa and Central and South America. These regions also have relative maxima in precipitation as shown in Figure 1.5. By contrast the relatively cloud-free areas over the sub-tropical oceans and the Saharan desert region of Northern Africa have maxima in out going terrestrial radiation.

SIMULATED CLIMATE CHANGE

Only a few fields representing the simulated change in equilibrium climate due to a doubling of CO_2 from 330 to 660 ppm are presented. A much more detailed presentation of the results is given in Boer, McFarlane and Lazare (1991).

Average changes for the entire globe and for land and "ice-free" ocean are given in Table 1.1. The change in the global annual average surface air temperature for this simulation is 3.5°C. Temperatures warm more over land than over the ice-free ocean. An increase of 3.8% in the vigor of the hydrological cycle is found, which is somewhat smaller than previously reported values. There is a decrease in soil moisture of 6.6% for the annual average, with larger values occurring in northern summer.

Total cloud cover decreases by 2.2% and the mass of sea-ice decreases by 66% for the annual average and by 72% in northern summer.

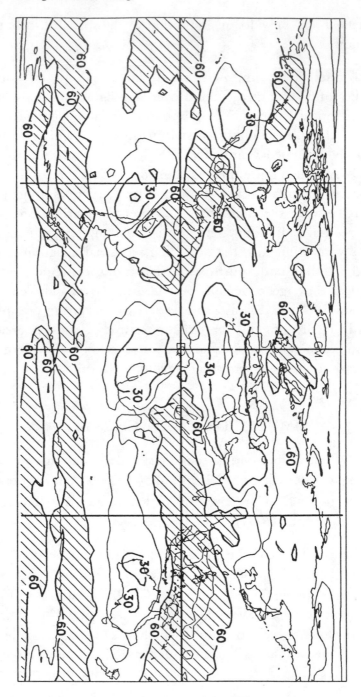

Figure 1.6: Simulated annually averaged percent total cloudiness.

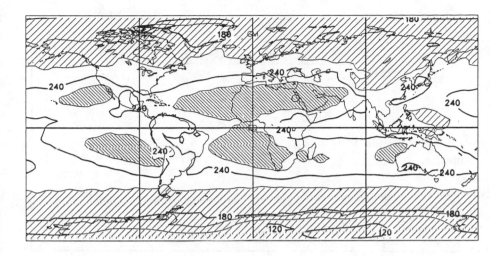

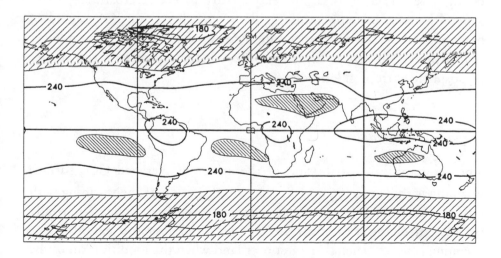

Figure 1.7: Annually averaged out-going terrestrial radiation (a) simulated, (b) observed from Nimbus7 data. Units Wm^{-2}.

Table 1.1

Mean changes due to doubled CO_2

	Annual Globe	Land	Ice-free ocean
Surface air temperature °C	3.5	4.4	2.7
Precipitation	3.8%	0.9%	4.3%
Evaporation	3.8%	3.8%	3.3%
Cloud cover	-2.2%	-1.9%	-3.1%
Soil moisture		-6.6%	
Sea ice mass	-66%		

TEMPERATURE

In the body of the atmosphere

Figure 1.8 displays the zonal cross-section of the annual average temperature change. The general features of the simulated temperature change are: (1) a decrease in temperature in the stratosphere; (2) a general increase in temperature in the troposphere; and, (3) a band of maximum tropospheric temperature increase which stretches from lower tropospheric levels in high latitude winter regions to the upper troposphere at tropical latitudes.

Surface air temperature

The geographical distribution of the annually averaged CO_2 surface warming is shown in Figure 1.9. The amplification of the warming with latitude is clear. The warming is largest in winter, at least partially because of changes in snow and sea-ice thickness and extent. The warming is never generally largest over land when the modification of the low level winter immersion occurs.

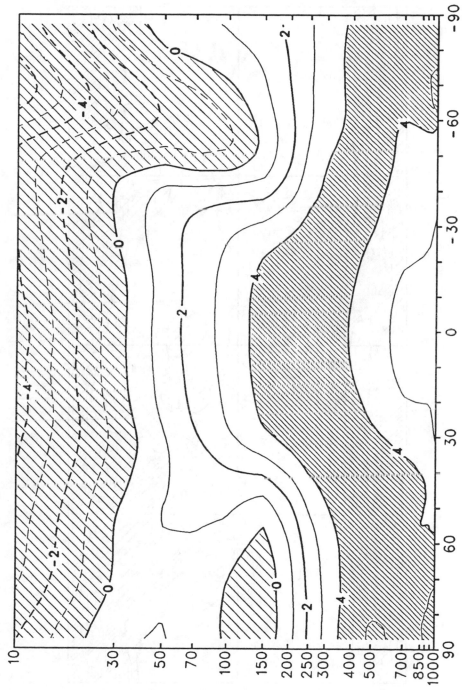

Figure 1.8: Simulated changes in annually averaged temperature due to a doubling of CO_2. Units °C.

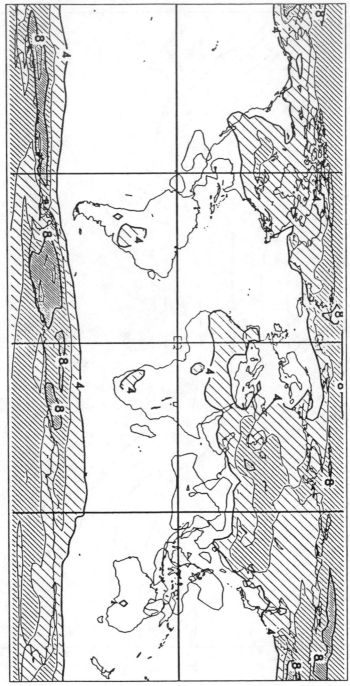

Figure 1.9: Simulated change in annually averaged surface air temperature due to a doubling of CO_2 Units °C.

The moisture budget

The expected increase in the vigor of the hydrological cycle due to a doubling of CO_2 is found with an increase of 3.8% in precipitation and evaporation on the global average. This is somewhat lower than previously published results and is a consequence, in this model, of the parameterization of cloud optical properties feedback. This is discussed more fully in Boer (1992).

Precipitation and evaporation

The zonally and annually averaged precipitation rates for the 1x and 2xCO_2 cases are shown in Figure 1.10. The changes are not large in an absolute sense but such changes may nevertheless have important consequences.

Evaporation is more uniformly distributed than precipitation and this is also true of the change in evaporation. The climatological distribution over the globe of both evaporation and precipitation is poorly known. This has implications for the assessment of the simulation of the current climate and for possible changes in climate. Moreover, a quantity like soil moisture is seldom measured so must be inferred from estimates of evaporation and precipitation.

Soil moisture

Possible changes in soil moisture due to greenhouse warming could have important effects on agriculture and water supply. Although average precipitation increases in the 2xCO_2 case, evaporation also increases so that it is quite possible for soil moisture to decrease as it does on average in this simulation. This is shown in Figure 1.11 which displays the annually averaged change in soil moisture associated with the doubling of CO_2.

The change in state from frozen to liquid soil moisture is also available for this simulation and shows, not surprisingly, a decrease of the frozen

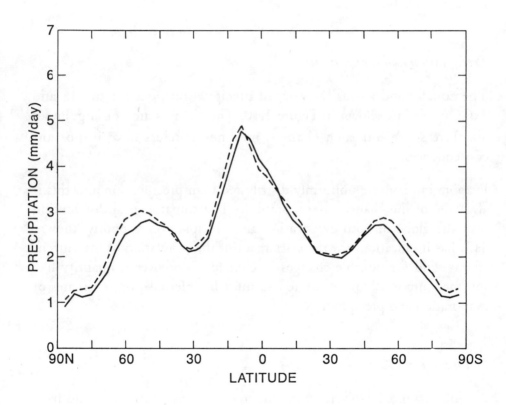

Figure 1.10: Simulated zonally averaged precipitation rate for the 1xCO$_2$ (solid line) and 2xCO$_2$ (dashed line) cases for the annual average.

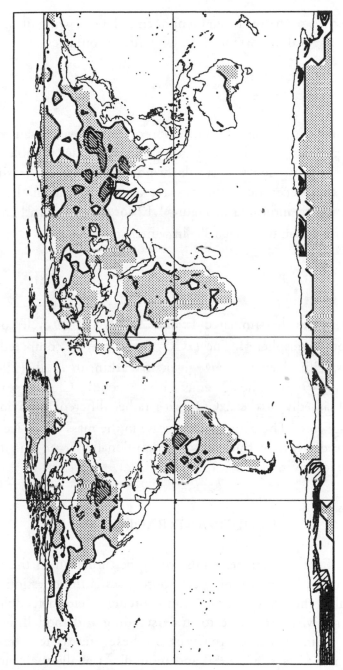

Figure 1.11: Simulated annually averaged soil moisture availability change due to a doubling of CO_2. Regions of decreased soil moisture are indicated by shading. The contour interval is 20% and changes in excess of 20% are also indicated.

and an increase of the unfrozen component. This thawing of frozen soil may be of practical importance for high latitude countries.

Snow

There is some climatological information on snow cover obtained mainly by satellite. There is little information on the model variable which is snow mass. Snow depth is similarly poorly known. The simulated retreat of the December-February average snow line in the warmer $2xCO_2$ climate is indicated in Figure 1.12 for the northern hemisphere. There is a reduction of about 18% in winter snow cover.

Sea ice

Figure 1.13 gives the simulated 1x and $2xCO_2$ annual cycles of sea ice area for both hemispheres. The $1xCO_2$ curves may be compared directly with the satellite-based curves given in Parkinson et al. (1987) and Zwally et al. (1983). The agreement is very good. Clearly sea-ice area decreases markedly in the $2xCO_2$ with rather different behavior in the two hemispheres. The simulated decrease in the mass of sea ice is about 66%. The decrease in thickness is proportionally larger than the 53% decrease in ice cover.

CLOUDS AND RADIATION

How the climate system responds to the perturbation in the radiative balance implied by increasing greenhouse gases is the question at issue. In particular, the questions of "cloud forcing", "cloud feedback" and model "sensitivity" are basic to understanding and modelling climate change. Some indirect analyses of these quantities have been undertaken in Cess et al., 1990 and more direct analyses are underway. Satellite measurements are the only way of observing the climate system to obtain the required quantities.

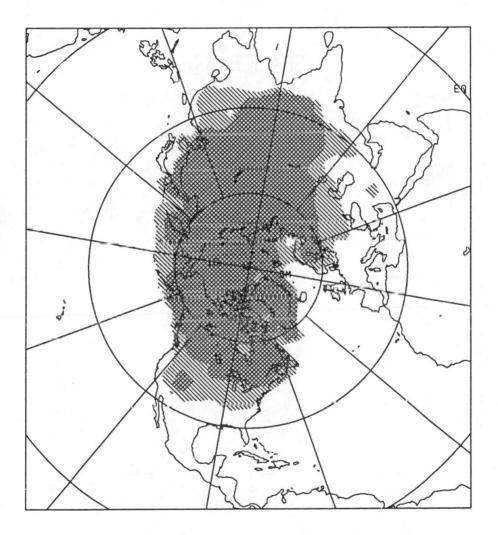

Figure 1.12: The 1xCO$_2$ (light shading) and 2xCO$_2$ (dark shading) snow lines over the Northern Hemisphere for December-February. Values greater than 10 Kg m^{-2} are shaded.

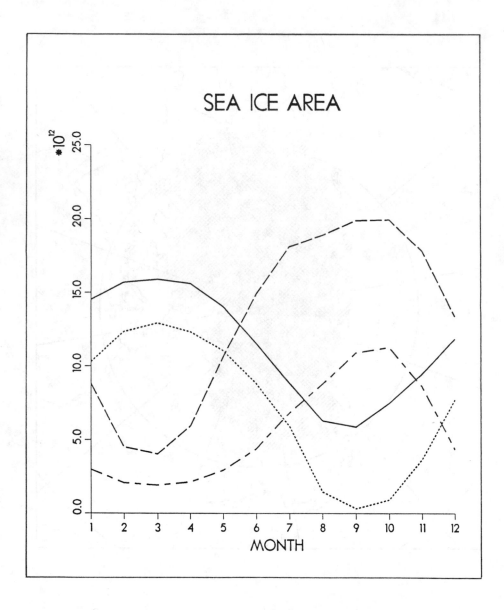

Figure 1.13: The simulated annual cycle of the area of sea-ice for concentration greater than 15%. The curves for each hemisphere and for both 1x and 2xCO$_2$ are plotted. Units 10^{12} m^2.

The difference in the zonally and annually averaged cloud amount is shown in Figure 1.14. The pattern is similar in a general way to that found in other simulations. What is especially important in the current simulation is that cloud properties are allowed to vary. The changes in cloud amount and distribution, temperature and moisture are not simply related to the changes in radiative quantities.

The radiation balance $R = Q - F$ at the top of the atmosphere (TOA) is one of the most basic climatic parameters. Here R is the net radiation and Q and F are the solar radiation absorbed by the system and the outgoing long-wave radiation (OLR) respectively. When globally averaged, $<R> = 0 = <Q> - <F>$ and the difference between the 2x and 1xCO$_2$ equilibrium climates gives $\partial<R> = 0 = \partial<Q> - \partial<F>$. Rather surprisingly, $\partial<Q>$ and $\partial<F>$ are separately zero even though the energy balance requires only that their difference be zero. Fig. 1.15 shows the difference in the net radiation at the TOA between the 1x and 2xCO$_2$ climates. It is clear that R changes with latitude, although the global average change is zero. There is a decrease in radiative input in the tropics (where R is positive) and a decrease in radiative output in the extra-tropics (where R is negative). The decrease in radiative input in the tropics is a consequence of a simulated increase in cloud optical depth in the upper troposphere in the region of maximum warming. It has important consequences for the surface energy balance and the change in the strength of the hydrological cycle (Boer, 1992).

DYNAMICAL CHANGES

Some discussion of changes in dynamical quantities is given in Boer, McFarlane and Lazare (1991) but will not be given here. Although satellite data are thought of as most naturally providing information on "thermodynamic/moisture" variables as opposed to "dynamical" ones, this situation may well change in future.

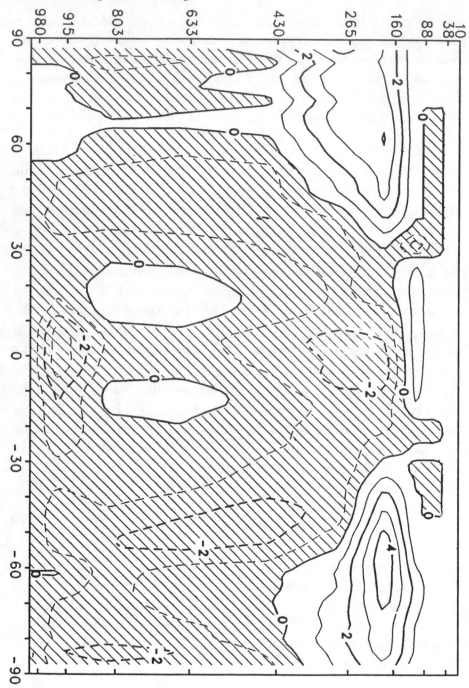

Figure 1.14: Simulated changes in annually average cloud amount due to a doubling of CO_2. Units %.

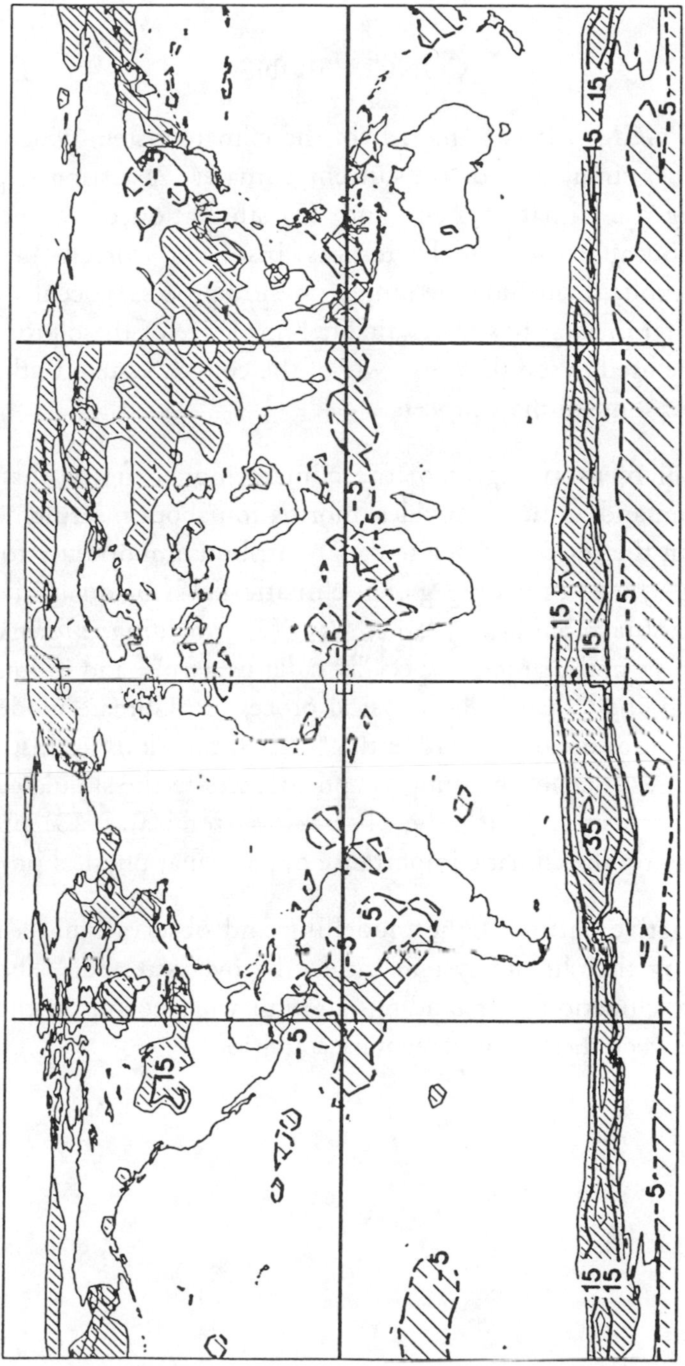

Figure 1.15: Difference in annually averaged net radiation for the 1x and 2xCO$_2$ cases. units Wm^{-2}.

CONCLUSIONS

The CCC GCM offers a "model" of the climate system which may be used for: (1) simulation of the current climate; (2) testing hypotheses concerning the climate system; and, (3) simulation of the perturbed climate. Because the model attempts, insofar as current knowledge allows, to explicitly include the proper physical processes occurring in the climate system it depends on a suitable knowledge of these processes. It also may be used to test the sensitivity of the climate system to the proper inclusion of some of these process.

This complementary aspect of the climate model means that it may benefit from and, in turn, provides information about measurements and processes in the system. Satellite data contribute importantly to climate modelling by: (1) providing global climatic fields of quantities which may be unobtainable in any other way; (2) providing information on basic balances in the system, especially radiative terms; and, (3) providing information about particular physical processes. Climate models make use of this information by: (1) testing their simulations against climatic observations; (2) analyzing budgets and balances in the simulated system for their consistency with the observed system; and, (3) providing information on the climatic importance of particular physical processes.

The interactive nature of the modelling and observational aspects of investigating the climate system cannot be over stressed. The rate at which new climatic understanding is found will depend on the proper balance between these complementary activities.

CHAPTER 2

REMOTE SENSING OF
THE OZONE LAYER

W. F. J. Evans

INTRODUCTION

In recent years there has been an increasing awareness of pollution problems that affect our global environment; remote sensing has played an important role in the study of many of these problems. These range from local scale problems such as garbage disposal, through regional scale problems such as air pollution, to international scale problems such as acid rain and water pollution in the Great Lakes. However, in the last decade we have become aware of several pollution problems that are of truly global scale, such as climate warming due to the carbon dioxide greenhouse effect. Another global problem with correspondingly long time scales is the threat of increased ultraviolet radiation posed by depletion of the stratospheric ozone layer. This is the first global environmental problem that geophysical scientists have attempted to solve. What is learned may be of intrinsic value in the solution of other global problems for which we need scientific data and knowledge. It is also a problem in which remote sensing has played a particularly valuable role.

STRUCTURE OF THE OZONE LAYER

Our atmosphere consists of the troposphere, the lower portion in which we live, and the stratosphere, an upper layer that lies above 12 km. This latter region of the atmosphere contains the ozone layer, which is a vertically distributed layer of gas about 25 km thick starting about 15 km from the earth's surface. If compressed to surface temperature and pressure, the "effective thickness" of this layer would be only 3 mm.

Figure 2.1 shows a photograph of the ozone layer taken from space in limb viewing mode by astronauts on board the space shuttle. The top of the dark clouds marks the tropopause or upper boundary of the troposphere. The white band above this is caused by sunlight scattered by the stratospheric aerosol layer between 15 and 30 km. Above this, a faint violet band shows the upper levels of the ozone layer from 30 to 40 km; this is due to a combination of Rayleigh scattering and ozone absorption. Above 40 km, the sky is black owing to the lack of Rayleigh scattering from atmospheric nitrogen and oxygen. The actual ozone layer extends from 15 to 40 km and the resulting absorption of violet light makes the aerosol layer look even whiter. The nomenclature of these layers is demonstrated in Figure 2.2.

However, because ozone is a powerful absorber of ultraviolet light, this thin layer shields the surface of the earth from the damaging short wavelength radiation coming from the sun. The penetration of various wavelengths of light into the atmosphere is shown in Figure 2.3; of particular importance is the partial screening of ultraviolet B radiation of wavelengths between 290 and 320 nanometres (nm). Without a protective ozone layer there would be no life on a planet such as earth. Despite our ozone shield, some ultraviolet light still penetrates to the surface and can cause skin cancer and eye aging in humans and animals and retard the growth of many plant species including cereal crops, resulting in reduced agricultural yields. It can also affect the phytoplankton yield and hence the ocean food chain.

The ozone layer also plays a key role in the climate of the earth since it blocks heat radiation from escaping to space and causes heating in the stratosphere by absorbing short-wavelength sunlight; this absorption of sunlight produces a temperature increase with increasing altitude in the stratosphere. Future temperature changes due to changes in the ozone layer may well affect the surface climate significantly.

CHEMISTRY OF THE OZONE LAYER

The amount of ozone in the stratosphere is controlled by a balanced set of chemical reactions. Ozone is created by the breakup of molecular

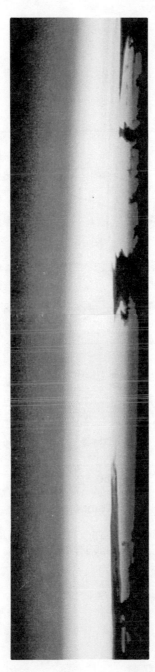

Figure 2.1: The actual ozone layer extends from 15 to 40 km and the resulting absorption of violet light makes the aerosol layer look even whiter in this view of the limb of the atmosphere from the shuttle. The nomenclature of the atmospheric layers is demonstrated in Figure 2.2. Figure courtesy of NASA.

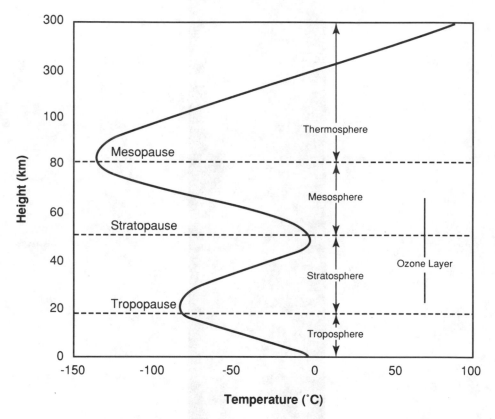

VARIATION OF ATMOSPHERIC TEMPERATURE WITH HEIGHT
delineates four atmospheric layers: troposphere, stratosphere, mesosphere,
and thermosphere.

Figure 2.2: The nomenclature of the structure of the atmosphere showing the ozone layer in the stratosphere.

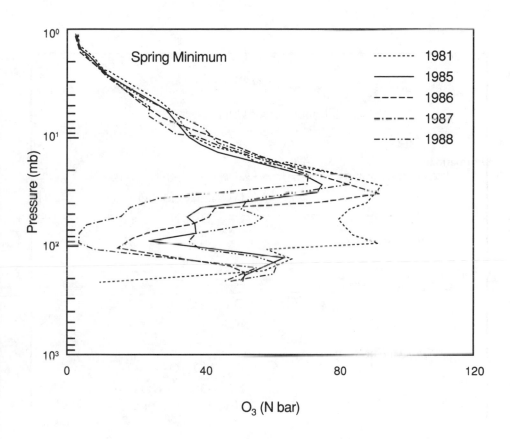

Figure 2.3: The penetration of light into the earth's atmosphere showing the screening effect of the ozone layer on ultraviolet B radiation.

oxygen by electromagnetic radiation in the ultra-violet region of the spectrum below 230 nm (reaction 1, in Table 2.1) and is destroyed by nitrogen chemistry (reactions 4 and 5), by water chemistry (reactions 6 and 7) and by chlorine chemistry (reactions 8 and 9). Although this is a simplification of all the chemical reactions occurring, it is clear that any increase in nitrogen or chlorine compounds in the stratosphere can lead to a depletion of ozone.

Table 2.1

Chemistry of the Ozone Layer

Formation:
    by photolysis of O_2

$$O_2 + ultraviolet \_ O + O \qquad R1$$
$$O_2 + O_2 + N \_ O + N \qquad R2$$

Destruction:
    Oxygen only Chemistry

$$O + O \_ O + 0 \qquad\qquad\qquad R3$$

    Nitrogen Chemistry

$$O_3 + NO \_ O_2 + NO_2 \qquad R4$$
$$NO + O \_ O + NO \qquad R5$$
$$Net\ O_3 + O \_ O + O$$

    Water Chemistry

$$O + OH \_ O + HO \qquad R6$$
$$O + HO \_ O + OH \qquad R7$$
$$Net\ O_3 + O \_ O_2 + O_2$$

    Chlorine Chemistry

$$O2 + Cl \_ O + ClO \qquad R8$$
$$O_2 + ClO \_ O + Cl \qquad R9$$
$$Net\ O + O_3 \gg 2\,O_2$$

Problems with the ozone layer were first anticipated in 1970 when scientists began to worry that water vapour from the exhaust gases of supersonic transports would cause a decrease in the ozone layer. With the discovery that nitrogen oxides play a key role in the chemistry of the ozone layer, this concern was extended to include the nitrogen oxides that would be emitted in the exhausts of large fleets of supersonic transports proposed for the 1990s. About 1972, scientists at the National Aeronautics and Space Administration (NASA) began to study the effects of chlorine compounds that would be emitted by the space shuttle planned for the 1980s.

It turned out that the amounts were too small to be significant. However, these calculations led to the recognition that large amounts of chlorine were already being injected into the atmosphere by the use of freons (chlorofluorocarbons or CFCs as they are now called) which areused for propellants in aerosol spray cans, for refrigeration and airconditioning and for manufacturing foamed plastic products. Professor Sherry Rowland at the University of California realized that because the CFCs were so stable, that any of them released in the air at ground level would eventually be transported upward into the upper atmosphere and be broken down by sunlight to release chlorine in the ozone layer.

The depletion of ozone by CFCs has now been studied for a decade, and current estimates of ozone depletion by CFCs are, if anything, larger than the original estimated by Rowland. However, it has been found that the overall problem is much more complex than originally estimated and that there are several other pollution sources for the ozone layer that have to be considered together because they interact with each other and the atmosphere. For example, increases in lower atmosphere nitrogen oxides from jet traffic have actually led to increases in the amount of tropospheric ozone. Furthermore, temperature changes in the high atmosphere that accompany the greenhouse effect produce ozone increases in the stratosphere. These and other gases may be causing a partial compensation for depletion of the ozone layer due to the CFCs.

However, very recent developments in the knowledge of ozone layer chemistry indicate a potential for a future disaster. In an effect called the "chlorine catastrophe," ozone would be depleted by only 5% at current usage rates of CFCs, yet if the global usage rate increased by only 4% a year, the ozone layer could deplete precipitously by more than 30% within 50 years! It might take more than 100 years after that to recover.

GLOBAL OZONE DISTRIBUTION

In the last few years, satellite images from the NIMBUS weather satellite, which carries a remote sensing instrument at an altitude of 600 km, have given us the ability to study actual global ozone distributions. The TOMS (Total Ozone Mapping Spectrometer) is used to image the ozone layer by measuring spectrum of the reflected sunlight from the lower atmosphere and surface. The satellite image in Figure 2.4 provides an example of the kinds of images obtained and shows the distribution of ozone with latitude. Low amounts of ozone below 2 mm are shown as violet on the colour scale while large amounts of ozone over 5 mm are shown as red. It is apparent that the ozone layer is thinner at the equator and thicker at the poles. This distribution of ozone determined the ultraviolet radiation distribution which in turn has influenced the evolution of the human species; dark skinned races are well suited to live under the low ozone conditions in equatorial regions, while light skinned people are better adapted to the northern regions. Skin cancer rates for example, are much higher among fair skinned people living at tropical latitudes in places such as Australia. This is a graphic demonstration of our environmental dependence on the ozone layer. We also note that the ozone layer is strongly affected by the location of the jet stream, which we can easily see in the satellite image in Figure 2.4 as a sharp gradient in the ozone field at mid-latitudes. Thus the ozone layer moves north and south with the daily motions of the jet stream at mid-latitudes.

Although the most recent calculations that attempt to account for the rather complex reactions involving many chemicals show that only small changes in the total column amount of ozone are expected over the next 5 years owing to the compensation effects of increases in several atmospheric gases, we do know that the altitude profile of the ozone layer has been altered, especially over Antarctica in spring.

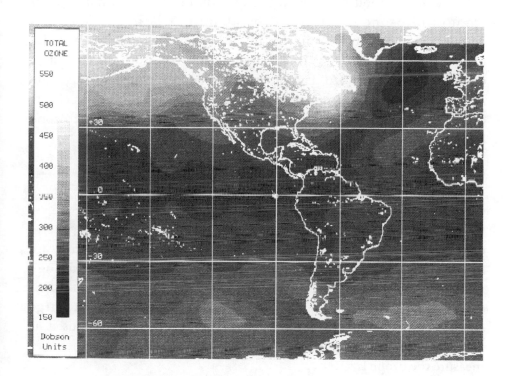

Figure 2.4: The global distribution of total ozone for the Western Hemisphere on January 15, 1986, derived from data recorded by the TOMS (Total Ozone Mapping Spectrometer) instrument on the NIMBUS 7 satellite. (data courtesy: Dr. Arlin Kreuger, NASA Goddard).
Ozone amounts vary with latitude from about 2.5 mm in the tropics to over 4.5 mm at the poles. 100 Dobson Units (DU) = 1mm.

Ground-based remote sensing measurements and satellite measurements of the 40 km height of ozone indicate that the ozone layer over the globe at these upper levels has been depleted by about 5% at 40 km because of chlorine build up from CFC usage. On the other hand, the ozone at lower levels, below 10 km, has increased by a small percentage, owing to ozone production by nitrogen oxides emitted in jet aircraft exhausts. Satellite and ground-based monitoring indicate that the total column amount of ozone has declined by about 2.5 % in the northern hemisphere and about 5 % in the southern hemisphere in mid-latitudes over the last decade. Its altitude distribution has also been altered as demonstrated by the SAGE profiles (like Figure 2.5) measured in the Arctic spring months. Scientists are not certain what the climatic effects of the change will be; however, there is definite evidence that the ozone layer is being altered and will continue to change.

MEASURING THE OZONE LAYER

One important facet of understanding the ozone layer is the measurement of the concentrations of ozone and other gases that are important in the chemistry of the ozone layer. High-technology instrumentation is being used to study an environmental problem created by high technology industry. High altitude aircraft, large stratospheric balloons, satellites and even the space shuttle are used as platforms on which to mount remote sensing and *in situ* instruments to measure the ozone layer.

Canada is one of the most advanced nations in the study of the ozone layer and the upper atmosphere. Beginning in 1976, large stratospheric balloons were launched from Yorkton, Saskatchewan, carrying the Atmospheric Environment Service payload which is part of Project Stratprobe. This payload, shown in Figure 2.6, carries ten remote sensing instruments up to 40 km above the earth's surface to measure the altitude distributions of many atmospheric gases including ozone, water vapour, methane, nitrogen dioxide, nitric acid and hydrochloric acid. The payload was brought back to the earth on a parachute after a twenty-four hour flight.

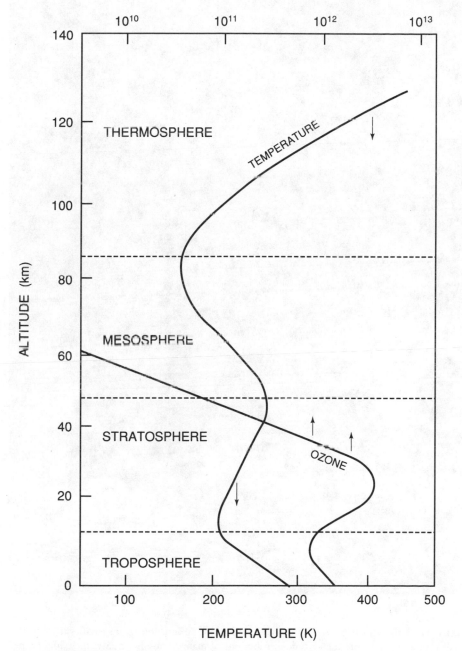

Figure 2.5: Depletions of ozone in the altitude distribution profile can be studied with the SAGE satellite as shown in this Figure for the Arctic.

Figure 2.6: This balloon payload carries ten remote sensing instruments up to 40 km above the earth's surface to measure the altitude distributions of many atmospheric gases including ozone, water vapour, methane, nitrogen dioxide, nitric acid and hydrochloric acid. The payload is brought back to the earth on a parachute after a twenty-four hour flight.

Both remote sensing and *in situ* instruments are used to measure these atmospheric gases. Radiometers, spectrometers, interferometers and photometers are some of the types of remote sensing instruments flown. Gas chromatographs, mass spectrometers, absorption photometers, and turnable diode lasers are some of the *in situ* instruments flown on balloons and aircraft in the atmosphere.

BIOLOGICAL IMPACTS

On the medical front, there is new evidence that ultraviolet radiation is more damaging than previously thought. A 1% ozone depletion will lead to at least a 4% increase in skin cancer. There is new evidence linking malignant melanoma to ultraviolet exposure and the discovery that ultraviolet exposure can lead to a depression of the human immunological system resulting in increased sensitivity to viral infections and carcinogenic factors such as toxic chemicals in the environment. It is also evident that the skin cancer rate is increasing because of the increased exposure of the general public to ultraviolet radiation resulting from such lifestyle changes as vacations in southern latitudes. Increases in ultra violet light levels are harmful to many other forms of life. Animals and small marine organisms have lower productivity. Plants and even agricultural crops may be adversely affected. Recent work indicates that soy bean, wheat and southern corn yields may be reduced.

THE GREENHOUSE EFFECT OF CFCs

Recently, we have heard many predictions that the increase of carbon dioxide concentrations due to the burning of fossil fuel will lead to a warmer climate within about 100 years. But CFCs have a more powerful effect per molecule than carbon dioxide. The greenhouse effect is so powerful that if humankind deliberately wanted to warm up the global climate by 5^0C, the current CFC production would only need to be increased by a factor of 10 above current production levels! It is expected that the greenhouse effect from CFCs will be at least a third as large as that from carbon dioxide. Currently, the CFC greenhouse effect is estimated to be about one quarter of the carbon dioxide greenhouse effect; CFC concentrations are increasing at 6% per year whereas carbon dioxide concentrations are increasing at only 0.3% per year. This effect may be a compelling argument by itself for limiting CFC usage, quite aside from the ozone issue.

THE ANTARCTIC OZONE HOLE

In 1985, scientists of the British Antarctic Survey at Halley Bay, Antarctica, using a ground-based remote sensing instrument called the Dobson spectrophotometer, noticed that the ozone column amount during the spring months, particularly October, had been decreasing since 1978 at the rate of 5% per year. When this station's data were checked against satellite data it was found that there was a crater-like structure in the ozone field over the Antarctic continent that had been getting progressively deeper since 1979, the first year for which satellite data were available. This crater-like feature, or ozone "hole" as it is called, is shown in Figure 2.7; the ozone field ranged from over 4 mm (400 DU) in the rim at 55 N down to less than 170 DU in the floor of the crater in October 1986. This hole became even deeper in 1987 and in 1989 with the ozone amounts falling below 130 DU in early October; this is over a factor of 2 deeper than in 1979! There was much debate about the cause of this hole, but the evidence now strongly implicates CFCs, since large amounts of free chlorine in the form of chlorine monoxide have been found in the altitude regions from 16 to 20 km where the hole is formed. It is thought that this free chlorine is produced by chemical reactions on the ice clouds that form in the cold temperatures of the winter polar vortex. Depletions of the ozone profile can be studied with the SAGE satellite as shown on Figure 2.5.

THE ARCTIC OZONE HOLE

Canadian scientists have been searching for evidence of a similar phenomenon occurring in the Arctic during the late winter. The bottom colour map in Figure 2.8 is a satellite image for mid-March

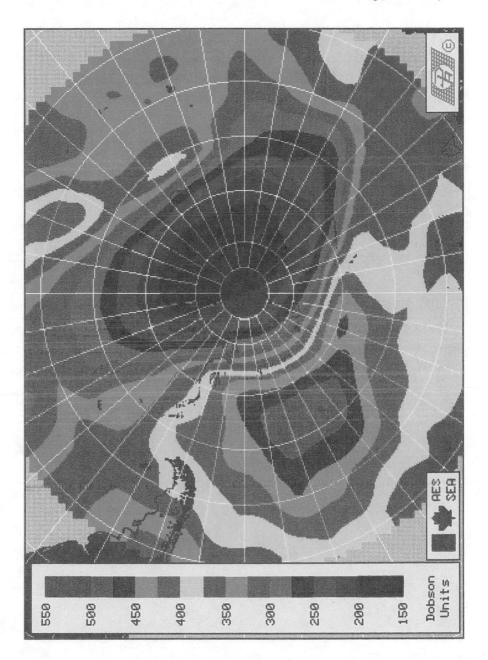

Figure 2.7: The crater-like feature or Antarctic ozone "hole", as it is called, is shown in this image; the ozone field ranged from over 4 mm (400 DU) in the rim at 55 N down to less than 170 DU in the floor of the crater in October 1986.

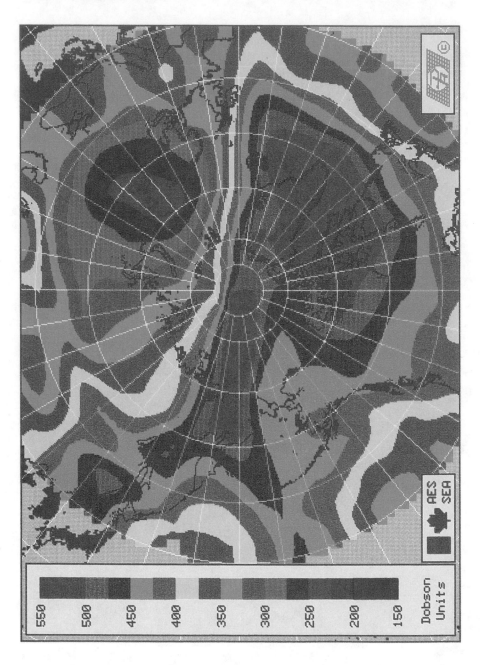

Figure 2.8: The bottom colour map is a satellite image for mid-March 1986, which should be compared with the other map in Figure 2.5; there appears to be a crater-like structure in the ozone field very similar to the Antarctic hole. Note that there is over 500 DU of ozone in the rim, but less than 225 DU in the valley.

1986, which should be compared with the other map in Figure 2.5; there appears to be a crater structure in the ozone field very similar to the Antarctic hole. Note that there is over 500 DU of ozone in the rim, but less than 225 DU in the valley. A search of satellite data from other years has revealed other structures not as obvious as this, but similar phenomena are indicated in some other winters including 1984. In 1989, the feature appeared again with ozone amounts below 200 DU for a week in late January over Scandanavia. Measurements of the ozone altitude profile from SAGE and from ozonesonde flights close to the floor of the crater have demonstrated notches or depleted layers in the profile similar to the notches discovered in the Antarctic and associated with the hole by American investigators from McMurdo Base. Hence it appears that the ozone depletion may exist in the Arctic, although it only became obvious in 1986. We do not have definite evidence that a deepening hole exists in the Arctic, but its reappearance in the 1990s would lead to the likely conclusion that a hole is developing in the Arctic ozone layer. The case for chemical depletion has been established and the appearance of an increasing Arctic hole during the 1990s is a good possibility.

MODELLING THE OZONE LAYER

Owing to the complexity of the chemistry and motions of the stratosphere, scientists require the use of the most advanced supercomputers to predict future changes in the ozone layer. The chemistry of the ozone layer is extremely complex; there are over 100 species of molecules and over 300 reactions among these species. Most of these are incorporated in the large computer models used to study the stratosphere and the ozone layer. In addition to chemical reactions, models must include a representation of the atmospheric circulation and transport of the gases including ozone. A range of sophistication of models is used, from simple "back of the envelope" models that can be run on personal computers to global climate models that must be run on supercomputers such as the Cray computer.

One-dimensional models are frequently used with altitude as the variable. Two-dimensional models have both altitude and latitude in their representation of the globe. The most sophisticated models represent the variations in the chemistry at various altitudes, latitudes and longitudes; these are usually derived from climate models called general circulation models. Models may include time as a variable in order to simulate changes in the ozone layer over future decades as in Figure 2.9, or they may simply be equilibrium models that assume the changes in the ozone layer are slow enough that equilibrium would result.

The kinds of scientists that work on the ozone problem also have a wide range of skills; chemists, meteorologists, computer scientists, and physicists all work in this field. Another development in the last four years has been the simulation of multiple scenarios in which the predictions of the increase of several atmospheric gases are included at the same time. In the past, scientists had considered only the increase in nitrogen oxides by themselves in model calculations. The result of these multiple scenario calculations has changed the outlook for the depletion of the ozone layer during the next twenty years. Because of the combined effect of all the substances that affect the ozone layer, any decrease will be delayed for at least 20 years; this makes it difficult to use the monitoring of total ozone as a early warning for global long term ozone depletion.

GLOBAL IMPLICATIONS

Although there is now concern that the Antarctic hole does permit more ultraviolet radiation to penetrate to the surface, there is little concern that the ultraviolet levels will be serious in the Arctic in late winter, since there is 15% more ozone in the Arctic to start with and the sun angle is low in the late winter. The real concern is that the mechanism producing the hole represents a new chemical sink for the ozone layer; as a result the ozone levels at lower latitudes could be affected annually and allow more ultraviolet rays to reach the earth's surface in the summer at the latitudes where most of the world's population lives. The analogy of adding another drain to your bathtub, so that the level of water in the bathtub is lowered, is appropriate. If the rate of disappearance of the

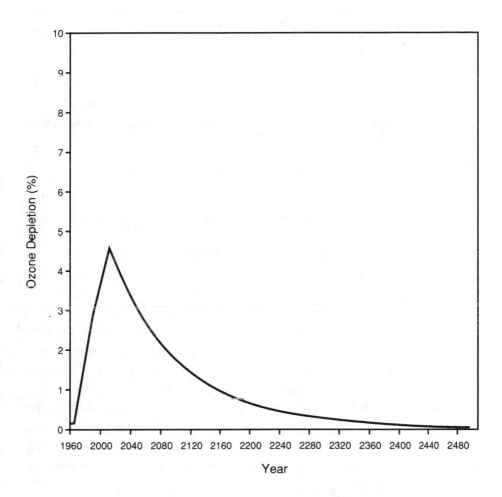

Figure 2.9: A future scenario model calculation of the fate of the ozone layer over the next 300 years from a large atmospheric computer model which incorporates both chemistry and transports.

ozone in the Antarctic is scaled to a world level, then ozone depletion may occur at a rate four times faster than predicted in computer model simulations of the effects of CFC usage using currently accepted schemes for ozone chemistry. Most of these scenario models predict a 2% depletion will not occur until the year 2030; yet the ozone monitoring records indicate that a depletion of 2.5 % in the Northern hemisphere has already occurred.

If the Antarctic hole sink is included in large computer models, the predicted ozone depletion may be over 5% by the year 2000! This is why it is so urgent for scientists to understand the cause and mechanism for the hole. Figure 2.9 shows the prediction from a simple future scenario calculation.

GOVERNMENTAL ACTIONS

The regulatory action taken in the United States and Canada against the use of CFCs as propellants in aerosol spray cans has resulted in a stabilization of CFC usage at the 1977 levels. In the United States this regulation is in the form of a total ban on propellant use, while in Canada, CFC use as a propellant has been banned only in hair sprays, antiperspirants and deodorants since these constitute the major uses. Most other nations, with the exception of the Nordic countries, have been much slower to discourage CFC usage. The most effective strategy for Canada and the United States now is to severely limit their usage. However, if global usage continues to increase, we will have serious long term ozone depletion. The Montreal protocol was a pioneering international agreement in the reduction of a global problem; under this agreement, signatory countries agreed to reduce the use of CFCs by 50% before the year 2000.

It is quite apparent that there is need for international action to limit global usage of CFCs to a safe level and provide the framework to protect the ozone layer against future threats as they occur. A United Nations Environment Program (UNEP) group had drafted an international convention for the protection of the ozone layer, which was signed on March 22, 1985 by 20 nations. In September 1987 at Montreal, diplomats from 40 countries met to negotiate a control protocol on CFC usage. On September 16, representatives from 23 countries signed a UNEP protocol agreement. Over the next year this was legally ratified by the governments of over 40 countries. As soon as 11 countries that produced over 67% of the world's CFCs had ratified it, the protocol came into effect; this occurred on January 1,1989. Under the terms of the agreement, the signatory countries agree to reduce CFC consumption to 50% of the 1986 base year consumption by 1999.

Halons are CFCs containing bromine which are widely used in fire protection systems; the production level of these compounds was frozen at the 1986 production level in 1992.

Underdeveloped countries are allowed to increase their annual consumption of CFCs to 0.3 kg per person (the United States uses 2 kg per person per year). The USSR is allowed to use 1990 as the base year. The European Common Market countriesare permitted to pool their consumption for accounting purposes. The protocol will be reviewed every four years to see if the status of scientific predictions has changed; then, if necessary, the consumption quotas will be adjusted in light of the knowledge at the review time. The first review was held in 1990, so that if harmful global effects have been detected to result from the Antarctic ozone hole by that time, then consumption levels could be lowered. A meeting was held in London in June, 1990 to strengthen the protocol. This treaty represents a unique example of international cooperation, and the Canadian Minister of the Environment at that time, the Honourable Tom McMillan hoped that it might lead to a "Law of the Atmosphere Treaty" by the United Nations. This more general treaty could, in principle, provide a solution to the greenhouse and acid rain problems as well.

CONCLUSIONS

It appears that the world's ozone layer is under more severe threat from CFCs than predicted five years ago. The Antarctic ozone hole and changes in the Arctic ozone layer have appeared due to chemical depletion by chlorine from CFC usage. On the positive side, a global

UNEP treaty has been signed to protect the ozone layer and the level of knowledge has advanced substantially. It has never been more true that more scientific research and monitoring of the ozone layer is needed urgently; in response to this need, new remote sensing satellite experiments such as the Upper Atmosphere Research Satellite are under development. This satellite will carry several experiments to measure ozone and ten other gases which are crucial in the chemistry of the ozone layer.

CHAPTER 3

MAPPING ACIDIC LAKES USING REMOTELY SENSED DATA: THE LAURENTIAN EXPERIENCE

J. R. Pitblado and F. A. Gallie

INTRODUCTION

In 1972, at the U.N. Conference on the Environment held in Stockholm, the problems of transboundary air pollutants and their deposition impacts on surface waters were brought to the attention of the world. Soon after, the number of reports outlining the adverse impacts of "acid rain" on both terrestrial and aquatic environments quickly multiplied. What was initially thought to be an isolated Scandinavian phenomena, acidic precipitation, is now recognized as a global problem, with particular relevance throughout Europe and eastern North America. In hindsight, this problem was recognized much earlier, even in Canada (see, for example: Gorham and Gordon, 1960; Beamish and Harvey, 1972).

Acid and toxic rain and their adverse environmental impacts continue to be global political, social, economic, biological and physical problems. In September 1990, in whole or in part, two international conferences grappled with some of the difficulties in monitoring these impacts and our efforts at rehabilitation. These were: the ISPRS Commission VII mid-term symposium, Global and Environmental Monitoring: Techniques and Impacts (Victoria, B.C., Sept. 17-21); and the International Conference on Acidic Deposition: Its Nature and Impacts (Glasgow, Scotland, Sept. 16-21).

Many scientists at Laurentian University (Sudbury, Canada) have participated in research projects, symposia and workshops associated with the problems of acidic precipitation. This paper focuses only on those efforts to employ remote sensing as a tool for monitoring the spatial and temporal characteristics of acidic lakes. Completed work and plans for the development of remote sensing monitoring techniques are briefly outlined.

BACKGROUND

In regions where lakes are numerous, remote in location, and scattered over an enormous geographical area, routine or even special-purpose limnological surveys pose considerable challenge and expense. Remote sensing offers a capability of gathering at least some of the surface water parameters that are required. Undertaken prior to more traditional lake survey methods, remote sensing results may then be used to guide the sampling programs of more intensive *in situ* surveys. They may also provide spatial and temporal information for a set of study lakes that is impossible to acquire in any other manner.

Northeastern Ontario provides a unique opportunity to test these proposals. Located in this area is the world's largest, single point-source of sulphur dioxide emissions, the Sudbury nickel-copper smelting complexes of the Inco Metals Company and Falconbridge Nickel Mines Limited. The adverse effects of acidic deposition on the freshwater systems of the region are major environmental and economic concerns and have long been recognized (Gorham and Gordon, 1960; Beamish and Harvey, 1972).

Over the past decade and a half, major changes in smelting processes, the adoption of pollution abatement measures, an extended strike, and numerous shutdown periods have substantially reduced airborne emissions. For example, estimated annual sulphur dioxide emissions ranged from 3,663 to 6,383 tonnes per day over the period 1970-1977 compared to the range of 1,065 to 2,562 tonnes per day during 1978-1983. In the late 1980s, those emission levels rarely exceed an average of 2,000 tonnes per day (Keller and Pitblado, 1990) and further cutbacks in emissions have been called for by control orders of the Province of Ontario.

During the summers of 1981 to 1983, 209 lakes within a radius of 250 km of Sudbury (Pitblado and Keller, 1984) were sampled by the Ontario Ministry of the Environment (M.O.E.) to compare the water chemistry characteristics of those same lakes that had been sampled in the summers of 1974 to 1976 (Conroy et al., 1978). Between the study periods, sulphur dioxide emissions from the Sudbury metal smelters were reduced by close to one-half. Observed water quality changes included increases in pH (an average decrease of nearly fifty percent in hydrogen ion concentrations) and decreases in sulphate, nickel, and copper concentrations. The degree of observed changes showed a general relationship with distance from the Sudbury smelters, indicating that reduced contaminant depositions from Sudbury sources were likely responsible for the observed improvements (Keller and Pitblado, 1986; Keller et al., 1986; Keller and Pitblado, 1990).

By way of example, Table 3.1 has been included here to illustrate the changes in pH levels (from 1974 to 1983) for a small number of lakes in Northeastern Ontario. These lakes are located in the Temagami area, within 50 km to 150 km northeast of the City of Sudbury.

Although water quality improvements (by natural processes and through rehabilitation interventions) have occurred in the Sudbury area, many lakes remain acidic and metal-contaminated. Monitoring continues to be required and remote sensing has a role to play in these efforts.

Digital data from the Multispectral Scanner (MSS) of the Landsat series of satellites have been employed since the launch of Landsat-1 in 1972 for a wide range of lake water quality assessment programs (Brooks, 1975; Fisher et al., 1979; Scarpace et al., 1979; Lillesand et al., 1983; Verdin, 1985). These activities have only been partially successful due to the relatively coarse spatial, spectral, and radiometric resolution of MSS data (Middleton and Munday, Jr., 1980; Witzig and Whitehurst, 1981; Hilton, 1984; Pitblado, 1984; Lindell, 1986). But with the launch of Landsats 4 and 5, satellite water quality assessments have been enhanced.

Table 3.1

1974-1983 pH values for selected lakes in the Temagami area, Northeastern Ontario.

Lake Name	1974	1975	1976	1981	1982	1983
Emerald	7.10	7.00	7.00	7.18	7.18	7.11
Temagami	7.00	7.60	7.30	7.20	7.18	7.26
Obabika	6.50	6.80	6.50	6.73	7.02	6.88
Lady Evelyn	6.30	6.60	6.20	6.43	6.49	6.45
Diamond	5.70	6.30	6.00	6.26	6.28	6.26
Yorston	6.00	5.80	6.00	6.19	6.09	6.01
Stull	5.30	6.20	6.10	6.13	6.22	5.97
Sunnywater	3.80	4.60	4.70	4.63	4.65	4.59
Florence	4.50	4.50	4.50	4.76	4.84	4.79
Mountain	-	6.90	6.90	6.92	7.05	6.99
Jim Edwards	-	5.60	5.50	5.61	5.82	5.72
Shack	-	5.20	5.30	5.52	5.55	5.63
Makobe	-	4.80	4.70	4.93	4.96	5.05
Solace	-	5.00	6.00	5.99	6.21	5.49
Klock	-	-	4.50	4.74	4.79	4.65
Lahay	-	-	4.70	4.79	4.83	4.82
Landers	-	-	5.00	4.91	4.95	5.07
Whitepine	-	-	4.40	4.80	5.01	4.85
Jerry	-	-	5.50	5.84	5.93	5.97
Bob	-	-	5.80	5.55	5.80	5.70
Smoothwater	-	-	6.10	5.55	5.69	5.53
Chief	-	-	5.40	5.71	6.05	5.66
Lady Sydney	-	-	6.40	6.27	6.21	6.43
Trethewey	-	-	6.70	6.70	6.62	6.92
Sugar	-	-	5.70	5.64	5.85	5.67
Aston	-	-	6.70	6.99	6.91	6.87
Banks	-	-	7.20	7.29	7.14	7.37
Gull	-	-	6.10	6.16	6.37	6.09
Kokoko	-	-	6.50	6.43	6.33	6.51
Anvil	-	-	4.70	4.80	-	4.78
Mendelssohn	-	-	6.30	6.74	6.60	6.64
Wabun	-	-	6.90	6.91	7.02	6.97
Clearwater						
Cookee						

(Sources: Conroy et al., 1978; Pitblado and Keller, 1984)

Studies in Northeastern Ontario using satellite imagery for water quality assessments have focused on the use of Landsat digital data, with most success coming from the use of the Landsat Thematic Mapper (TM) as opposed to MSS scanner data. In feasibility studies designed to discriminate between clear acidic lakes and non-acidic lakes, classifications in the order of 90% correct have been achieved (Pitblado et al., 1987; Pitblado, 1987a, 1987b and 1988).

Spectral responses acquired by the Landsat-5 TM are now being gathered for all water bodies larger than ten hectares (if they are detectable by the satellite) in the region of Northeastern Ontario that extends from the North Channel of Lake Huron to Highway 11 (south to north) and from Wawa to Temagami (west to east), an area of approximately 120,000 sq.km. Empirical relationships have been or are being derived between Landsat-measured reflectance values and selected surface water chemical or optical properties.

EMPIRICAL OBSERVATIONS

Principal Components Analyses

To find the underlying dimensions of remotely sensed data, a commonly used technique is that of principal components analysis (PCA). As described by Richards (1986) and characterized by Fung and LeDrew (1987), the PCA transformation involves three steps:

> -derivation of the variance-covariance matrix;
> -computation of eigenvectors; and,
> -linear transformation of the dataset.

It has long been recognized that multispectral data from remote sensing scanners of the Landsat series of satellites (as well as from other scanners with similar band selections) exhibit high interband correlations and therefore may involve a considerable degree of redundancy. Thus, the uncorrelated linearly transformed components are derived from the original data set in a manner such that the first principal component accounts for the maximum possible proportion of the variance of that data set. The additional components, in a descending ordered sequence, account for the remaining residual variance. With Landsat MSS and TM data it is not uncommon to find 80+ to 90+ percent of the explained variance in the reflectance data set to be found in the first or first plus second principal components.

Virtually all applications of PCA to remotely sensed data have been employed to assess terrestrial (vegetation, geology, etc.) targets. An excellent review of some of the more significant uses of PCA for such purposes, as well as a discussion of alternative approaches within the technique itself, is provided by Fung and LeDrew (1987).

In our examination of lakes in Northeastern Ontario (Pitblado and Dempsey, 1989), we have computed the eigenstructure of Landsat-5 reflectance data using mean pixel values for 633 lakes. In that analysis, the visible bands TM3 and TM2 were loaded heavily on the first component (PCA-1) and the visible (blue) band TM1 was moderately loaded on that same component. The mid-infrared bands, TM7 and TM5, were heavily loaded on PCA-2, and the near-infrared band, TM4 was loaded highly on PCA-3. These three components together accounted for 88.2% of the overall variance of the lakes reflectance dataset. They provide evidence of the expected contrast between the spectral responses of water bodies. This is attributed to the fact that water bodies, for the most part, absorb infrared radiation but are highly reflective in the visible portion of the spectrum.

The visible-then-infrared sequence of components is in direct contrast to many published works on the terrestrial applications of PCA in remote sensing. As illustrated by the work of Fung and LeDrew (1987), the normal expectation in terrestrial applications is for an infrared-then-visible series of components. There, the great variety of vegetation types results in a PCA-1 that discriminates between the high infrared reflecting targets of forest and crop land to the low infrared reflecting surfaces of plowed fields, cutovers, or lands in rural-to-urban conversion.

Dissolved Organic Carbon Relationships

In order to display contrasting PCA results the lakes were subdivided into three subsets based on arbitrarily selected categories of dissolved organic carbon (DOC). DOC was chosen because of the high correlations that have been found with this parameter and the pH of lakes. In our study areas, acidic lakes (with pH values of less than 6.0 and in particular below 5.5) invariably have low concentrations of dissolved organic carbon, unless associated with bogs or similar organic environments.

One of our subsets consisted of lakes with a DOC concentration of 2.0 mg/L or less. The actual range of DOC for this group of lakes was from 0.1 to 2.0 with a mean of 1.04 mg/L and a 0.66 standard deviation. A second subset had a mean of 3.06 mg/L and a standard deviation of 0.52 mg/L. This group contained lakes with DOC ranging from 2.1 to 4.0 mg/L. The final set of lakes ranged in DOC concentration from 4.1 to 6.5 mg/L. Here, with slightly greater within-group variation as expressed by a standard deviation of 0.71, the average concentration was 5.13 mg/L.

One would anticipate that a group of lakes with little or no (<= 2.0 mg/L) dissolved organic carbon would be highly reflective with little variability in the visible wavelengths. This is, in fact, the case. The eigenstructure of this group (Table 3.2) of lakes indicates that the visible bands TM1 (blue) and TM2 (green) load most heavily only on the third and fourth components, respectively, and explain little of the variance of the data set. In Northeastern Ontario, to explain the variance in these highly reflective lakes, one must look to subtle differences in the near- and mid-infrared bands.

Turning to the other extreme of the DOC groups, with measured concentrations greater than 4.0 but less than 6.5 mg/L, we see that the eigenstructure (Table 3.3) is the reverse of that for the low DOC group. There, the visible bands (TM1, TM2, TM3) are loaded highly on PCA-1 and the near- to mid-infrared bands (TM4, TM5, TM7) occupy positions of heavy loadings on the third and subsequent components. This reversal of the loadings can be attributed to the fact that these more

highly coloured lakes are darker, but more variably reflective in the
visible.

Table 3.2

Eigenstructure of Northeastern Ontario lakes
with dissolved organic carbon (DOC) less than or equal to 2.0 mg/L.

Band	COMPONENTS				
	PCA-1	PCA-2	PCA-3	PCA-4	PCA-5
TM4	.81683	.29187	.29963	.34576	.09168
TM3	.77896	.24608	.27155	.35891	.29471
TM5	.77052	.39471	.28362	.28125	.23271
TM7	.58217	.39484	.32558	.27416	.56904
TM6	-.29191	-.89631	-.25985	-.15238	-.14342
TM1	.32203	.32169	.82727	.28793	.15914
TM2	.48070	.19454	.34352	.76570	.16276
eigenvalues	5.67212	.53282	.37403	.18416	.14453
% variance	81.0	7.6	5.3	2.6	2.1
cum. % variance	81.0	88.6	94.0	96.6	98.7

Table 3.3

Eigenstructure of Northeastern Ontario
lakes with dissolved organic carbon (DOC)
greater than 4.0 but less than or equal to 6.5 mg/L.

Band	COMPONENTS				
	PCA-1	PCA-2	PCA-3	PCA-4	PCA-5
TM1	.85530	.20133	.31260	.20102	.25944
TM3	.80799	.23296	.31487	.26436	.25207
TM2	.79851	.14144	.42693	.29174	.22051
TM6	-.16677	-.95785	-.11389	-.14902	-.13929
TM4	.45945	.15411	.82685	.20768	.19484
TM5	.47206	.34172	.31388	.68498	.30377
TM7	.51248	.31080	.28998	.31057	.67806
eigenvalues	5.44773	.78674	.28567	.23464	.14303
% variance	77.8	11.2	4.1	3.4	2.0
cum. % variance	77.8	89.1	93.1	96.5	98.5

Separation of acidic from non-acidic lakes using these observations and more recent work dealing with water colour designations (Pitblado 1990a and 1990b) has been achieved, with classification accuracies ranging from 70% to 95%.

Temperature Characteristics

Of great interest to us was the contribution of the thermal band (TM6) when undertaking these principal components analyses. While only explaining from 8% to 11% of the variance within the various DOC categories, the thermal band (TM6) consistently appeared as the second principal component. That placement in the eigenstructure supports earlier observations (Pitblado 1987a and 1987b) that clear, acidic lakes (i.e. highly reflective in the visible) tend to be cooler at the surface than non-acidic lakes. Limnological investigations have demonstrated, in association with increased transparency, that acidic lakes may have deeper epilimnia but higher hypolimnetic temperatures (Yan, 1983). It is a great pity that the TM6 spatial resolution is so coarse (120 m). It is to be hoped that future satellite scanners will provide superior thermal sensing capabilities that will enable us to more easily detect the extremely important differences of within- and between- lake temperature differences. Even so, we are continuing to investigate the apparent ability of TM6 to discriminate between various lake types.

Multiple Regression Analyses

Multiple regression analyses has been widely adopted as a technique for assessing the relationships between remotely sensed data and water quality. Some of the best known efforts come from the lake monitoring work undertaken in Minnesota and Wisconsin (Fisher et al., 1979; Scarpace et al., 1979; Lathrop and Lillesand, 1986) and in Sweden (Lindell, 1986).

Secchi disc depth, a measure of transparency, and dissolved organic carbon are the two surface water parameters in the data sets that we have been employing that are optically significant. Much of the optical variability in the Sudbury area lakes is thought to be controlled by the presence of dissolved organic carbon. It is felt that Al is strongly tied to pH through watershed mobilization, with possibly increased rates accompanying enhanced weathering associated with the impacts of acidic precipitation. And there is some evidence that Al will interact with DOC, resulting in the loss of dissolved organics from the water column and therefore increased transparency (Dillon et al., 1984; Effler et al., 1985; Pitblado et al., 1987).

These relationships translate into successful multiple regression models where Landsat data from various bands, combinations of bands, or band ratios are used as predictors. The resulting correlation coefficients for Secchi disc depth and DOC range from 0.70 to 0.90 or greater (Pitblado, 1988; Pitblado 1987a and 1987b). Concern has been expressed that the relationships so derived are location-specific and therefore cannot be transferred to other regions or even, sometimes, to other portions of the same Landsat scene. While this is frequently true for the analysis of Northeastern Ontario lakes, the technique has been successfully applied in our study areas, with instructive information being provided.

FUTURE RESEARCH STRATEGY

The statistical work described above and elsewhere (Pitblado 1990a and 1990b) clearly identifies that relationships exist between water quality parameters (or groups of parameters) and water colour, and that satellite sensors can measure water colour with sufficient sensitivity to monitor changes in water quality. The next step is to develop a fundamental understanding of why these relationships exist and what controls them. This work will further our ability to interpret water colour and water clarity in terms of water quality and to understand the conditions under which empirical relationships will hold. In addition, because this work is fundamental in nature rather than depending on local statistical relationships, it should have application to other optically- complex inland and coastal waters.

Some of our work focuses on the development of a theoretical optical water quality model for Northern Ontario. The model is based on the reflectance equations of Gordon et al. (1975) relating reflectance to the inherent optical properties of the water body as well as accounting for atmospheric and water surface effects (Gallie, 1990). The model requires input on the concentration and optical properties of the relevant materials, and our initial focus will be on collecting this data and testing the basic model. Once operational, the model will allow us to explore the effects on simulated remote sensing data of varying concentrations and types of algae, dissolved organic material and sediment, thereby clarifying the optical basis for the empirical relationships found in previous work. The model will also provide a basis for deconvolving reflectance spectra measured by remote sensors in order to solve directly for water parameter concentrations.

The second focus of our modelling work will be to define the links between optical parameters, acidity and temperature. Much is known about the biological and chemical effects of acidity but relatively less work has been done on the optical effects. Development of the model will proceed in two steps: first, definition of the physical links between temperature and lake optics so that the influence of water clarity and colour on water temperature can be described; and second, definition of the effects of acidity on the concentration, type and optical properties of relevant materials in order to link acidity to the model. The objective is to arrive at a fundamental understanding of the relationship between increased acidity and lower surface temperatures which we have observed in TM images in Northern Ontario. Not only will this improve our ability to remotely monitor acidity and other water quality parameters, but it will contribute to a broader understanding of the role of lakes as heat sinks and the interactions between water quality and the ability of lakes to absorb heat.

THE ROLE OF REMOTE SENSING IN UNDERSTANDING THE EFFECTS OF SEA ICE ON GLOBAL CHANGE

E. F. LeDrew

INTRODUCTION

The concept of Global Change has focussed attention on the idea that a perturbation in any one component of the planet system will have far reaching ramifications throughout the system. A useful image is that a kick will result in a bulge in some other, unidentified sector. The system that is affected includes pervasive linkages throughout the physical, biological, economic, social, and political components. The significance of the polar regions for Global Change is that there are particular feedbacks between the atmosphere and the cryosphere that enhance any perturbation. The result is that the global effect will be considerably greater than that for a comparable process in any other region. The effect of the snow and ice covered surfaces of the polar regions is far out of proportion to its geographic area.

To illustrate, the climatic result of the feedbacks is clearly evident in the temperature record. In Figure 4.1 the annual averages of temperature since 1880 are plotted for the northern hemisphere as a whole and separately for the region between 65^0 and 85^0N (note the difference in vertical scales). Although the overall trends are similar, the trend in temperature is magnified approximately three times in the Arctic sector in comparison to the hemispheric values. The 'kick' is amplified in the polar regions.

In this chapter, I will review the process linkages between the atmosphere and the polar sea ice that result in this amplification and the implications

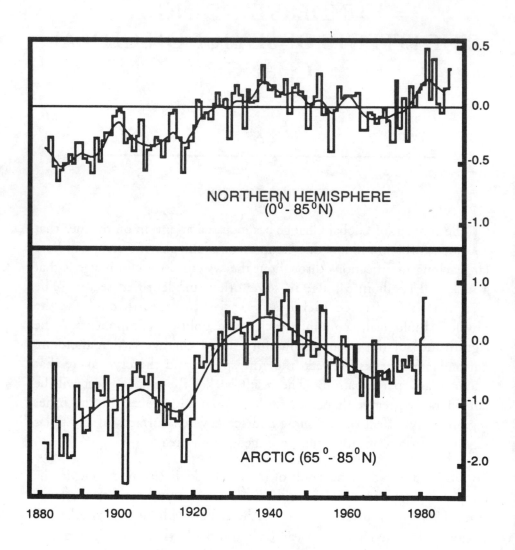

Figure 4.1: Annual temperature departures from the 1946-60 mean (Celsius) averaged over the Northern Hemisphere and the Arctic. After Jones and Kelly, (1983) and updated by Jones (1988).

for Global Change. I will also examine the crucial role that remote sensing plays in understanding these linkages and the importance of remotely sensed data in modeling Global Change scenarios.

CLIMATE VARIABILITY AND CHANGE

What is not clear from the temperature trends of Figure 4.1 is the nature of the perturbation; however, the parallelism of the trends in the two graphs does indicate that the cause of the perturbation is global. During the period of this instrumental record, there have been both significant warming trends and cooling trends. There is a variety of explanations proposed and several may be acting in concert.

The annual changes in temperature and the change in temperature trends may be due to the natural variability of the climate system. This system may be viewed as a delicate clockwork mechanism with several wheels or process loops of different sizes working together. Unlike a clock, however, the wheels are elastic with the processes changing in rate and direction in response to the seasons and the effects of other linked processes. If we trace any one indicator through time, such as temperature, there will be variability as that indicator responds to the myriad of processes affecting it. The time scale may range from seconds to centuries.

There also may be natural or anthropogenic changes in the climate system. That is, the system may be moving to a new state of quasi-equilibrium with certain forcing variables. These variables may be the quantity or quality of solar radiation, the amount of dust in the atmosphere from volcanic eruption or poor farming practices, or from natural or artificial increases in the 'greenhouse' gases such as carbon dioxide, methane, nitrous oxide, chlorofluorocarbons and tropospheric ozone. Carbon dioxide is increasing at approximately 0.4% per annum as a result of burning of fossil fuels and deforestation. Methane is increasing at approximately 1.1% per annum as a result of biological activities related to increasing human and bovine populations. Chlorofluorocarbons released from industrial processes are increasing at approximately 6.0% per year. Climate simulation models indicate that the observed increase in all of the greenhouse gases may account for a warming of from 0.3 to $1.1C^0$ between 1900 and 1980AD. Between 2030 and 2050 a further warming of 1.5 to $4.5C^0$ is anticipated if emissions are not curtailed.

The greenhouse effect does not account for the apparent cooling between the early 1940s and the late 1970s in Figure 4.1, however, and another, yet to be determined, process must also be at work in concert with the greenhouse effect. Consequently, scientists have been reticent to attribute the recent vagaries of weather to the greenhouse effect, although five of the years in the 1980s have been the warmest during the period of instrumental record.

FUNDAMENTAL ROLE OF SEA ICE IN GLOBAL CHANGE

Variability of Sea Ice

The areal extent of sea ice in the Arctic and Antarctic undergoes tremendous seasonal variations in response to the surface radiation receipt as well as the import or advection of energy from lower latitudes by means of the atmospheric and oceanic circulation. The average thickness is only three meters which means that small perturbations in the energy absorbed will have tremendous effects on the spatial extent of ice due to the small thermal capacity of this relatively thin layer. Generalized maps of the average and extreme ranges are presented in Figure 4.2. The winter extent in the northern hemisphere is approximately 15×10^6 square kilometers, yet is reduced to approximately 8×10^6 square kilometers in the summer. For the Antarctic, the corresponding figures are 20×10^6 square kilometers and 3×10^6 square kilometers. If we include the area of snow on land, the seasonal range is from 64×10^6 square kilometers to 10×10^6 square kilometers in the northern hemisphere and 34×10^6 square kilometers to 16.5×10^6 square kilometers in the southern hemisphere.

Superimposed upon this significant seasonal variability is an interannual variability or change. This is illustrated for the Arctic Ocean for the

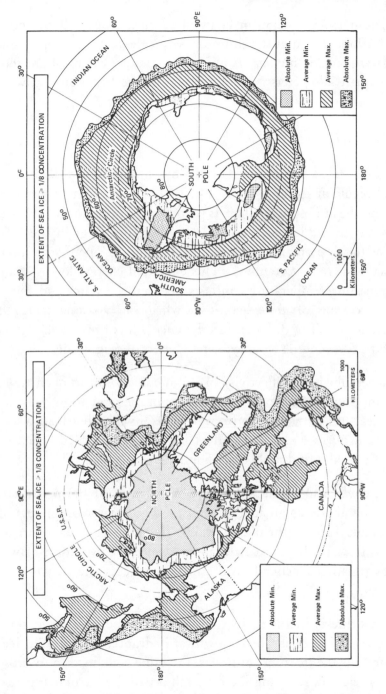

Figure 4.2: Seasonal extent of the Sea Ice in the Northern Hemisphere (top) and Southern Hemisphere (bottom). After CIA, (1978).

period from 1924 to 1980 in Figure 4.3. In the early 1950s and again around 1960, the August minimum sea ice extent was approximately 5.6 x 10^6 square kilometers. A minimum summer extent of greater than 7 x 10^6 square kilometers was observed in the late 1920s and early 1960s.

Process Controls

The sea ice serves several critical functions in polar regions. It acts as a thermal regulator through control of the energy exchange between the ocean and the atmosphere. This is particularly important for the areas of open water in the ice such as leads (fracture openings in the ice) and polynyas (large permanent or transient regions of open water). These areas act as thermal volcanoes.   This enhanced energy flow is related to the very strong temperature contrasts between the water and the much colder air coming off the adjacent ice which forces strong energy fluxes from the ocean. The difference in the energy flux from open water with that of the surrounding ice may be two orders of magnitude.

The higher albedo or reflectivity of ice in comparison to open water has important implications for the absorption of solar radiation. The albedo for the sea surface may range from 3 to 10% while that for sea ice may range from 30 to 45%. The effect is that the absorbed radiation for water may be almost double that of an ice cover.

The ice cover also modulates the wind forcing of the ocean surface currents by acting as an inertial barrier. The greater roughness of the compression ridges in the older ice also affects the frictional contribution by the surface to the wind field above, hence the evolution of weather systems passing overhead, and similarly affects the ocean currents underneath.

Initially, brine is included in the ice during the beginning stages of freezing as well as subsequent downward advancement of solid ice into the water. As the freezing continues, the brine contained in macroscopic pockets is ejected, reducing the bulk salinity of the ice in comparison to sea water. Thus the formation and melting of ice affects the brine content of the water column and hence the density stratification which

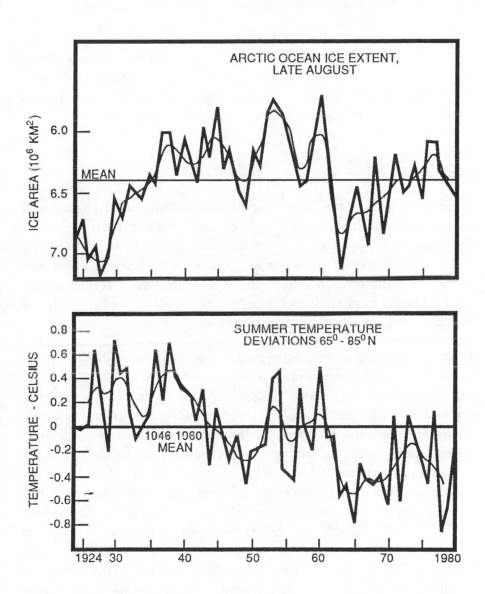

Figure 4.3: Ice extent for the Arctic Ocean compiled by Zakharov in 1981 and summer temperature deviations after Kelly and Jones, 1981 (from Barry, 1984)

in turn has an effect on the vertical circulation in the ocean. It has been estimated that 75% of the water masses of the world oceans acquire their properties in the polar latitudes (Sarmiento and Tottweiler, 1984).

The mass movement of drifting ice has an important effect on global energetics. As ice is created in the polar regions it serves as an energy source. As a consequence of the migration of ice to temperate latitudes it serves as an energy sink through melting. The spatial and temporal variability of the drifting sea ice can have significant consequences.

Potential Feedbacks

These control processes have a variety of effects on polar climate and subsequently on global climate through feedbacks and teleconnections. These feedbacks are incompletely understood, however. We are currently exploring the nature of the feedbacks and have yet to determine how they interact and affect each other. Only the simplest of feedbacks are included in the numerical models of climate which are used to study the effects of an enriched carbon dioxide atmosphere.

As an illustration, a simple model for the albedo/sea ice feedback is given in Figure 4.4. The symbolic conventions used in feedback theory are described in the caption. According to this model, a regional temperature rise resulting from warm air advection from the south would be accompanied by a rise in the atmosphere to surface heat-flux. This prompts melting of the highly reflective ice-cover which is replaced by the water surface of lower albedo or reflectivity. The increased absorption of solar irradiance forces a greater temperature increase. As a strong surface temperature inversion is typical of the Arctic, vertical mixing of this warmed air is inhibited, and the near-surface heating rate is augmented even more. A numerical model developed Parkinson and Kellogg (1979) that incorporates this positive feedback concept with an initial $5C^0$ warming simulated a complete disappearance of the Arctic pack-ice in August and September and its reappearance in the following winter. In a recent climate simulation by Hansen et al. (1984) for an atmosphere with two times the current carbon dioxide concentration, it was found that $1.1C^0$ of a $4C^0$ globally averaged temperature increase

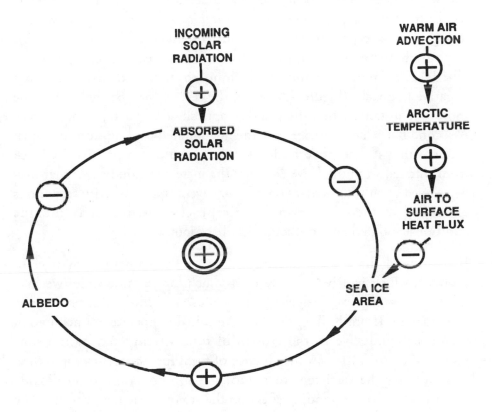

Figure 4.4: Albedo/sea ice feedback loop. The pluses in the diagram indicate each time that a change in a parameter causes a change of similar direction in the effect. The entire loop is negative if there is an odd number of negative linkages.

was attributed to this feedback. This illustrates the sensitivity of the global climate to small perturbations in the polar regions through amplification, which is a consequence of such feedbacks.

Recent investigations have indicated that there may be also negative feedback loops in polar regions. One proposed interaction can dampen the above mentioned albedo feedback effect at the margins of the pack-ice. Enhanced evaporation over open water, as well as steering of cyclones along the sea ice boundary, can lead to increased cloudiness in this region. If the cloud is optically thick, the increase in the planetary albedo associated with increased cloud cover would result in a net negative feedback (Figure 4.5) while the reverse may be the case in the more rare instance when the cloud is optically thin (Barry et al., 1984). A second but related linkage may include infrared cooling from the open water with a net negative feedback (Figure 4.5), or a positive feedback from infrared warming if we consider the increased cloud cover that may be formed from the evaporation. In any event, the sensitivity scenario is expanded to include synoptic scale processes which may include additional and perhaps conflicting feedback loops.

If we extend the albedo/sea ice feedback loop to include changes in biomass, which will be effective on a much longer time scale, we may have another negative feedback loop, as illustrated in the third schematic of Figure 4.6 (from Kellogg, 1983). An initial temperature amelioration would be conducive to the growth of forests (tempered by the slow retreat of permafrost). In the absence of fossil fuel sources in the future, this sink may be sufficient to reduce the atmospheric carbon dioxide density, with a corresponding effect on the atmospheric temperature. The net result of this scenario may be stability, an ice-free Arctic Ocean, and a northward shift of the tree-line.

We are far from agreement with respect to cause and effect in understanding such cryosphere-atmosphere-biosphere process linkages. The feedback scenarios get more complicated as we include additional processes to more realistically model the situation for the real atmosphere. The net sign of the feedback becomes more difficult to determine. Nevertheless, because of the sensitivity illustrated above, the cryosphere may be the most significant focus of research into climate variability and change in polar regions and hence Global Change.

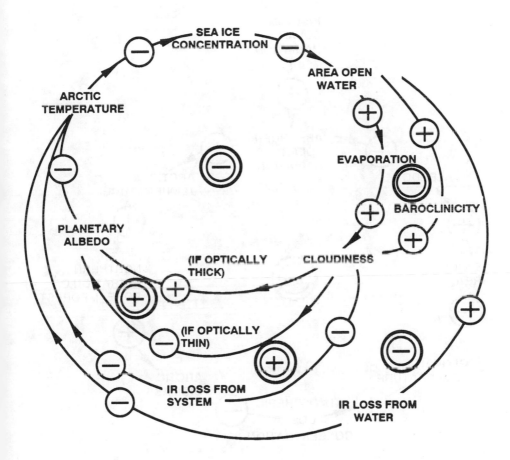

Figure 4.5: Cloud/sea ice feedback loop.

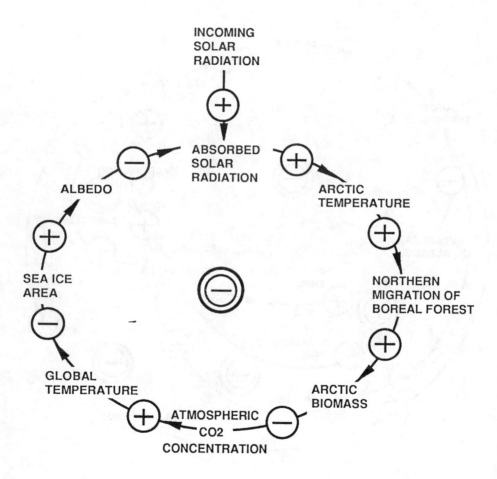

Figure 4.6: CO_2-biomass feedback loop, after Kellogg (1983)

Synoptic-Scale Linkages

The nature of these feedbacks has been explored through the study of the spatial patterns of cloud and ice that can be observed on satellite imagery. From monthly statistical analysis of the relationships between cloud patterns and the ice and snow margins, it has been observed by Carleton(1985) that there are very strong associations between developing weather systems and the ice margin in the spring season and with the snow margin for the fall and mid-winter. Furthermore, as these margins move towards the equator in anomalously heavy snow and ice years, the weather systems also move towards the equator. These relationships have been identified for both the northern and southern hemisphere.

Insight into the processes involved can be gained through study of the surface pressure patterns associated with particular types of ice movement. In Figure 4.7, the top graph illustrates the sea ice area for the Bering Sea and the Sea of Okhotsk for the period from December 1975 through April 1976 (from Cavalieri and Parkinson, 1987). These data have been derived from analysis of the microwave imagery of the Electrically Scanning Microwave Radiometer (ESMR) on the NIMBUS 5 weather satellite. The microwave wavelengths of this sensor have the property of penetration through non-precipitating cloud so we have all-weather coverage of much of the globe, which is particularly important in the cloud covered sea ice margins. Good quality data from this sensor are available from 1972 to 1976 and it has been succeeded by more sophisticated microwave systems. The major waves in the northern circumpolar vortex or westerly wind belt have been broken down into the two major wave patterns or Fourier harmonics and the relative strength of these are plotted in the next chart of Figure 4.7. The vertical bars highlight the March 6 and 15 cases. Figure 4.8 includes the surface pressure maps for these two cases. On March 6 the ice in the Bering Sea was retreating while that in the Sea of Okhotsk was advancing. Harmonic number 2 of the circumpolar vortex, which reflects the position of the Aleutian and Icelandic lows, was predominant. In the surface pressure chart the position of the Aleutian low over the Bering Sea may be seen to contribute to geostrophic south-westerly surface air flow over the Bering Sea which would account for the ice recession, while

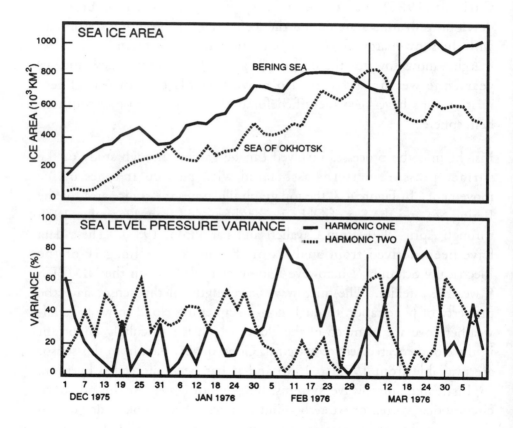

Figure 4.7: Sea ice time series for the Sea of Okhotsk and the Bering Sea derived from three-day sea ice composite maps based upon ESMR satellite data (top), and the variance attributed to each of the first two harmonics of sea level pressure derived from hemispheric analysis (bottom) after Cavalieri and Parkinson (1987). The vertical bars highlight the cases of March 6 and March 15, 1976.

MARCH 6, 1976

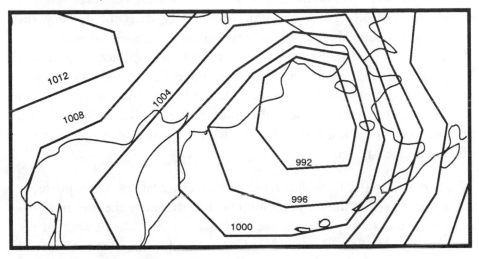

MARCH 15, 1976

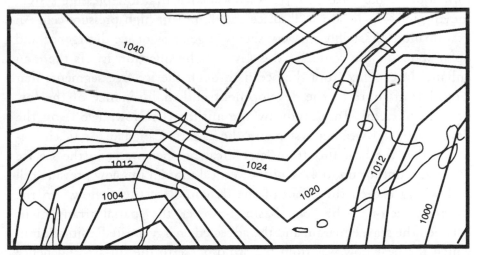

Figure 4.8: Surface pressure maps for the two cases highlighted in Figure 4. 7.

the north-easterly flow over the Sea of Okhotsk would explain the ice advance. On March 15, the ice motion was reversed and there was predominance of Harmonic number 1 which represented the semipermanent Siberian high. From the surface chart for this day, the southerly flow over the Sea of Okhotsk and north-easterly flow over the Bering Sea may be seen to explain the retreat and advance, respectively. It is clear that the sea ice margin can respond very rapidly to shifts in forcing by the atmospheric wind field, although in studies in other regions of the Arctic it has been shown that advection or import of warm air can result in *in situ* melting of the ice pack and force similarly rapid changes in ice pattern.

While these studies have illustrated the influence of the atmosphere on the sea ice, to close the feedback loop we must identify the link from the sea ice to the atmosphere. Some evidence for this can be seen in the August reversal of the Beaufort Sea Gyre. On the annual mean maps of ice motion in the northern Polar Basin, there is an anticyclonic or clockwise Gyre in the Beaufort Sea. Recent analysis of weekly data by McLaren et al. (1987) has revealed a shift on an annual basis to a cyclonic Gyre in the late summer that may persist for several weeks. The formation of the cyclonic Gyre is associated with a low pressure system moving into the region to displace the dominant high pressure cell. An examination of satellite imagery shows large areas of ice divergence and open water in the center of this Gyre. The question is: Is there an enhanced heat flux from the ocean through the ice free segments that would contribute to the development and maintenance of the low pressure system? In a study by the author (LeDrew, 1988) on the development of weather systems in the eastern Canadian Arctic, it was found that the heat flux from large areas of open water in the sea ice could account for up to 47% of the vertical motion in a low pressure cell and would exceed the effect of the dynamics of the airflow. In the Eurasian sector of the Polar Basin, however, the spatial arrangement between the sea ice margin and the advected energy created a situation in which the heat flow was from the atmosphere to the surface and hence opposed the vertical motion in the region of active synoptic development. It is possible for the enhanced heat flux to contribute to development of the depression but it is not always the case that it will.

Global Linkages

The polar regions play a major part in the global balance of energy. The role of these regions as an energy sink ties them strongly to the global atmospheric and oceanic circulation and as a result any perturbation will have far-reaching implications. In Figure 4.9 the energy fluxes over the north polar cap and south polar cap are given for annual means as well as for winter and summer seasons. The imaginary 'wall' identified for the purpose of this illustration is at 70^0 latitude. The importance of the energy advected from mid-latitudes with the circulation systems (Fwall) is evident. On an annual basis it contributes 98% to the radiative energy loss to space in the northern polar region and 106% in the southern polar region. The balance required to bring the total to 100% is the energy exchange with the underlying surface.

The long-distance linkages between climate events in one region and those in another by means of the features of the circulation are called teleconnections and several illustrations of teleconnections between cold regions and elsewhere have been identified. There is evidence, for example, for a link between anomalous cold regimes over Hudson Bay and drier-than-normal conditions over South America. Decreased ice cover and warming over the Bering Sea, which is physically related to intensification of the Aleutian low pressure systems, has been statistically linked with El Nino events in the South Pacific which are periods during which the cold upwelling of the Peru Current slackens. The Bering Sea events also have been linked to abnormally high pressures over the Yukon and Northwest Territories. There are also strong linkages between surface pressures within the Arctic Basin and those in the North Atlantic. It is important to note that these teleconnections have been identified statistically; as yet there is little understanding of the physical mechanisms giving rise to the associations and we cannot identify cause and effect with confidence.

General Circulation Models

The urgency in resolving the net effect of the myriad of feedbacks in the Arctic is evident in the discrepancies between various computer

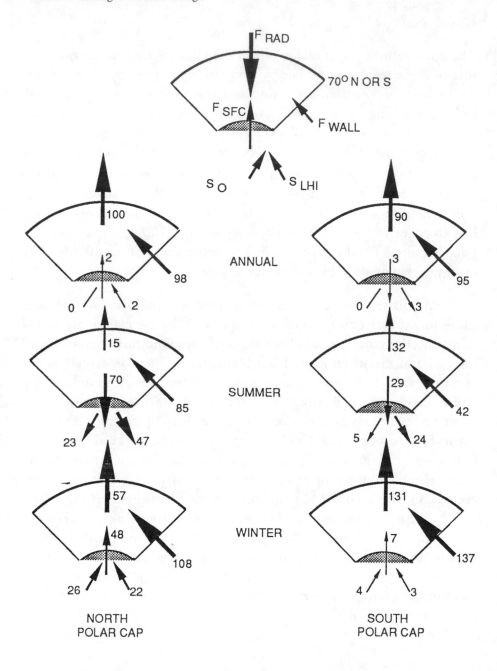

Figure 4.9: Schematic illustration of major energy fluxes (Watts metre^{-2}) for June, July and August (NH summer and SH winter) and December, January and February (NH winter and SH summer) and for the year as a whole. The data are a combination of observed and modelled data compiled by Naskamura and Oort (1988)

simulations for the general circulation of the atmosphere. In Figure 4.10 the latitudinally averaged temperature changes for a two times CO_2 enrichment of the atmosphere are presented for six General Circulation Models (GCM's) (Schlesinger, 1984). These are the models upon which climate dependent planning scenarios for the next several decades are based. Whereas the various state-of-the-art models yield similar global averages for the temperature increase, and are comparable in mid- and tropical-latitudes, they differ considerably in the Arctic and Antarctic. Some yield the amplified temperature change in these regions, as expected from analysis of observational data, while others do not. This is largely attributed to the different methods used to handle sea ice growth, decay and transport, and the consideration of the atmosphere-cryosphere feedbacks in the models. An evaluation of one model in particular indicated a weak sensitivity to snow and ice extent due to parametric limitations.

CLIMATIC OASIS

Not only is the presence of ice and snow important, but their absence in the polar regions is also significant. For a variety of reasons related to climatic and/or oceanic processes, there are regions with distinctly different energy regimes that provide stark contrasts to their surroundings. These can have considerable ecological significance, acting as refugia in times of climatic stress and therefore as conservation areas for the unique gene pools of the polar regions. The ecological character and diversity of these oases also can be sensitive indicators of climate variability and change.

Several such oases have been discovered through microclimate expeditions. A large-scale thermal anomaly on Truelove Lowland, Devon Island, studied by Bliss (1977) is an example. This anomaly is attributed to the dissipation of the normal Arctic cloud decks by adiabatic warming of winds coming down from the Devon Island Icecap, as well as to solar warming of a west-facing granite outcrop. This warming influences animal activity such as calving, and contributes to the diversity of the local ecosystem.

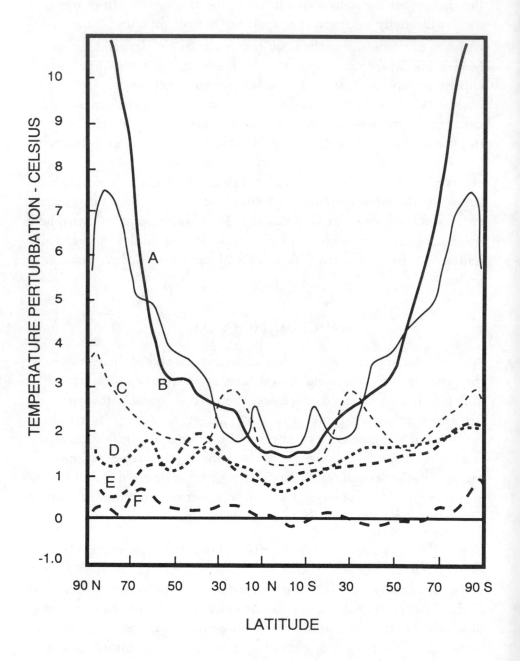

Figure 4.10: Latitudinally averaged temperature perturbations for six General Circulation Model simulations of a two times CO_2 atmosphere. Data compiled by Schlesinger (1984).

Other types of oases are large permanent or transient areas of open water bounded by land and sea ice. These are known as polynyas and have been the focus of considerable scientific inquiry. Around Antarctica, the katabatic winds that are a constant feature of the cold ice cap blow over the sea ice and produce polynyas through the effects of shear stress on the ice. The most persistent polynyas are at the mouths of glacier tongues where the draw-down in the ice cap by the flowing ice creates channels that focus the power of the wind. These polynyas are regions of accelerated cooling of the upper water layers through the enhanced heat and moisture flux to the atmosphere. As a consequence they are important areas of creation of cold Antarctic bottom water.

An interesting feature that was discovered through the study of satellite imagery is the Weddell Polynya off Queen Maud Land, Antarctica. This polynya was actually evident as a reduction in per cent ice cover as opposed to being an area of no ice. It seemed to appear in some years but not in others in the early 1970s, and exhibited a longitudinal displacement from year to year. Numerical simulations by Parkinson (1983) indicated that the wind field is an important factor in formation, but warm-water upwelling may also be significant, perhaps through wind-induced divergence in the surface currents. This area of reduced ice concentration has been balanced by positive ice anomalies elsewhere in the region, implying that as yet unknown compensation processes are at work. The polynya has not appeared since 1978.

In the Arctic a famous polynya that does recur every year, and which can be traced back to William Baffin's voyage in 1616, is the 'North Water' in the northern reach of Baffin Bay in Smith Sound (Steffen, 1989). This region has been extensively studied for more than two decades using airborne reconnaissance, satellite imagery and observations of climate transects (Aber and Vowinckel, 1972; Mueller et al., 1976; Steffen and Lewis, 1988; Steffen and Maslanik, 1988). There is clear evidence of an anomalous climate around the margins during the winter. According to observations taken by Mueller in the early 1970s (Mueller et al., 1976), the mean monthly screen level temperature within the polynya is $15C^0$ above that for comparable stations elsewhere in the Arctic, and the heating by the open water surface extends up to 850 mb. There is a clear intensification of cyclones moving through the region as a consequence.

There is also creation of storms of sub-synoptic scale. The result of this enhanced weather activity is an estimated 30% increase for precipitation in the region compared to areas outside the influence of the polynya.

The significance of these oases for Global Change is that these features, and the ice margins, are the regions of anomalously high energy and biological activity in the Arctic and Antarctic. These are the regions where change will be first evident. These are the repositories of 'early warning' indices.

REMOTE SENSING EVIDENCE OF CHANGE AND VARIABILITY

Evidence of climate variability and change does not exhibit coherence around the globe - it is not evident to the same degree in all regions. Because of the horizontal wave structure of the prevailing westerlies of the mid-latitudes, cold episodes in one region are typically balanced by warm episodes elsewhere. If the observational network is not truly representative, it may be difficult to reconcile these differences and extract any true indication of hemispheric variability and change. Even in the well charted mid-latitude regions, there are many more stations on land than on sea.

In the Arctic and Antarctic, the biases are more extreme. Any long-term stations are at readily accessible coastal locations and are far between (Bradley and England, 1978). The provision of an adequate Arctic data-base was a principal objective of the Polar Experiment of the late 1970s. Even today there are significant errors in regional weather analysis, and data for the central Arctic are missing from recent compilations.

Satellite imagery is proving to be an important data-source for mapping surface variables that are significant in climate analysis. The synoptic coverage fills in the spatial detail that is lacking in the traditional *in situ* observational networks, and for some sensors we have a consistent historical archive of almost two decades from which to draw information. The microwave sensors that have been orbiting in various generations of satellites since December 1972, with short interruptions, provide cloud penetration capability and coverage of most of the polar regions every two to three days. Considerable progress has been made in the mapping of ice margins, ice type and ice concentration from these data. As is evident from the preceding discussion, these variables are critical indices of change in surface energy regimes and hence global processes.

The out-of-phase relationships around the globe related to the wave structure of the westerlies are readily apparent in the imagery. In Figure 4.11 the total ice concentration and the fraction of multi-year ice are plotted for three-day intervals in late January/early February of 1979, 1980 and 1981 (Cavalieri and Zwally, 1985). In 1979, the extent of the maximum concentration is far south in the Sea of Okhotsk while it is far north in the Bering Sea. In 1981 the relative sea ice extents are reversed. A similar out-of-phase relationship can be detected in the maximum extent of the multi-year fraction at the north coast of Alaska versus the Siberian coast of the Laptev Sea.

The interannual variability of sea ice is best illustrated for the Antarctic since there are no land masses immediately towards the equator to constrain the expansion and contraction of the ice cover, and hence confusion in climatic interpretation is minimized. In Figure 4.12 the areas of ice extent in the southern ocean and for selected sub-sectors are plotted from 1973 to 1981 (Zwally et al., 1983). These data are from a combination of ship and aircraft reports of opportunity and a variety of satellite data types including microwave imagery. The graphs represent 12 month running means so the annual changes are highlighted and the very large seasonal cycles are removed. The decrease from 1973 to 1977, and again from 1979 to 1980, is suggestive of a notable change over the decade and have led some to believe that this is the first evidence of the CO_2 warming effect. The reduction averages 2.3 per cent per year over the period of this record. At this rate, only 20 years would be required to reduce the summer ice extent to zero and the winter maximum to 70% of the original area. Analysis by sector, however, reveals that the majority of this change was in the Weddell Sea which also showed a sharp rebound in the last half of this record. The only sector that had a persistent downward trend was the Pacific sector and this was relatively small. The strong regional variability emphasizes the need for caution when interpreting such a short record of data in terms of climate processes. The issue is complicated further by independent analysis of

TOTAL CONCENTRATION **MULTI-YEAR FRACTION**

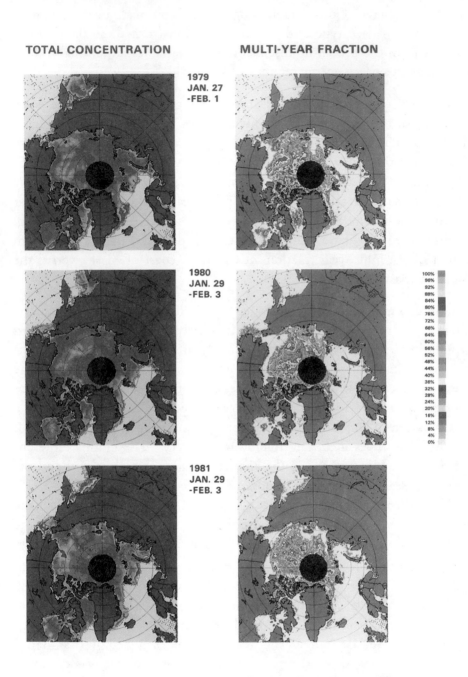

Figure 4.11: Color coded maps of total ice concentration and the multi-year fraction derived from Scanning Multispectral Microwave Radiometer (SMMR) imagery for identical intervals in three successive years. Produced by Cavalieri and Zwally (1985).

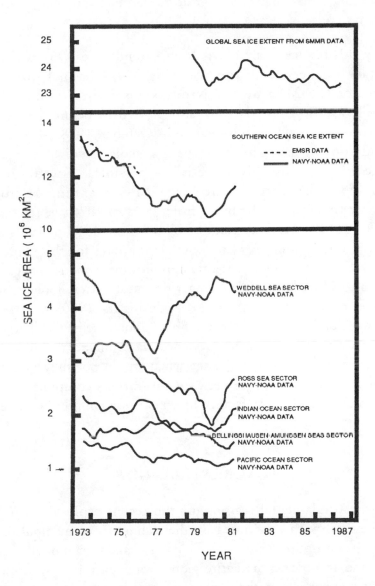

Figure 4.12: Twelve-month running means for sea ice extent in the southern ocean and component sectors derived by Zwally, Parkinson and Comiso (1983) from Navy-NOAA ice charts and ESMR data, and for the globe as a whole, derived by Gloersen and Campbell (1988) from SMMR data.

the surface temperature data for Antarctica by Sansom (1989) which indicates that since 1958 there has not been a statistically significant trend, although there has been a great interannual variability with large short term trends.

Recently this sea ice analysis has been extended to 1987 using only microwave imagery from the Scanning Multichannel Microwave Radiometer (SMMR) on the Nimbus 7 satellite (Gloersen and Campbell, 1988). These data are also plotted in Figure 4.12 for the period since the launch of this satellite in October, 1978. The data are 12-month running means for the globe as a whole so a direct comparison with the other data of this figure is not possible. If we do include comparable global data for the Electrically Scanning Microwave Radiometer (ESMR) on Nimbus 5 from 1973 to 1976, we see that the maximum global ice extent decreased by 6% from 1973 to 1986. Again the critical question arises as to whether the data for this short time interval in Figure 4.12 represent a trend indicating climatic change or are part of natural variability on the longer time scale. Certainly one would hope to see major effects in the ice cover during the 1980's when we had the five warmest years in the history of global measurements. There is an active controversy regarding this 'evidence'. It highlights the difficulty in looking at indices of Global Change when we do not fully understand the complex process linkages between the various components of the planet system. Unknown factors may mask or counter the effect of change.

FUTURE STRATEGIES

One of the fundamental reasons for the recent explosion in Global Change research is that we now have the technology to manipulate large data sets in computers with the speed necessary to model complex systems, and to observe the entire globe from space in a synoptic and consistent manner. From the satellite imagery we can derive parameters that can be studied in their own right as well as be used in the numerical models to understand the regional and global processes of change. This is particularly important in polar regions where traditional *in situ* data have not provided the spatial coverage required. From the satellite imagery we are discovering and attempting to understand atmosphere-cryosphere-ocean phenomena that could not have been imagined two decades ago.

In planning for the International Geosphere-Biosphere Program (IGBP) agenda, the joint Canada-US Working Group on Arctic Regions has identified several issues of Global Change that are particularly amenable to study in northern Canada (UCAR, 1988). The following subset is relevant to this discussion:

> "...effects of year-to-year variation in snow cover on land and arctic seas, changing the yearly pattern of energy absorption or reflection, through positive feedbacks that accentuate variations in the relatively small amount of energy available;
>
> ...global patterns of atmospheric circulation and surface energy distribution, which appear to have the effect that warming or cooling of the global atmosphere will have its greatest surface manifestation in sub-polar latitudes, with consequent effects on ocean circulation, sea ice, and boreal vegetation belts;
>
> ...the tendency for industrial air pollution from temperature latitudes to drift to high latitudes (causing 'arctic haze') and be deposited on snow, producing minor albedo changes that trigger effects much greater than those due to pollution alone." (UCAR, 1988)

Data collection is a critical element in these themes, both in terms of providing 'early warning' data for Global Change and for analysis and modelling of temporal variability or change. Remotely sensed data are recognized as providing the temporal and spatial resolution necessary for observing significant change. When coupled with *in situ* measurement in order to develop transfer functions to derive meaningful geophysical parameters from the image data, we have a powerful data base to drive integrated models of the earth system.

The following program elements were identified in the UCAR document for the sea ice themes :

> "Obtain high-resolution observations of ice kinematics and characteristics and lower-resolution observations of hemisphere-wide ice extent, using multifrequency, satellite-mounted sensors.
>
> Obtain surface observations of sea ice growth and decay and the interrelations between the physical characteristics of the ice and its growth history.
>
> Measure the geographic distribution of sea ice thickness and its variations in space and time.
>
> Study the role of seasonal sea ice in regulating the supply of nutrients to ice-edge plankton blooms.
>
> Coordinate the development of suitable ice models that can be used in interactive atmosphere/ice/ocean/biota models.
>
> Conduct year-round studies of ice biota for areas of perennial and heavy seasonal sea ice, determine the ecological factors involved in the summer bloom, and study the responses of these organisms to interannual changes in sea ice conditions." (UCAR, ibid)

This decade will be particularly important for understanding these aspects of polar variability and change as well as the global significance. Canada can play a preeminent role on the international stage. The launch of RADARSAT in the mid-1990s will initiate a massive stream of high resolution active microwave imagery of the north polar regions that will provide a level of detail now only available from the limited airborne missions normally planned in support of Arctic navigation. We will be able to study the microscale processes that are fundamental in atmosphere-cryosphere feedbacks.

In its recommendations to the House of Commons, the Standing Committee on Research, Science and Technology recognized the importance of RADARSAT and stated that:

> "The Committee recommends that studies be undertaken, or supported, by the Federal Government to determine how the RADARSAT project...could be used as part of the International Geosphere-Biosphere Program (the Global Change Project), as adopted by the International Council of Scientific Unions."(House of Commons, 1987, Recommendation 11).

It is imperative that we put these good wishes into operation and develop the science infrastructure in universities, government laboratories and in industry that is necessary to make use of these data and address the Global Change issues in a state-of-the-art manner. We must go far beyond collection and storage of the data and generate credible science. Unfortunately, there are relatively few Canadian scientists trained in the issues raised in this paper and even fewer laboratories with the critical mass of personnel necessary to provide the synergistic approach necessary to tackle some of the global scale models that are required to understand the processes. One such endeavor is described by Barber, Piwowar and LeDrew (1990).

The IGBP objectives cited above closely parallel those of NASA's Earth Observation System (EOS), which are "...to understand the processes and interactions that lead to large-scale changes in the Earth's environment, and to monitor these changes on a global basis over a significant time period of at least a decade" (NASA Instrument Panel Report, vol. 11f, no date). The plan is for a low-orbit multi-instrument platform. The Instrument Panel for the High-Resolution Multifrequency Microwave Radiometer (NASA Instrument Panel Report, vol. 11e, no date) has identified the measurement requirements for sea ice envisaged for the next decade as a basis for instrument design. The parameters include sea ice boundary, concentration of sea ice, ice type, albedo and state of surface melting. An adequate resolution of 25 km represents the diurnal range of the ice boundary and the ideal requirement of 1 to 10 km will reveal convergence and divergence processes in the ice that affect mass balance and thus heat exchange with the atmosphere.

One instrument designed to address these needs is the Advanced Mechanically Scanned Radiometer (AMSR). This sensor will have six microwave channels, each with dual polarization, and with sufficient resolution to discriminate the geophysical phenomena of interest including study of wave-ice interactions, polynya dynamics, eddies and upwelling features in the ice. The 18 and 37 Gigahertz bands are critical for sea ice. These are the same wavelengths as the most useful bands on the SMMR but with considerably finer spatial resolution of 6 and 3 km, respectively.

Considerable synergism is envisioned between the passive microwave AMSR and the active microwave Synthetic Aperture Radar (NASA Instrument Panel Report, vol. 11e, no date) planned for the same platform. The SAR X (9.6 Ghz) and C (5.3 Ghz) bands are particularly suitable for studies of snow cover, water equivalent, ice grain size and sea ice dynamics. The high resolution SAR swaths (50 to 100 m) planned for selected regions in the Southern Beaufort Sea, Arctic Ocean, Bering Sea, Greenland Sea, and North and Baltic Seas will complement the hemispheric mapping capability of the AMSR.

The science plan for the NASA EOS is in an advanced stage of development. Several Canadian university and government scientists are involved in the EOS proposal named CRYSYS which is directed by the Atmospheric Environment Service. The proposal addresses a wide variety of issues related to the cryosphere including sea ice, snow, glacier ice, permafrost and lake and river ice.

A related initiative is PIPOR (Program for Polar Ocean Research) which has been designed to make the interactions between the European Space Agency and the polar oceans research and applications community easy and efficient while at the same time utilizing the ERS-1 SAR data to the fullest (PIPOR Proposal, unpublished document). The science programs stress the process linkages among the atmosphere, ocean and ice in an integrated polar system. They involve scientists from several European, American and Canadian agencies.

The international collaboration evident in these two programs bodes well for the future of Global Change research for which the scope and complexity demands a highly integrated and synergistic strategy. These programs will be instruments that will permit Canadian scientists to have the impact that is appropriate for a nation dominated by the consequences of the cryosphere.

CONCLUSIONS

According to some analyses, we are currently in one interglacial of an ongoing glacial epoch. It has been 10,000 years since the recession of the last major continental ice sheets and the interglacials of the Pleistocene typically lasted from 10,000 to 15,000 years. It is conceivable that we may shortly, from the perspective of a geological time frame, move into a new glacial. According to the theory of astronomical control on radiation receipt (the Milankovitch variations), this may occur from 6000 to 8000 years from now.

In the short term, however, there will be changes in global climate that will have an effect on the current generation and our children. It is probable that the greenhouse effect will result in a warming before the causative factors are brought under control. We must immediately plan for the consequences which may include changes in agricultural practices, adaptation to drought, changes in international trade of food and fibre, geopolitical realignment and disruptive changes in lifestyle and societal structure. Other factors which complicate the warming scenarios are potential regional coolings that may be attributed to increased atmospheric particulate from slash-and-burn agriculture, soil erosion and industrial pollution. Additional climate processes not yet fully understood may also have to be considered in the planning process. In polar regions these effects will be exacerbated because of the potential amplification due to the feedbacks amongthe atmosphere, cryosphere and ocean. When this is coupled with the marginal existence and fragility that exists under the current climate regime, the importance of fully understanding the processes controlling variability and change in these regions becomes obvious. It is imperative that we build upon our internationally recognized strengths in remote sensing and embark upon a clearly focussed research agenda that provides answers to the nature of the atmosphere-cryosphere-ocean feedbacks and their role in future variability and change on regional and global scales.

CHAPTER 5

REMOTE SENSING OF SNOW COVER

B.E. Goodison

INTRODUCTION

The study of regional and global water cycles, including the study of future changes, requires not only a good understanding of processes, but also reliable, accurate and consistent data sets for all elements of the hydrological cycle. In high latitudes and in alpine regions, snow is a significant component of this cycle and is a major factor in short term and seasonal basin runoff forecasts. Snow can serve as an insulator for the soil and agricultural crops and provide spring moisture recharge for crop growth. Over larger areas, seasonal snow cover plays an interactive role in the regional and global climate system. The land area potentially covered by seasonal snow (i.e. snow cover that forms almost every year, but is not stable) includes 60% of all of the Northern Hemisphere and 87% of the land north of 25°N (Robinson and Kukla, 1985; Hall and Martinec, 1985). For northern countries, such as Canada and the USSR, snow is a factor which must be included in any proposed study of the energy and water cycle, or research on geosphere-biosphere interactions or climate change. Over large areas and for remote regions, remote sensing will be an important data source for snow cover determination.

Snow cover variables that are important in the study of energy and regional and global water processes, and ones which should be considered in global change/climate change monitoring and detection programs, include extent, depth, density, water equivalent, structure, wetness, and albedo. This paper provides a brief review of the ability of some airborne and satellite sensors to provide these data with special emphasis on studies in Canada. Details on the satellite and airborne sensors themselves are not discussed here. Instead the reader is referred to Kuittinen (1988), Johnson (ed.)(1986), and Goodison (ed.)(1985) for information with respect to hydrological applications.

In any discussion of remote sensing one must consider the spatial resolution and frequency of observation of a satellite sensor in the context of the problem to be studied. The greatest single difficulty for the processing and archiving of remote sensing data still involves the large data volumes produced. Kuittinen (1988) provides a useful comparison of the amount of data per square kilometre and the frequency of imaging for current and future satellite systems. Basically, an increase in the temporal frequency of observation results in a decrease in spatial density of data as there is a limit in the amount of data which can be processed rapidly. Weather satellite data, with hourly or daily coverage, are particularly useful for studying phenomena such as snow cover, which require frequent coverage. For snow studies, Kuittinen (1988) indicates that satellite data with a temporal resolution from six hours to two weeks and with a spatial resolution from 0.5-6.0 km are generally used the most. However, depending on the size of the study area and the nature of the investigation, high resolution and lower frequency data from the Earth Resources satellites such as Landsat or lower resolution data from passive microwave sensors may be totally adequate. It is highly unlikely, however, that one would try to use 10m resolution data to construct a global map of a particular element or 30 km resolution data to map distributions over a 400 km² basin.

This naturally leads to the question of the observational requirements for snow parameters with respect to resolution, frequency and accuracy of the observation. This is perhaps one of the most difficult tasks to be resolved realistically for any geophysical element derived from satellite observations. It is also something that changes as new sensors become available. Table 5.1 summarizes the observational requirements presented by Kuittinen (1988). This is a synthesis of the needs stated by the various World Meteorological Organization (WMO) Commissions which may have quite different requirements. Rott et al. (1985) present even more detailed observational requirements for land-cryosphere parameters for climatological and glaciological application as part of their review of the use of synthetic aperture radar for land snow and ice studies. A similar exercise is currently on-going within the Earth Observing System (Eos) Program of NASA. Scientists are trying to provide a common statement of observational requirements for Eos sensors and derived products. This requires a blending of optimism (what one would like to be available in the future) with reality (what is likely to be available and achievable in the future), and is by no means a simple task.

Table 5.1

Observational requirements for snow surveys

Variable	horiz.res. (km)			frequency (days)			accuracy		
	max	min	opt	max	min	opt	max	min	opt
free water content	0.03	10	1	0.5	7	1	1%	5	2
water equivalent	0.03	10	1	0.5	7	1	1mm	100	10
extent	0.03	10	1	0.5	7	1	2%	10	5
surface temperature	0.03	10	1	0.5	14	1	0.2C	1	0.5
albedo	10	100	25	1	30	7	1%	10	5

max. = maximum; min. = minimum; opt. = optimum.
(Kuittinen, 1988)

ALBEDO

Satellite remote sensing of snow cover is not new - it was one of the first applications of satellite data in the water sector. The reflectance of snow in the visible and near infrared parts of the electro-magnetic spectrum is much greater than that of any other naturally occurring material on the ground and thus in many regions, the areal extent of snow cover can easily be determined. In addition, on land, it is the snow cover which produces the largest annual and interannual variation in the surface albedo.

Albedo of the snowcover governs the amount of energy absorbed by the snowpack, and hence is important in determining the rate of melting. As well it has a very important role in governing the earth-atmosphere energy budget. Albedo depends on age and depth of snow, grain size and density of the snowpack, sun angle, method of illuminating the surface (by direct or diffuse radiation), surface roughness and the type and density of the vegetative cover (Robinson and Kukla, 1985; Gray and Male, 1981). The spatial and temporal variability of albedo over snow has been examined at local and regional scales (O'Neill and Gray, 1973; Robinson et al., 1983) and at the hemispheric scale (Robock, 1980).

Remote sensing is a data source which could be used to assist in the determination of the albedo of snow cover over large or remote areas. It is important to know the spectral reflectance characteristics of snow for different snowpack conditions at different wavelength bands rather than for the entire solar spectrum. To map snow and determine snowpack characteristics (e.g. impurities and grain size) from satellite data one must distinguish snow from other surfaces and from clouds. At near infrared wavelengths, the reflectance is lower than for visible wavelengths (Zeng et al., 1985). At the 1500-1600nm wavelength the reflectance of snow falls to almost zero, whereas both ice and water clouds will be appreciably brighter, thus allowing for the discrimination of snow from clouds (Dozier and Marks, 1987). For Landsat 4 and 5 satellites, Thematic Mapper band 5 covers this wavelength range and can be used in conjunction with the visible wavelength bands (TM 1 and 2) and near-infrared band (TM4) in the study of snow cover and its properties.

Kukla and Robinson (1980) used satellite data to estimate the surface albedo over snow-covered terrain for a specified interval. More recent work (Robinson and Kukla, 1985) developed a map of maximum surface albedo of land covered with snow in 1° x 1° latitude-longitude cells over the Northern Hemisphere in selected clear sky scenes using Defense Meteorological Satellite Program (DMSP) imagery. Surface albedo was determined by assuming a linear relationship between brightness measured on an image processor and albedo. The spectral range of the DMSP sensor was between 400 and 1100nm, where the majority of the solar radiation reaching the ground is found (Robinson and Kukla, 1985). The global map resulting from their analysis is shown in Figure 5.1.

A broad zonal distribution of vegetation is seen in Figure 5.1. In Asia the albedo rises from 0.36 over the boreal forests at 60° - 65°N to 0.76 over the tundra regions. In Canada a similar effect can be seen with the lower albedo outlining the boreal and coastal forest zones. Of note, is that the

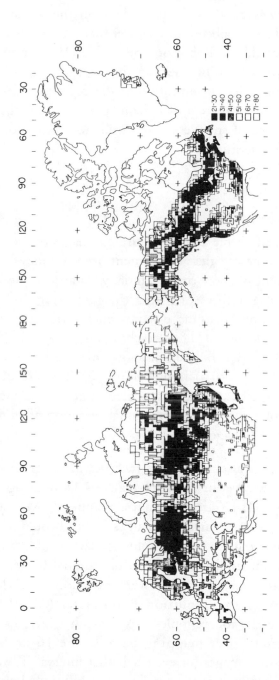

Figure 5.1: Maximum surface albedo of land covered with snow as estimated from DMSP imagery (Robinson and Kukla, 1985).

albedo of snow is very much dependent on the regional vegetation, which can produce an albedo much lower than the text-book value of 0.8 - 0.9 often quoted. As Robinson and Kukla (1985) note, this type of map may also be of use in assessing the distribution of biomass, since winter albedo provides an indication of the vegetation density. Further work in assessing local, regional, hemispheric and global albedo and spectral reflectance of snow-covered terrain will be important in future geosphere-biosphere studies.

SNOW COVER EXTENT

The availability of visible and near-infrared images of the earth since the early 1960's has allowed the development of techniques for the mapping of the areal extent of snow cover. Initially, data from the US NOAA or Soviet "Meteor" satellites provided the resolution and frequency of observation to allow mapping of snow cover extent for even relatively small basins (200 km²) if digital techniques were used (Andersen and Odegaard, 1980). A handbook of snow cover mapping techniques has been published to assist users in making effective use of satellite data (Bowley et al., 1981). Cloud cover, dense forests, and mountain slopes still present problems for the operational mapping of snow cover using visible and infrared imagery.

Landsat multispectral scanner data (MSS) with 90m resolution can be used to map snow cover in basins as small as 10 km² using digital analysis (Rango, 1985). If Landsat thematic mapper (TM) data with 30m resolution are employed, areas as small as 2.5 km² could be mapped. For cost effectiveness, the very high resolution data would be most suited to experimental basin studies rather than operational snow cover mapping. For larger basins, sensors with lower resolution (e.g. 1km of NOAA Advanced Very High Resolution Radiometer (AVHRR)) are more feasible. In Canada, for example, it is difficult to use Landsat data for operational snow cover mapping because the 16 or 18 day period between successive images (or even half that interval if two satellites are operating) is generally inadequate. The probability of cloud free coverage every 16 days is low and during that time interval the snowpack could disappear entirely (Peteherych et al., 1983). For large basins such as the Saint John River (55,220 km²), the increased spatial resolution of Landsat means that satellite overpasses on five consecutive days are required for coverage of the entire basin. Cloud cover is a problem in snow cover mapping, both in obtaining coverage of the basin and in distinguishing between cloud and snow. Daily coverage of target areas by the weather satellites is often more suitable for obtaining usable and timely data.

Snow cover mapping techniques for selected basins using weather satellite data have been reported by several authors. Andersen and Odegaard (1980) studied snow cover disappearance in small Scandinavian basins characterized by an irregular snow-line. Waterman et al. (1980) using digital methods and Johnstone and Ishida (1984) using an analogue-digital procedure employed multiple-channel NOAA/ Televison Infrared Observation Satellite (TIROS) or Goestationary operational Environmental Satellite (GOES) data to determine snow cover extent in the heavily forested Saint John River basin in Canada. Prokacheva (1985) described work in the Stanovoe Upland region where snow cover extent was mapped for basins ranging in size from 4,000-21,000 km² using cloud-free Meteor satellite images for the 1969-1981 period. Their study was to develop forecast correlations between snow-line dynamics and the volume of snowmelt runoff. Dhanju (1985) reported similar type research for basins in the Himalayas. Lucas et al. (1989) have recently reported a scheme applicable to areas of temporary snow cover, such as the United Kingdom, using daily NOAA AVHRR imagery to produce weekly composites of the areal extent.

The US National Weather Service, Office of Hydrology operates a co-operative National Remote Sensing Hydrology Program (USNWS, 1988). During the 1989 snow cover mapping season (January - July), AVHRR visible and infrared data from the NOAA polar orbiting satellites were used to map the areal extent of snow cover over the Western USA, Great Lakes region and New England. During the 61 day mapping season, 3,799 snow cover analyses were completed by basin. Products were delivered in real-time over Acronym for National Weather Service Computer Network (AFOS) using Standard Hydrologic excange Format (SHEF) format, by facsimile and by electronic mail. Such readily available snow cover products could be useful to researchers involved in biosphere studies in these regions.

For studies at the hemispheric and global scale, the most often used product is the NOAA Northern Hemisphere satellite derived snow cover data base which was initiated in 1966 by the National Environmental Satellite, Data and Information Service (NESDIS). The snow charts are produced weekly from a visual interpretation of photographic copies of daily NOAA satellite imagery. Currently, visible and thermal infrared (IR) data from NOAA polar orbiters, GOES and occasionally Meteorsat, are used in the analysis. The snow boundary is plotted on a 1:50,000,000 polar stereographic base map. The method of preparing these maps is outlined in Wiesnet et al. (1987) and Matson and Wiesnet (1981). The creation of a digitized data set of the NOAA Northern Hemisphere Weekly Snow and Ice Cover Chart (Dewey and Heim, 1982) (Figure 5.2) and the publishing of the Atlas of Northern Hemispheric Snow Cover (Matson et al., 1986), which shows monthly frequency maps (Figure 5.3) is a major contribution to snow cover analyses involving climate, hydrology, or biosphere studies. Assessment of the accuracy of this product by Wiesnet et al. (1987) concluded that except for the fall season, the data are accurate enough for climate studies at the continental or hemispheric scale. For regional studies, they recommend comparison with conventional data which may be available. As for all data sets that one might use, users should be aware of its limitations in order to minimize misinterpretation.

SNOW DEPTH AND WATER EQUIVALENT

For relatively shallow snowpacks, McGinnis et al. (1975) indicated that visible data from NOAA polar orbiters could provide an estimate of snow depth. As snow covers lower vegetation, albedo increases for depths up to about 30cm, but greater depths have no effect on brightness. Over large areas it is difficult to establish firm relationships because of the natural variability in the height of vegetation.

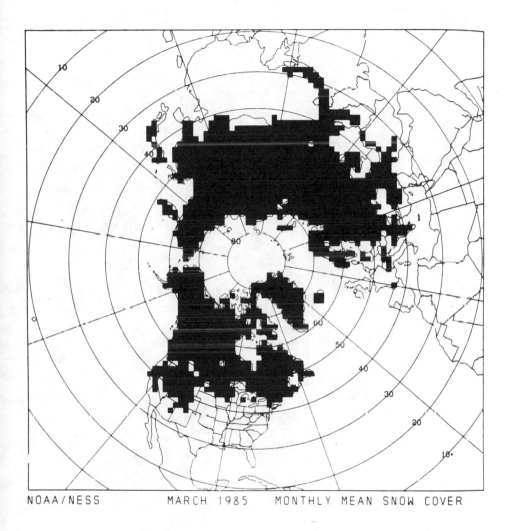

NOAA/NESS   MARCH 1985   MONTHLY MEAN SNOW COVER

Figure 5.2: Digitized monthly mean Northern Hemisphere snow cover over land for March 1985 (after Matson et al., 1985).

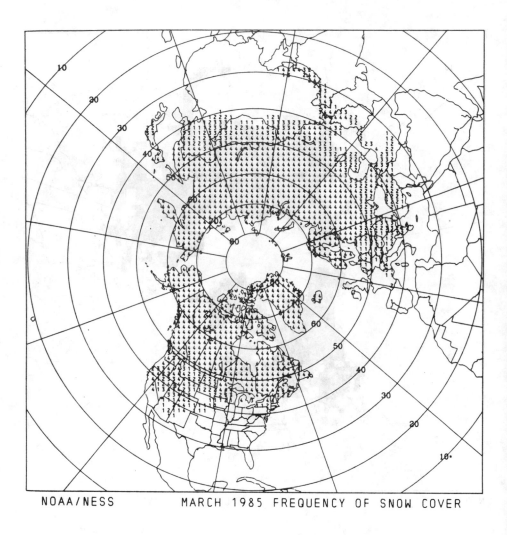

NOAA/NESS   MARCH 1985 FREQUENCY OF SNOW COVER

Figure 5.3: Monthly frequency of snow cover for Northern Hemisphere for March 1985. Numbers represent number of weeks with snow cover during the month (after Matson et al1985) et al., 1985).

However, these data can be used in combination with other conventional data to provide an estimate of depth and water equivalent. In an effort to determine basin water equivalent, Power et al. (1980) tested the use of Landsat digital data to delineate various vegetation categories in a basin and then used concurrent snow course data obtained within the given vegetation category to distribute the snow water equivalent over areas within the basin containing that category of vegetation. For many biosphere experiments where snow cover must be considered, this is one feasible method for combining satellite and ground data for the determination of areal snow water equivalent. In Finland, Kuittinen (1986) found a relationship between the area of bare spots on the ground during snowmelt determined from weather satellite data and snow water equivalent. In his study, bare areas began to form at about 150mm snow water equivalent. This does provide another method to estimate snow water equivalent using weather satellite data in conjunction with conventional measurements.

A viable and operational procedure to determine snow water equivalent using remote sensing is the airborne gamma ray method. The airborne survey method is based on the attenuation by water, in either the liquid or solid phase, of gamma radiation emitted by natural radioactive decay in the ground. The intensity of gamma radiation is measured along the same flight line before snow accumulation in the autumn (no snow) and then during the snow-covered period. Allowing for differences in soil moisture between the two surveys, the snow water equivalent is a function of the ratio between the gamma emission from bare ground and that from snow-covered ground. Typically, the aircraft might fly along a 16 km flight line at 150m altitude measuring the signal over a 300m wide swath. Each line would then provide a measured areal average snow water equivalent of a 5 km^2 area. The method has a root mean square error of 10-20mm (higher in forested deep snow regions) or 5-10%, whichever is greater (Carroll et al., 1983; Carroll, 1987; Kuittinen, 1986). The method is not suitable for swampy regions since water layers of about 450mm can absorb all of the terrestrial gamma radiation. As well, the method is not adaptable to satellite sensing.

The aerial gamma method was first developed in the USSR (Vershinina, 1985). It has been subsequently used operationally for spring runoff forecasts in the USA, (Carroll, 1987), Sweden (Bergstrom and Brandt, 1985), Finland (Kuittinen, 1986) and Canada. The technique has also been shown to be an excellent method for "ground-truthing" in the development and validation of algorithms for deriving snow water equivalent from satellite passive microwave data (Goodison et al., 1986). It is a method which is applicable in a variety of regions and landscapes and will be a useful remote sensing tool in future proposed geosphere-biosphere studies.

As noted, the use of visible and infrared satellite data for snow cover determination is limited in many regions by frequent cloud cover, and in Arctic areas by darkness for part of the year. Using sensors in the microwave region of the spectrum, snow cover could be monitored under almost all weather conditions. As well, microwaves are capable of penetrating the snowpack and responding to changes in snowpack properties. Recent investigations (Rango et al., 1979; Kunzi et al., 1982; Chang et al., 1982; Hallikainen et al., 1986; Goodison et al., 1986; Chang et al., 1987) using data from ground experiments, airborne missions and satellites (ESMR on NIMBUS 5 and 6; SMMR on NIMBUS-7) have shown that there is potential for using passive microwave sensors to monitor snow cover, notably areal extent, snow depth, snow water equivalent and wetness.

Data from the 18GHz and 37GHz channels of the SMMR sensor on NIMBUS-7, have been used to develop algorithms for snow cover properties. Brightness temperature data are available for grid cells of 60x60 km (18GHz) and 30x30 km (37GHz). For dry snow over bare soil or short vegetation (e.g. Canadian prairies), the 37GHz brightness temperature decreases with increasing snow water equivalent (or depth), due to increased scattering of the deeper snow. The 18GHz temperatures are not as sensitive to changes in snow water equivalent. Very shallow dry snow (less than 2.5cm) is very difficult to detect. Wet snow has an emissivity similar to wet bare ground and may not be distinguishable from snow free areas. However, by continuous monitoring, the onset of melt can be readily identified in snow-covered areas. In regions where depth hoar may form, the emissivity of the snowpack will be lower than for snow of a similar depth but without the depth hoar (Hall et al., 1986). Different algorithms for determining snow depth or water equivalent would be required for accurate retrieval of snowpack properties. This is also the case when deriving snow cover for forested areas, particularly coniferous forest regions, where the forest partly masks the emission from the ground and snow. Hallikainen (1984) investigated the effect of the major surface types in Finland on the microwave emission from snow-covered land and found the need to use different coefficients for determining snow water equivalent in forested compared to open areas.

Various algorithms have been developed to derive snow water equivalent and depth. Kunzi et al. (1982) and Chang et al. (1987) have produced maps of extent and depth using 18 and 37GHZ data from SMMR. Hallikainen et al. (1986) focused on the need to consider land cover type in the retrieval of snow water equivalent. Similarly, Goodison et al. (1986) emphasized the need to develop regional algorithms for snow water equivalent, in their case for the Canadian prairies. All investigators agree on the need for continuing validation of their snow cover products in order to refine and improve the retrieval procedures and to compare the maps with other conventional products. Chang et al. (1987) compared their weekly global snow cover map with that produced by NOAA/ National Environmental Satellite, Data, and Information Service (NESDIS) described above. Goodison et al. (1986) compared their results with both conventional snow course measurements and airborne gamma survey data.

Goodison (1989) extended the research to use data from the Special Sensor Microwave/Imager on the US Defense Meteorological Program (DMSP) F-8 satellite. This sensor has 19GHz and 37GHz channels and has a 1,400 km swath width, thus allowing operational use of the data. In this validation experiment, data were acquired daily and snow water equivalent maps for the Canadian prairies were produced weekly for distribution to local users. Conventional snow course data and airborne gamma data were used to compare with the microwave maps. The demonstration showed generally good agreement between the various products and indicated that passive microwave data can be used to map regional snow water equivalent on a real-time basis. An example of a snow cover map for this region for 1988 (a drought year) is shown in

Figure 5.4. Areal extent of the snow cover matched almost exactly that derived from NOAA AVHRR data. It is clear that this technique offers the promise of augmenting and complementing, if not replacing, some of the conventional observations by providing greater spatial coverage on a repetitive basis.

One of the limitations of passive microwave data was the ability to determine depth or water equivalent when the snow was wet. Synthetic Aperture Radar (SAR) data at X and C band frequencies may be useful to detect areas of wet snow (Goodison et al., 1980; Rott et al., 1985). Rott et al. (1985) report that SAR systems can provide the areal extent of wet snow, but that the application of SAR to snow cover mapping of dry snow is questionable. Complementary sensors to SAR would be necessary for the monitoring of snow cover through the entire snow season. On the other hand, SAR systems with their high spatial resolution (e.g. 15-20m) supplement passive microwave radiometer data for mapping wet snow and for mapping in regions of complex terrain where the spatial resolution of the radiometer may not be sufficient. Certainly the mapping of the extent of snow cover during the runoff period, particularly in mountainous areas, is especially important for hydrology and water management investigations.

INPUTS FOR HYDROLOGICAL MODELS

One of the major challenges is the effective use of remotely sensed data with other conventional data in hydrological models. Schultz (1986) provides a general discussion of this problem and Rango (1988) focuses specifically on snowmelt-runoff models. The snowmelt-runoff model (SRM) is one of the models that requires remote sensing derived input, specifically the areal extent of snow cover. The model has been run with snow cover data from ground-based, airborne and satellite derived observations. Rango et al. (1985) outline the details for satellite snow mapping with respect to frequency of observation and resolution requirements in order to use SRM for various sized basins. By using historical snow cover depletion curves for different basin snow water equivalent values at the beginning of the snowmelt period, an estimate of snow cover depletion during the forecast period can be made for the

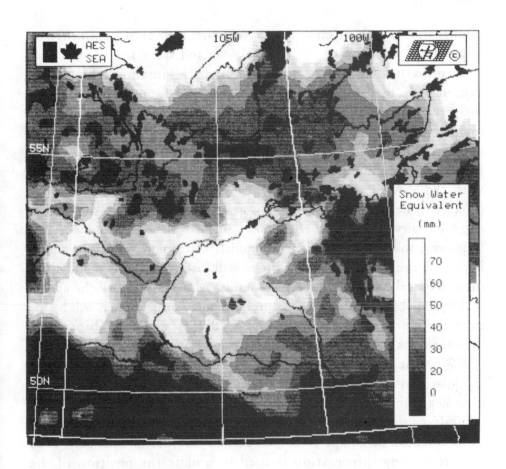

Figure 5.4: Snow cover over Southern Saskatchewan, February 24, 1988 as derived from SSM/I passive microwave satellite data. Note: snow cover values over forested areas north of 54°N are low.

forecast period. The actual curve being used can be updated with remotely sensed snow cover data that becomes available during the snowmelt season. The model is well suited to mountain basins where snow cover in different elevation zones is of importance in runoff forecasting.

Similar studies with different models for other regions of the world lend support of the utility of remotely sensed data for snow cover determination for use in runoff models. Ramamoorthi (1987) demonstrates that snow-covered area, as derived from NOAA AVHRR imagery, is the main factor in forecasting seasonal snowmelt runoff in the major mountain basins of the Himalayas. In western Canada, Ferner and Sutherland (1987) found computer processed NOAA satellite data for a 2,200 km² mountainous basin to be useful for snowmelt modelling with the SSARR (Streamflow Synthesis and Reservoir Regulation) forecast model. The NOAA data were used to update the snow cover depletion curve rather than relying on a single depletion calculation, thus improving the performance of the model. As remote sensing products become more readily available, there will be increasing demand for a more physically based hydrological model which would use the spatial and temporal information derived from remote sensing. Such will be the case for studies of global change and for geosphere-biosphere investigations as part of Global Energy and Water Cycle Experiment (GEWEX) or IGBP. Fortin et al. (1985) report on efforts to develop a modular grid-square forecasting model based on remotely sensed data. One key component is the updating of snow-covered area and water equivalent using satellite data. In their approach, the modelled map of snow cover can be compared to that derived from satellite imagery. The remote sensing information is used to update the position of the snowline and the water equivalent from the percentage of snow cover area of each grid cell. This development work is continuing as the HYDROTEL (acronym) model.

CONCLUSIONS

This paper has provided a brief review of the current status of the remote sensing of snow cover, with special emphasis on hydrological applications. Areal snow cover information is an important element for the study of regional, hemispheric and global water balances. For the future, many international projects are being proposed within UNESCO's Man and the Biosphere Programme and International Hydrological Programme, the International Geosphere-Biosphere Programme (IGBP) and the World Climate Research Programme. The study of water and energy budgets will be a focus of many of them, particularly in the context of global change. Coordination among these studies and between agencies and scientists is of utmost importance.

For snow cover data, like many other remotely sensed elements, to become a fully accessible and useful component in future regional and global studies of the energy and water balance and change detection, several actions need to be considered. These include:

- Integration of conventional and remotely sensed data to create more complete snow cover data sets;

- Creation of regional data bases for key regions for monitoring climate change impacts;

- Continuation of development and validation of algorithms to derive snow cover depth and water equivalent from microwave data for different biomes;

- Establishment of a data management system which will allow effective use of satellite derived information for hydrological, agricultural and climatological purposes, at various temporal and spatial scales; and,

- Cooperation between national and international agencies and international programmes (e.g. MAB, IHP, WCRP, IGBP) to maximize the efficient use of resources.

These recommendations apply to more than just snow studies. Hopefully, there will be progress in this direction in the near future.

CHAPTER 6

GLOBAL CHANGE: IMPACT ON OCEANS AND FISHERIES, CONTRIBUTIONS OF REMOTE SENSING TO FUTURE STUDIES

J.F.R. Gower

INTRODUCTION

The fact that the oceans cover about 70% of the surface of the earth gives them an automatic major role in climate and global studies. Their enormous heat capacity compared to the atmosphere (the top 2.5m of the ocean has as much capacity as the atmosphere above it, while mean ocean depth is about 3,800m) means that the ocean provides the greatest part of the thermal inertia that will moderate rapid change in climate, or perpetuate a change once made. The properties of the atmosphere (particularly cloud cover) largely determine the radiation balance of the earth with in-coming solar radiation, but the oceans are responsible for about half of the heat flux away from the equator, and contain most of the carbon that determines the long-term greenhouse effect.

Many other properties of the ocean are directly important to humankind, and are expected to change with any long-term climate variations. These include changes in sea level, polar ice, storm tracks and fish populations. A slightly less direct, but very significant, effect would be changes in mean precipitation patterns over large areas.

In terms of the present discussion, which concerns the contribution that can be made by remote sensing to monitoring and understanding global change, the inaccessibility and expanse of the oceans make observations from satellites relatively more important than in the case of land. Satellite observations also make use of techniques such as scatterometry and altimetry which can only be applied over large areas of open water.

BACKGROUND FACTS ON CLIMATE CHANGE

> Who sees with equal eye as God of all,
> A hero perish or a sparrow fall,
> Atoms or systems into ruin hurl'd,
> And now a bubble burst, and now a world.
> (Alexander Pope, from "An essay on man")

The equilibrium temperature for the earth can be calculated as T_s X square root $(a_s/2)$, where T_s is the effective temperature of the sun, and a_s is the apparent angular radius of the sun in radians. This assumes both earth and sun are thermodynamically "black" (zero albedo). Given that the sun appears 32 arc minutes in diameter and has an effective temperature of 5785^0K (degrees absolute), the result is 279^0K, or 6^0C. In fact, the cloud cover of the earth increases the albedo in the visible, while thermal albedo remains near zero. This reduces the calculated absolute temperature by the fourth root of (1 - the optical albedo), ie to -18^0C for the mean global albedo value of 0.3 (Stephens et al., 1981).

Radiatively active gases in the atmosphere have maintained the earth's mean temperature about 33^0C warmer than this calculated value, giving it a comfortable average of 15°C for much of its history. Mean temperatures have dropped about 10°C in ice ages, (Barnola et al., 1987), while recent climatic variations referred to as the "Medieval warm epoch" (800-1200 AD) and the "Little ice age" (1400-1800 AD) correspond to average temperature changes of less than 1^0C. The above figures show that even a slight increase in average global optical albedo, due to greater cloud-cover or to volcanic eruptions, can cause a significant temperature drop (Ramanathan et al., 1989). Any resulting glaciation will raise the albedo further, causing more cooling. The possibility of such an instability leading to an "run-away" ice age was a major concern of climate studies in the 1970's (Budyko, 1974).

The clearest signal of a change in the present global environment is the increase in atmospheric CO_2 concentration. Linked to increases in other radiatively active greenhouse gases, this is predicted to lead to a global warming with far-reaching consequences (Bolin et al., 1986;

Ramanathan, 1988; Ramanathan et al., 1989). It is generally agreed that doubling the CO_2 will cause a global temperature increase of several degrees (1.5 to 5.5^0C, Bolin et al., 1986), although the expected increase in optical albedo, due to increasing cloud and leading to cooling, is one of the major sources of uncertainty. The CO_2 increase is only one of a number of other effects of human activities which are described in a very readable article by McKibben (1989) as implying the "end of nature."

The atmospheric CO_2 change has been observed directly since 1958, but has recently been measured in air bubbles trapped in ice cores back to 160,000 years ago. The concentration has varied from 180 to 300 parts per million over this period, with higher values correlating with warmer temperatures (Barnola et al., 1987).

Compared to these past changes, the present observed atmospheric CO_2 increase is very rapid, from about 275 ppm in 1850, to the level of over 350 today. The increase is only half as great as expected from known human activities (fossil fuel burning, deforestation), and it is supposed that the other half has been dissolved in the oceans. It is, however, an open question as to what extent the oceans can continue to absorb such a large fraction. The surface waters become rapidly saturated. Continued absorption depends on water exchange with deeper layers, and on the extent to which the carbon in CO_2 fixed in photosynthesis leaves the surface layers and sinks to the sea floor. Table 6.1 summarizes the global carbon inventory.

Only the first two fluxes represent the results of human activities. It can be seen that only 3.3 billion tons (Bt) of the 6 Bt introduced annually into the atmosphere is observed to stay there, and to lead to the observed increase in CO_2 concentration. A slow increase in upper ocean CO_2 concentration has been reported, which could account for the remainder, but the figures are very uncertain. Annual ocean photosynthesis of 40 Bt is vastly greater than the missing carbon, but most of this is recycled in the surface layers. An increase in the small fraction (about 10%) which is lost to the sea floor and must be made up each year as "new production" would also contribute to balancing the increased input to the atmosphere.

Table 6.1

Carbon in billions of tons (Bt) or 10^{15} grams:

Inventory:

In the ocean:	40,000
In the atmosphere:	740 (350 ppm)
In the biosphere:	600
In soil:	1,400
In oil, coal, gas	15-20,000
In sedimentary rocks	20,000,000
Earth's core and crust	2×10^{11}

Fluxes (per year):

Human input to atmos.:	6
Observed atmos. rise:	3.3
Air/sea exchange:	90
Air/land exchange:	120
Upper ocean increase:	0.3 - 3
Ocean photosynthesis:	40
Flux to bottom:	4?
Volcanoes on land:	.05
Sea-floor spreading:	.05

The above carbon budget is based on Bolin et al. (1986). The huge amount given above for the earth's core and crust assumes that 3% is carbon. This enters into the atmosphere through volcanoes, and into the deep ocean through sea floor spreading. Fluxes are based on Arthur et al (1985). More recently Gerlach (1989) gives a number 10 times smaller for the sea floor spreading (mid-ocean ridge) flux. The reserves of coal, oil and gas include an estimated 10,000 Bt of methane clathrate whose partial transfer to and from the atmosphere may have important effects on climate (Macdonald, 1990).

Given the dramatic climate changes that are known to have occurred in the past, humanity is right to feel nervous.

EFFECTS ON THE OCEAN

Ocean circulation is important in distributing the dissolved carbon and, at the same time, heat and salt. It is estimated that half of the global heat transported pole ward (across 30°) is carried by the ocean, and half by the atmosphere. However the accuracy of this estimate is only ±25-50%.

One suggestion, illustrating the possible sensitivity of this transport to climate change, is that the global-scale thermohaline circulation of the oceans, whose net effect is to take heat from the southern Pacific and releases it in the northern Atlantic, might be subject to sudden interruptions (Broecker, 1987). There is evidence that these have been triggered in the past by fresh-water inflow. The resultant cooling could have a disastrous effect on the climate of Europe. A slight warming, on the other hand, could lead to an ice-free Arctic, and cause a strong increase (Roots, 1989) or decrease (Marko et al., 1992) in the number of icebergs off the Canadian east coast.

A link has also been suggested between marine primary productivity and global albedo, through the production of cloud condensation nuclei from the emitted dimethyl sulphide (Charlson et al., 1987; Ayers, et al., 1991). This provides another feedback mechanism in the climate problem.

The oceans are also expected to have an effect on human activities through a rise in mean sea level, due to a combination of thermal expansion and melting of ice caps and glaciers. The rise is estimated at anywhere from .2 to 1.5m per century, but will be masked locally by tectonic and post-glacial movements (Bolin et al., 1986). The rise will also be affected by changes in ocean circulation (Mikolajewicz, 1990). Since so many cities are built on low-lying land, this could be the most important immediate climate-related effect (Bardach, 1989).

Shorter time scale variations indicate the contribution of the oceans to the instability of the world's climate. The most famous example is the ENSO (El Nino/Southern Oscillation) in which the interaction of winds and warm surface water in the tropical Pacific changes state for a period of a few months at intervals of 3-4 years (Cane and Zebiak, 1985), causing alterations in ocean and weather patterns that affect roughly half the globe for about half a year. The phenomenon is now closely monitored, partly for prediction of the resulting changes, and partly so that it can be used as a tool in climate research.

EFFECTS ON FISHERIES

"Of all the human endeavors, no activity has been so consistently fruitless as fisheries management."

"Essentials of
Oceanography,"
H.V. Thurman, 1990.

In his book "Climate and Fisheries," Cushing (1982) gives an interesting review of historical changes in fisheries, emphasizing evidence for climatic influences. Recently, the efficiency of fishing gear and the high capability of world fishing fleets have meant that harvesting has been a dominant cause of the variation and disappearance of many commercial stocks. These dramatic, human-induced changes make it hard to be certain of climatic effects. The separation of natural causes from overfishing is discussed by Kawasaki (1985). Fluctuating fish populations have made management a frustrating task, as noted by Thurman, above (1990).

In general, world fisheries have increased to the level where 10 to 20% of the top predators of the ocean are harvested every year. Reduction of the rate of increase with time suggests that we are near the maximum yield for presently fished species. Recently, exhausted stocks have been replaced by larger commercial harvests of species at lower trophic levels, helping to maintain the increase. Growth of aquaculture will cause new impacts on the ocean environment.

Climatic effects must be expected, but predictions are very uncertain. The transactions of a 1988 symposium on "Effects of climate change on fish" (Regier et al., 1990) concluded that progress was being made "...in efforts to adapt the scientific method to forecast the potential effects...".

The indirectness of this type of progress reflects the problems involved. A more recent special issue of the journal "Fisheries" contains papers using past changes in fishery patterns as examples (Glantz, 1990) and calling for increased monitoring efforts to watch for future changes (Regier and Meisner, 1990).

Changes in ocean circulation must be expected to affect the patterns of primary productivity. A recent paper (Bakun, 1990) presents evidence for world-wide intensification of the wind stress that drives coastal upwelling. Data series span only 1950 to 1985, but all show an increasing trend. Bakun points out that a CO_2 increase would be expected to have this effect through an increase in the temperature contrast between land and ocean. At the same time a reduced temperature contrast between equatorial and polar areas should slow the large scale ocean circulation.

Species and productivity distributions are strongly influenced by climate. Southern and northern limits of populations must be expected to move (eg. for salmon, squid, tuna, mackerel). The temperature limits of many species have been measured, but little is known about the effect of bottom temperatures on groundfish.

It has been noted that human-induced global change will be much faster than natural climate change, giving species much less time to adapt. On the other hand, the historical changes discussed by Cushing (1982) were all in response to sudden events with possible links to climate change. It has been suggested that changes in migration patterns of salmon on the west coast of Canada may be related to shorter-term temperature variations associated with El Nino (Mysak, 1986).

Fresh-water fisheries would be strongly affected by climate changes. Lakes exist because of precipitation excess over evaporation, and small changes in temperature or rainfall could easily lead to some of them drying out. Melting of permafrost could lead to an increase in lake area further north. A review of the problem, with suggested research requirements, has been prepared for the Canadian prairies and central Arctic (Hecky, 1987).

Glantz (1990) and Glantz and Feingold (1990) present summaries of the dramatic fluctuations that have affected fisheries in the past, and draw "lessons" about future effects of climate change. We should prepare to be flexible, and hope that whatever survives in the ocean is either palatable or valuable in some other way. There is no suggestion of any active role for fisheries management beyond attempting to reduce catch rates, but perhaps advances in aquaculture will change this view.

MAJOR PROGRAM COMPONENTS

The World Climate Research Programme wasstarted in response to concern about future climate changes. This in turn led to three major international ocean-related programs, TOGA, WOCE and JGOFS, which together should lead to greater understanding of the ocean's role in climate change.

The World Ocean Circulation Experiment (WOCE) is an international program of observation and modelling aimed at understanding the role of the oceans in the global heat budget. The immediate aim is to develop models useful for predicting climate change, while collecting the data necessary to test them. Three core projects have been identified:

- A global description based on extensive measurements which will provide a quantitative assessment of fluxes of heat and water in critical sections;

- A study of the entire Southern Ocean adjacent to Antarctica, which provides a connection between all other oceans; and,

- A gyre dynamics experiment which will study the North Atlantic basin in enough detail to allow major advances in modelling techniques, which can then be applied to other basins.

The first two projects will obtain a global circulation field using sea surface topography derived from satellite altimetry, from surface and deep drifters and from three-dimensional tracer fields. The

TOPEX/Poseidon mission will carry the precise altimeters and tracking system required for this, although earlier altimeter missions (GEOS-3, Seasat, and Geosat) have provided important data for planning purposes, and ERS-1 will also contribute in the near future.

WOCE will work closely with the Tropical Ocean Global Atmosphere (TOGA) experiment which is already underway in the tropical regions (20 degrees north to 20 degrees south). Many of the observing systems put in place for TOGA will simply be extended to higher latitudes for WOCE and the distinction between the two programs will gradually disappear.

Because of the major importance attached to modelling, the WOCE program requires a major effort in assimilation of remote sensing data into the models. This includes investigations of model behaviour to insertion of remotely sensed surface temperatures and topography, interpretation of interannual topography variations in terms of circulation and heat transport, and testing of procedures for estimating eddy transports of heat and freshwater based on satellite observations of altimetric variability.

Since WOCE will involve dealing with data sets covering large areas, remote sensing products will become more important. There is a need to develop facilities, including groups of scientists and technicians, for analysing and using such data. In addition, better data transmission capabilities are needed if such data are to be used in day-to-day operations before the end of the WOCE period.

The Joint Global Ocean Flux Experiment (JGOFS) is an international program to understand the exchange of carbon and associated elements in the ocean, and to investigate the related exchanges with the atmosphere, sea-floor and continental margins. A longer-term goal is to develop strategies for observing and predicting changes in ocean bio-geochemical cycles in relation to climate change.

An essential characteristic of JGOFS is that the fluxes are to be measured at regional and global scales. This means that, as for WOCE, conventional ship-borne oceanography has to be supplemented by studies based on remote sensing. Estimates of primary productivity on ocean basin scales require satellite observations because of variability in space and time.

Remotely sensed data of ocean colour can be used to interpret concentrations of phytoplankton pigments, and algorithms are being developed to allow estimation of primary production. Because carbon dioxide is an important component of photosynthesis, the study of marine primary production is an essential element of research into the greenhouse effect.

To improve the contribution that can be made by remote sensing, important tasks are to develop methods for integration of satellite-based and ship-based data on bio-geochemical properties of the ocean, methods for estimation of carbon fixation by phytoplankton from remotely sensed data, expertise in marine optics, and statistical procedures for integrating remotely sensed results to give reliable averages at a large scale.

Although the above two experiments represent the major focus of large scale climate research, a variety of other measurements will contribute. The warming of the ocean in response to the greenhouse effect may be measurable in historical time series of direct observations. Freeland (1990) presents the data for shore stations on the west coast of Canada. One interesting recent suggestion is to measure the mean, large scale warming of the ocean directly using acoustic travel times over very long paths. The expected change of .005C per year should cause a change of 0.1 to 0.2 seconds per year in travel time over a hemispheric path. Noise from mesoscale variations is expected to be about 1s. A 10 year experiment with a sound source on Heard Island in the southern Indian Ocean, and receivers around the world, should be able to measure the change and study some of the regional variations (Munk and Forbes, 1989).

A NATIONAL RESPONSE

The above summary of problems gives a global perspective to climate change, and WOCE and JGOFS describe programs representing an international response. How might an individual country react? The points below are the conclusions of a study undertaken by the Canadian Department of Fisheries and Oceans (Department of Fisheries and Oceans, 1989), titled "Global warming, the oceans, and Canada's fisheries" and submitted to the House of Commons Standing Committee on Environment. Similar conclusions would probably be reached by other government departments (with suitable changes in wording) both in Canada and abroad.

- Global warming could have an important impact on fisheries, ocean users and coastal residents.

- Improved scientific understanding and data are needed on the response of local areas and of fish populations to large scale changes. Such knowledge would also be immediately useful.

- "Strategies for fisheries management in conditions of change and uncertainty" are also needed. Such knowledge would also be immediately useful.

- Present projections of warming are uncertain, largely because of deficient knowledge of the oceans' role in transporting heat poleward and in mediating greenhouse gas build-up. Canada should participate in international efforts to address this.

- Canada needs improved large scale modelling capability, so as to be able to conduct independent and credible simulations of global warming.

- World-wide concern offers a market for Canadian knowledge-based industry.

- Canadian scientists have been active in climate change research, in both oceans and fisheries, and have the necessary expertise.

The above conclusions give the principal reasons for a national organization, in this case a Federal department responsible for fisheries management and ocean science, to participate in climate research. In

Canada's case, ship time is potentially available to take part in cruises. Image and data processing equipment are available for work on satellite remote sensing data. In both cases some up-grading will be necessary to meet the new, expanded research goals.

SATELLITE REMOTE SENSING TECHNIQUES

The large scale international experiments will make extensive use of satellite measurements of the ocean. The techniques have been reviewed before (SCOR Working Group 70, 1986, Canadian Global Change Program, 1989), and only a brief summary is given here.

Visible imagery

Optical measurements from space need to be made with high sensitivity in specific, narrow spectral bands, if they are to sense the colour changes caused by variations in phytoplankton pigments in near-surface sea water. As a result, the imaging sensors designed for use over land, such as the Landsat TM and MSS, or over cloud, such as the AVHRR, are only useful for mapping strong sediment patterns in coastal waters, or bright (eg. coccolithophore) blooms offshore. Global mapping of cloud cover from the geosynchronous GOES satellites has been used for mapping solar irradiance.

Only the CZCS, launched on the NASA satellite Nimbus 7, has so far provided the required radiance measurements for phytoplankton mapping. The sensor operated with diminishing efficiency from 1979 to 1986. Algorithms have been developed for processing the data (Gordon et al., 1983), to form global maps of pigment concentrations and hence of near surface irradiance attenuation. Recent work is directed at deducing primary production (Platt and Sathyendranath, 1988) and new production rates (Dugdale et al., 1989). A replacement sensor, although technically relatively simple, is not scheduled before about 1994 (SeaWIFS or OCTS on ADEOS). Future imaging spectrometer sensors should improve the capability of this type of measurement.

Infrared imagery

Measurements of sea surface temperature from space play an important part in the JGOFS, WOCE and TOGA programs. The AVHRR has been shown to be capable of measuring to better than 1 degree accuracy under cloud-free conditions (Bernstein, 1982). The ATSR, now in orbit on ERS-1, makes use of active cooling to give higher sensitivity, and dual viewing of the surface to improve correction of the measurements for atmospheric attenuation.

Altimetry

Precision of satellite measurements of sea surface height variations in response to water motion on the rotating earth has increased dramatically, from the 20-30cm of the GEOS-3 mission through the 7cm of Seasat to the 3cm of Geosat. This has allowed eddy fields and ocean height variability to be mapped for the first time. The accuracy of geoid and satellite orbit determination needed for deduction of absolute heights has also improved. Geosat ceased operation in 1990 after 5 years. ERS-1 is now in orbit to continue providing data. Recent summaries of results are given by Douglas and Cheney (1990) and Zlotnicki et al. (1989). Assimilation of altimeter data into models is discussed by Holland and Malanotte-Rizzoli (1989).

Passive microwave radiometry

Microwave radiometry is, in principle, capable of giving sea surface temperature through cloud, but has not so far achieved sufficient accuracy to replace infrared techniques (Liu, 1983). Measurements have been used for mapping ice (Parkinson and Cavalieri, 1989), water vapour and wind (Goodberlet et al., 1989). Sensors include the ESMR (1973 to 1979), SMMR (1978 -1986) and S/SMI (1986 to present).

Scatterometry

A scatterometer for measuring wind speed and direction was demonstrated during the brief Seasat mission in 1978. No sensor has been flown since then, despite US plans for NOSS and NROSS. Partial coverage will be given by ERS-1, where the instrument shares an antenna with the Synthetic Aperture Radar (SAR). Analyses of Seasat data continue to appear (Halpern, 1989; Davidson and Harrison, 1990), and future scatterometer data (ERS-1 and NSCAT on ADEOS) will form an important input to WOCE models.

Synthetic Aperture Radar

A Synthetic Aperture Radar (SAR) was also demonstrated on Seasat, and experimental missions have been flown with the Shuttle (SIR-A and SIR-B). Large scale climate uses are expected to be largely for ice mapping (Fily and Rothrock, 1990), although a variety of ocean feature mapping applications has been demonstrated (Barnett et al., 1989). After a 13 year gap since Seasat, the ERS-1 SAR has now started to provide images.

CONCLUSIONS

> Some say the world will end in fire,
> Some say in ice.
> (Robert Frost, Fire and Ice, 1923)

The understanding of future climate change has increased since 1923, but considerable uncertainty remains. The above summary outlines the present knowledge of the role of the oceans in climate change, the planned ocean research programs aimed at better defining this role, the possible Canadian response to these plans and the techniques of satellite remote sensing that will be applied.

I have tried to mention the more important and readable publications on the topic, and to include recent references to relevant satellite work. I have also included references to interesting suggestions (Broecker, 1987; Munk and Forbes, 1989). The literature, like the world's newspapers, is at present full of uncertainty, leading to many articles which are basically lists of questions (Bardach, 1989). The recommended "National Response" above, seems a reasonable reaction to the present state of affairs. It will be interesting to see answers appear in the years ahead.

CHAPTER 7

GLOBAL CHANGE IN AGRICULTURE

R.J. Brown

INTRODUCTION

The effect of predicted changes in the climate of the Earth on agricultural production and operation could be enormous, leading to a substantial reassessment of how we operate and manage this precious resource. This is particularly true for Canada where we tread a precarious line between abundance and scarcity. For example, crop yields for the Western provinces vary dramatically from year to year according to the annual rate of precipitation. At first glance, it may seem that a gradual warming of the atmosphere would be beneficial to Canada allowing us to extend the agricultural areas to the northern regions which are presently predominately forested. However, upon closer examination, in many cases, it is not the climate that now dictates the northern limits of the agricultural zones, but rather the soil type and fertility. If global warming were to occur there would be a further reduction in the forested areas of the earth, with a subsequent release of carbon dioxide, one of the greenhouse gases.

Global change would undoubtedly lead to changes in the type of crops grown within various regions. Such changes would put an enormous burden upon governments and planning agencies to have up-to-date information on the impact of these changes. Remotely sensed data can definitely facilitate the collection of data over large areas. In order to fully exploit remotely sensed data, it is necessary to use Geographic Information Systems (GIS) to take the extracted data, update existing databases, and make this information available to policy and decision makers in a readily useable form. The need for a convenient and effective means of transferring information between the GIS and the image analysis systems (IAS) that are being used to extract the information is evident. This transfer of data between the GIS and IAS is not a one-way street but there needs to be two-way traffic. Information from the GIS can be used to direct the analysis of the remotely sensed data within the IAS (by the transfer polygons of specific characteristics), and these can then be used to direct the subsequent classification of the data. In addition, the IAS/GIS system must be capable of integrating data from many different sources. Thought must be given to how this should be done both conceptually and technically. Remotely sensed data should be just another input to any analysis system. It should not be expected to answer all of the questions by itself, but it has a major role to play in supplying objective, multitemporal, direct observations of the vegetation and surface of the earth. No such system exists at the present time, although there has been a move in this direction with the establishment of the Crop Information System (CIS) in Winnipeg as a joint venture of the federal and Manitoba governments (Brown et al., 1990a). This system will be described in more detail later in this section.

In 1972, when the first environmental monitoring satellite, Landsat-1, was launched, most of the projected uses of these data were directed not so much towards global change and global monitoring as to specific problems. However, now we are in the 1990s, we realize how valuable and important these early images of the earth's surface are in assessing changes that have occurred over the last 20 years.

Remotely sensed data are very sensitive to agronomic parameters and are ideally suited for use in monitoring and quantifying the effect of climatic and environmental change. Remotely sensed data have a major role to play in the monitoring of agricultural landuse, rangeland management, vegetation type discrimination, changes in agricultural practices, monitoring of compliance with governmental programs and vegetation condition assessment. The sensors required to carry out such a program range from the low resolution (1 km) Advanced Very High Resolution Radiometer (AVHRR) carried on the National Oceanic and Atmospheric Administration (NOAA) satellite to the high resolution satellite sensors operating in the visible, near-infrared, and microwave regions of the electromagnetic spectrum. To monitor large areas, the AVHRR sensor is ideal to identify where changes are occurring and should be examined in more detail by either higher resolution sensors or by other means. For other applications, such as the monitoring of soil conservation measures, the high resolution sensors operating in the visible and near-infrared, or even the microwave, regions of the electromagnetic spectrum are necessary.

Synthetic Aperture Radar (SAR) imagery holds great promise as an important active microwave sensor for collecting valuable information related to agricultural applications and monitoring environmentally induced changes in the vegetation. One of the important requirements of monitoring operations is data timeliness and SAR, with its all-weather capability (able to image through clouds and at night), can collect data every time that the area of interest is within the field-of-view of the sensor. The 1990s will see a large number of satellite SAR sensors launched (Table 7.1). It is quite apparent from this list that there is a wide range of sensor parameters (frequency, incidence angle, and swath width) which will have a substantial effect upon the capabilities of these sensors to provide useful information for agricultural applications. Within Canada there is presently a vigorous Radar Data Development Program (RDDP) (O'Neil, 1990) underway to develop the procedures to use these data within operational programs. In agricultural research this includes participants from universities, provincial remote sensing centres, federal government agencies, and industry. Table 7.2 lists the various groups involved in a coordinated research effort to maximize the return to Canada from a concerted research effort.

The expertise which has been developed, in Canada, over the last couple of decades has put us in a strong position to use remotely sensed data effectively in Global Change programs. This chapter presents the current capabilities of remotely sensed data in meeting the requirement of agriculture in various application areas and follows up with an outline of the research and development requirements to meet the needs of a Canadian Global Change Program.

Table 7.1

Past and Future SAR Sensors in Earth's Orbit

Satellite/ Sensor	Launch Date	Freq./ Pol.	Incid/ Angles (Degrees)	Reso'n (m)	Swat Width (KM)
SEASAT	1978	LHH	23	25	100
SIR-A	1981	LHH	50	40	50
SIR-B	1984	LHH	15-60	17-58	20-40
ESA ERS-1	1990	CVV	23	30	99
JERS-1	1992	LHH	35	18	75
SIR-C	1993/4/5	X,L,C (QUAD POL)	15-55	10-60*	15-90*
RADARSAT	1994	CHH	20-60	10-100*	50-500*
EOS	1999	X,L,C	15-55	25-500	50-700*
ESA ERS-2	1990'S	CVV	23	30	99

* Depending on Mode

Table 7.2

Canadian Participants in the Agricultural RDDP

Canada Centre for Remote Sensing
Ontario Centre for Remote Sensing
Manitoba Remote Sensing Centre
Saskatchewan Research Council
University of Sherbrooke
University of Laval
University of Guelph
University of Waterloo
University of Saskatchewan
College of Geographic Sciences
Statistics Canada
Agriculture Canada
Canadian Wheat Board
Prairie Farm Rehabilitation Administration
Intera Technologies Ltd.
Terrain Resources Division of Polar Sea Research Ltd.

STATUS OF USE OF REMOTELY SENSED DATA IN CANADIAN AGRICULTURAL APPLICATIONS

Remotely sensed data capabilities within agricultural applications will be addressed as they relate to.
- vegetation type determination,
- crop condition assessment which includes soil moisture estimation, and
- other applications which include soil conservation monitoring, habitat mapping, rangeland condition assessment, landuse change, soil type mapping and soil erosion monitoring.

Vegetation Type Determination

Many studies have illustrated the capabilities of satellite sensors operating in the visible and near-infrared (VIR) portions of the electromagnetic

(EM) spectrum (Landsat Multispectral Scanner (MSS) and Thematic Mapper (TM), and the French Systeme Pour l'Observation de la Terre (SPOT)) to identify and map crop areas. These studies have shown that the success of such applications depends upon the mix of crops within the area and the time of data acquisition. For example, the determination of canola area in Western Canada (Brown et al., 1981; Pokrant and Magahay, 1986), and of potato area within Eastern Canada (Ryerson et al., 1980), on an operational basis has been demonstrated. In addition, these data have been used for the determination of various crop areas including corn, and soybeans in the United States (Hanuschak et al., 1982). This is an area where a great deal of research has occurred and where there is not much current activity except to investigate specific cases.

Since data collection in the VIR requires a cloud free atmosphere, there is always concern whether data will be available for input to operational programs. Hence the use of data, acquired in the microwave portion of the EM spectrum, is attractive because these data can be acquired regardless of the weather conditions. In fact, these data can even be obtained if it is raining, although in this latter case there is a change in target characteristics which must be considered. The methodology and understanding of the interaction between EM energy and vegetation are fairly well known within the VIR; this is not the case within the microwave portion. Considerable research is now underway in this area and we can expect that data from various satellite SARs will be used effectively for determining vegetation type within this decade.

A meeting in January, 1990, of the Radar Data Development Program (O'Neil, 1990) produced a status report on our understanding of the interaction between microwave radiation and vegetation. The main points are outlined below.

There are definite differences in the radar backscatter from the crops which are related to type and development stage. C- and X-band data are definitely superior to L-band data for discriminating crop type since, with the greater penetration of the L-band radiation (wavelength about 23 cm), the soil surface, in addition to the plant, contributes substantially to the magnitude of the radar backscatter. X-band is probably better than C-band but this has not been shown conclusively with airborne imagery. From ground scatterometer measurements, Ku band data was the best frequency (compared to C- and L-bands). In a comparison of the correlations of the radar backscatter values at X-, C- and L-bands, it was found that there was little correlation of field mean values between X- and C-bands for the grains and broad-leafed vegetation such as canola. This indicates that different parts of the canopy or different mechanisms are involved in determining the magnitude of the radar backscatter. Regardless, at both of these bands, there is good correlation with vegetation type. At L-band, on the other hand, there is little correlation of the radar backscatter values with crop type indicating that other factors, such as soil moisture and/or surface roughness, are more important in determining the magnitude of the radar backscatter values. In general, one cannot reliably separate the various grain classes (such as wheat and barley) but it is very easy to separate broad-leafed vegetation such as canola from the grains. This separation is possible very early in the growing season—approximately 3 to 4 weeks before it is possible using VIR imagery (Brown et al., 1984). However, some recent studies (Brown et al., 1990b) have indicated that separation of barley and several varieties of wheat is possible using VV (vertical transmit/vertical receive) polarization as opposed to HH (horizontal transmit/horizontal receive) at C- and X-bands.

Radar backscatter depends strongly upon the amount of water present on the plant surface or within the plant. Consequently, there is a substantial increase in the magnitude of the back scatter as the crop canopy develops (as the crop develops more biomass is produced which, in turn, produces more water). In general, the CVV data are superior to the CHH data for discriminating vegetation type, especially under wet crop conditions (either during or just after a rain). It appears that the vertical structure of most plants is coupled to a vertically transmitted electromagnetic wave and hence VV polarization is better than HH for crop type discrimination (Brown et al., 1990b). On the other hand, CHH data may be better for detecting soil properties. This CVV\CHH comparison suggests that the soil contributes more to the magnitude of the radar backscatter at HH. The cross polarization data, on the other hand, appear superior to both HH and VV. This is probably due to the multiple scattering of the electromagnetic wave within the canopy structure and hence higher correlation between the magnitude of the backscatter values and the canopy type, as characterized by plant structure and moisture content.

Dew does not seem to affect the relative radar backscatter at incidence angles greater than 45 degrees. However, the effect of dew on plants is apparent at smaller incidence angles and, in fact, for dew detection CHH data acquired at incidence angles of about 20 degrees is the best (Gillespie et al., 1990a; Gillespie et al., 1990b). It has been noted that the effect upon the relative radar backscatter from diverse canopy types is quite different between the situation where there has been a heavy dew and when there has been a light rainfall (Brown et al., 1990b)

In general, the time of data acquisition does not have a significant effect upon classification accuracy at large incidence angles (greater than 45 degrees), although there will be changes in the absolute values of the radar backscatter (Brisco et al., 1990b). Note that, except for some of the earlier planned SAR sensors, most will have the capability to acquire data at incidence angles greater than this value (Table 7.1).

Factors such as row direction, soil moisture and surface roughness (especially early in the growing season) can have significant effects upon the magnitude of the radar backscatter at C band or lower frequencies, and at small incidence angles (less than 40 degrees) (Ulaby et al., 1978; Ulaby et al., 1979; Wang et al., 1987; Hutton and Brown, 1987; Beaudoin et al.,1990). Changes in surface roughness often cause considerable confusion between a rough summerfallow field and those containing grains. However, multitemporal data or a combination of visible/near-infrared and SAR imagery can remove these ambiguities.

Preprocessing of the SAR data is important (for example median filtering and antenna pattern removal) (Hutton and Brown, 1986; Thomson et al., 1987; Begin et al., 1987). However, after implementing procedures to remove antenna or range effects, care must be taken in the analysis of the data as correlations of radar backscatter to incidence angle have been modified. Segmentation also improves the accuracy of crop classification when calculated on a polygon or segment basis.

Analysis of the data for discriminating crop type using texture measures has not shown great promise and, in general, there appears to be very little additional information in the texture that is not available in the image tones (Pultz and Brown, 1987).

Crop Condition Assessment

In the VIR portion of the EM spectrum, qualitative relationships between condition and vegetation indices have been demonstrated with both low and high resolution satellite imagery. Various studies have shown good empirical relationships between crop yields and various crop parameters such as leaf area index (LAI) and plant biomass (Tucker et al., 1981; Aase et al., 1986; Asrar et al., 1985). The inherent problem with using data acquired with the high resolution sensors is data availability (due to cloud cover) and the fact that data cannot be collected with sufficient temporal spacing to follow the development of the vegetation. Rather, one obtains a snap-shot of the area and thus, one needs to evaluate factors such as crop development stage from other sources. The AVHRR data are particularly attractive for the monitoring of vegetation as these data can be acquired twice daily for all of the agriculturally significant areas of the world. This is accomplished with a low spatial resolution and a correspondingly wide swath width greater than 2500 km.

Considerable preprocessing is required to generate useful data. This involves procedures to correct for geometric distortions due to scan angle, radiometric degradation of the data due to atmospheric effects, and procedures to generate a clear composite image from the daily images. Within the Crop Information System (CIS), established in Winnipeg, Manitoba, composite images are generated weekly from the afternoon AVHRR data takes.

Figure 7.1 illustrates the procedure which is followed to generate these cloud free data. The daily data are first geometrically registered to a map base and radiometrically calibrated. A map of the Normalized Difference Vegetation Index (NDVI) (the difference between measured radiance values in the AVHRR channel 2 [0.725 -1.10 micrometres] and channel

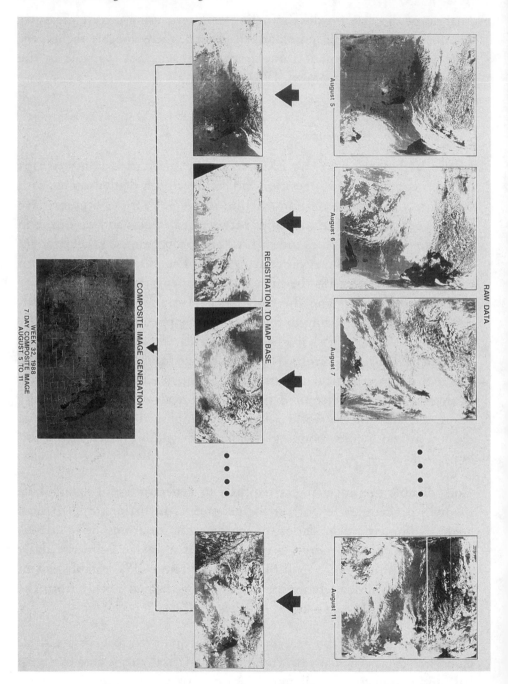

Figure 7.1: Procedure to generate cloud free AVHRR composite images from daily data.

1 [0.58 -0.68 micrometres] divided by their sum) is then produced. This index has been shown to emphasize the differences between healthy and stressed vegetation and serves as the basic tool in crop condition assessment. Besides being a measure of vegetation vigour, the NDVI can also be used to generate the cloud free composites. The NDVI is reduced by clouds and atmospheric haze. Hence, by choosing data from the daily image containing the largest NDVI, a cloud free composite image is produced for subsequent analysis (Holden, 1986).

This analysis usually involves extracting mean NDVI values for areas of interest such as Crop Reporting Districts (CRDs) or Rural Municipalities (RMs) within Canada on a weekly basis. These NDVI values have been shown to be related to final crop yield (Major et al., 1986). Research is presently underway to make this relationship more quantitative through the investigation of the relationship between the area under the curve (of NDVI plotted against time) and final crop yield.

Figure 7.2 shows a comparison of false colour infrared imagery produced by the CIS for corresponding weeks in 1987 and 1988 (areas of greater vegetation growth appear in deeper shades of red). Because the AVHRR records the reflected light from all of the area within the field-of-view of the sensor (not just individual fields), the measured reflectance depends upon the crop mix within an area. Hence, reliable interpretation requires a comparison of areas of similar crop, vegetation, and soil characteristics or a comparison of the same area from year to year. To illustrate the capabilities of the AVHRR sensor to monitor crop conditions, a comparison is made of the mean NDVI values of a RM in the Red River Valley of Manitoba between 1987 and 1988. In 1988 this area was severely affected by drought as is illustrated by the bluish tones on the 1988 composite image. Figure 7.3 is a plot of the NDVI values for one RM within this region for 1988, 1987 and a mean of the years 1985-1987 (Allison et al., 1989). It can be seen from this plot that the NDVI values are considerably reduced in 1988 from 1987 and from the mean of the three years. The wheat yield, estimated by Statistics Canada, for the CRD which contained this RM, was 14.7 bu/ac in 1988 compared to a value of 33.0 bu/ac in 1987 and a normal yield closer to 40 bu/ac.

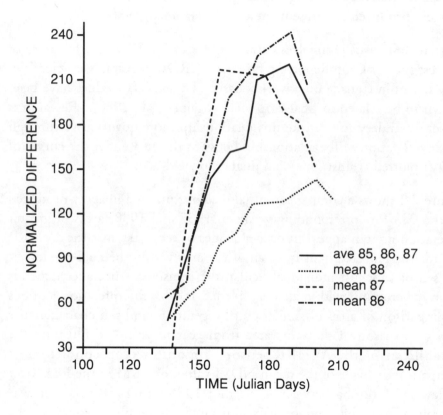

Figure 7.2: Plot of variation of mean NDVI for a Rural Municipality in southern Manitoba throughout the summer of 1987 and 1988.

CROP CONDITION ASSESSMENT

Figure 7.3: Comparison of composite AVHRR images of the Red River Valley, Manitoba, for the same time period between 1987 and 1988.

These AVHRR images have a major role to play in global change studies since this is truly a global data source. AVHRR data of every area on the earth are collected daily and at a resolution which makes the data files manageable. These data have been used extensively to monitor vegetation changes in Africa (Hastings et al.,1989; Henricksen, 1986; Tucker et al., 1986) and South America for such things as forest depletion, drought monitoring, and rangeland dryness (Paltridge and Barber, 1988). These data can also be used to monitor changes in the forest/agriculture or agriculture/rangeland interfaces and hence evaluate changes at these boundaries.

In the microwave region, studies have shown positive relationships between LAI and radar backscatter (Brakke et al., 1981; Ulaby et al., 1984; Le Toan et al., 1986). However, robust models are lacking to relate radar backscatter to LAI and to incorporate these measurements into yield models (as a surrogate for plant parameters) along with meteorological observations.

Crop density and vigour have a significant effect upon the magnitude of the radar backscatter which adds support to the potential use of SAR data for condition assessment (Le Toan, 1985; Le Toan et al., 1989). Some recent work by Brisco and Brown (1990) suggests that textural information can be used to differentiate between stressed and non-stressed wheat. In addition, the appearance of significant plant parts such as grain heads has a noticeable effect upon the magnitude of the radar backscatter which, again, adds considerable promise for the use of SAR data in this application. However, our understanding of the interaction of microwave energy as it relates to crop condition is sparse and considerable research is required in this area.

Soil Moisture Determination

Another approach to assess vegetation condition is to establish the soil moisture content. Microwave imagery is especially good for this purpose as the emission and reflection of the surface is strongly dependent upon the dielectric constant of the target which, in turn, is strongly dependent upon the moisture content.

Several approaches have been investigated for the determination of soil moisture. These range from the use of thermal sensors which relate soil thermal inertia to those measuring the microwave emission and backscattering. Considerable effort has gone into the evaluation of thermal infrared data using the thermal inertia approach. However, this has proven to be an unreliable approach due to limitations on the availability of data and on the resolution of the thermal sensors. Most importantly, we still lack knowledge of such important factors as the effect of vegetation cover on the thermal emission and how thermal emissivity might change when there is dew on the vegetation. Sensing within the microwave region of the EM spectrum appears to be the only feasible means of getting soil moisture information from remotely sensed imagery. These latter approaches are based on the premise that the dielectric constant of soil is about 3 compared to a value of about 80 for water. Hence, as the soil moisture changes, there is a significant change in the dielectric constant of the surface which, in turn, determines the magnitude of the emission or scattering from the surface.

There are many striking examples of the ability of SARs to distinguish between areas with different amounts of soil moisture. Figure 7.4 is an image of two fields prepared in exactly the same manner in an area near the town of Outlook, Saskatchewan acquired by the CCRS SAR-580. One of these has been irrigated and the other has not. The field which has been irrigated has a substantially greater radar backscatter which is represented in the image by the brighter tones.

For estimating surface soil moisture using SAR, it has been shown that small incidence angles are preferred because surface roughness effects are minimized at these angles, and there is more penetration through the canopy to the underlying soil (Ulaby and Batlivala, 1976). However, recent studies have shown that, even at the larger incidence angles of the order of 40-50 degrees, there is still a high correlation between soil moisture and radar backscatter (Pultz et al., 1989). From ground-based scatterometer measurements, C band has been identified as the best frequency for estimating soil moisture (Ulaby and Batlivala, 1976). Fortunately, this is the proposed frequency for the European Space Agency (ESA) Earth Resources Satellite (ERS-1) and RADARSAT. There are no universal models that quantitatively relate soil moisture to

Figure 7.4: CVV image of an area near the town of Outlook, Saskatchewan acquired on June 27, 1983. The two circular fields have been planted with the same crop but the irrigated field appears considerably brighter than the unirrigated one due to the differences in dielectric constant caused by the difference in soil moisture.

backscatter. The Michigan Microwave Canopy Scattering Model (MIMICS) (Ulaby et al., 1988) is perhaps the closest model for this purpose. This is a radiative transfer model (incorporating the Kirchoff scattering theory) which was developed for characterizing the radar backscatter from forest canopies (Ulaby et al., 1986). The tree canopy is divided into three regions which include the crown, the trunk and the ground. However, there is no inherent reason why it could not be used for agricultural applications, particularly since, by removing the forest or vegetation, we are left with the soil component of this model. The evaluation of this model for soil moisture estimation is presently underway at the University of Laval.

There is no agreement on how well soil moisture can be determined under a vegetated surface. Work by Pultz et al. (1989) has shown extremely good correlations between radar backscatter values at CHH and soil moisture in the surface layer even under a heavy vegetation canopy. This was an unexpected result which could mean that, at C-band, it is possible to determine soil moisture even under a dense canopy or perhaps we are measuring the changes in the soil. In 1990 a major experiment began involving CCRS, the Ontario Centre for Remote Sensing, the University of Laval, the University of Sherbrooke, the University of Guelph, the University of Waterloo, and Agriculture Canada to develop a robust model to relate radar backscatter to soil moisture, taking into account such factors such as surface roughness, vegetation cover type, and soil texture. As part of this work, there will be an evaluation of models which relate surface soil moisture to the subsurface moisture. It is this latter moisture regime that is very important for determining whether the vegetation will be under stress once a sufficient root structure has been established. This is important for many global change studies and results are promising that a relationship between surface and subsurface soil moisture can be established (Boisvert, 1990; Camillo and Schmugge, 1983).
It is felt that the SCANSAR mode of RADARSAT will be of great importance for determining soil moisture over a wide area especially as initial soil moisture input to vegetation development models. In this mode it will be possible to collect SAR imagery at 50 to 100 metre resolutions, 7 looks, at swath widths of 300-500 km. This would give

complete coverage of the agricultural areas of Canada approximately every 3 to 4 days.

Considerable success has also been obtained in relating microwave emission temperature to soil moisture. Schmugge et al. (1986) ascertained that L-band is the best single channel for relating soil moisture to radiometric emissions, although there is still a need to bring in other sensors to estimate the surface roughness (active microwave sensor) and the amount of vegetation present (VIR sensors) (Theis et al., 1986).

It should be noted that these microwave approaches measure the soil moisture content in only the top 0-5 cm at L-band and could be extended to greater depths by the use of P-band radiometers. Moreover, remote sensing gives a synoptic view of the area which cannot be obtained by conventional sampling means. A task for the future is to use this surface soil moisture information " in determining such things as the partitioning of energy at the land surface and its effect on surface runoff" (Schmugge et al., 1986).

OTHER APPLICATIONS

Soil Conservation

Radar imagery has a potentially large role to play in soil conservation programs. In estimating the potential for soil erosion, there are two factors of paramount importance: the presence of trash on the field in the form of stubble, and whether or not the field has been mechanically worked. The first factor can be evaluated using VIR imagery such as SPOT or LANDSAT TM (Schaal, 1986), while SAR is an ideal instrument to use for determining the roughness of the field on which cultivation has occurred (Brisco et al., 1989; Brisco et al., 1990a). Incorporating these data into an expert system to determine land cover type (the type of vegetation cover indicates the amount of trash which would be left on the field) and surface roughness along with topographic information and soil type is an important component of any program designed to evaluate potential erosion of our precious top soil and to implement remedial action.

Habitat Mapping

Combined SAR and VIR data have been shown to identify semi-permanent categories of marshland based upon vegetation type. Wetlands are easily identified within radar imagery because of the specular reflectance from the water, which results in a low backscatter from these areas. However, on water bodies suitable for water fowl nesting, there is also a high reflectance from the surrounding vegetation, which is probably caused by a corner reflector effect of the emergent vegetation and volume scattering from this lush vegetation (Manore et al., 1990).

Rangeland

Rangeland extent and condition can be mapped using various remotely sensed data sources. This can be of prime importance in global change applications as the change in climate is quickly manifested in change in rangeland areas. The AVHRR data can be used to outline the extent of rangeland areas and the changes which are occurring. Also, data from the Thematic Mapper can be used to determine rangeland condition in what is known as the short grass prairie region of the Great Plains (Brown et al., 1981). Within this region, it has been shown that these data, suitably enhanced to emphasize the information content within the rangeland areas, identify areas of high carryover, those where invading weeds are becoming a problem, and helps the rangeland operator to develop a management plan. Figure 7.5 is a Landsat MSS image of an area near the town of Scandia, Alberta acquired on June 29, 1980. This image has been contrast stretched to enhance the information content within the rangeland areas at the expense of the agricultural areas. Consequently, the tones within these cropped areas show little changes in tones as most of the digital values within these areas are saturated. Figures 7.6 and 7.7 are ground photographs to the east (right) and west (left) (north is to the top) of the sharp fence-line contrast which is seen at "A" in figure 7.5. The area to the east (lighter tones on the MSS image) is dominated by fringed sage (silvery plant in figure 7.6) which is an invading plant which becomes more prevalent as the native grasses are depleted. The area shown in Figure 7.7 is in good condition with considerable carryover.

Figure 7.5: Landsat MSS image of an area in southern Alberta acquired on June 29, 1980. This image has been enhanced to accentuate the information within the rangeland areas. Darker tones correspond to areas of greater amounts of biomass and hence better rangeland condition.

Figure 7.6: Ground photograph to the east of the fence-line contrast at "A" in Figure 7.5. This is an area of poor rangeland which is dominated by fringed sage which is an invader species which becomes more prevalent in areas where the native grass is depleted.

Figure 7.7: Ground photograph to the west of the fence-line contrast at "A" in Figure 7.5. This is an area of better rangeland which is associated with darker tones on the Landsat MSS image.

Changes in the climate can readily change the delicate balance which exists in the rangeland areas. Here, a small change in precipitation can have a large effect on the amount of biomass produced, which in turn will affect the carrying capacity of the area. Hence, if there is no corresponding change in the amount of cattle on the fields, there will be a noticeable change in the range condition which can be detected using satellite sensors such as SPOT or TM.

Land Use Change

The high resolution sensors operating in the VIR are excellent vehicles for detecting and mapping the extent of land cover change. Consequently, these data have a role to play in detecting and quantifying changes in vegetation. Changes due to the introduction of irrigation and transition of land use from or to agriculture, from either rangeland or bushland, are easily detected (Rivard et al., 1990). The monitoring of these transitional areas can become an important element of programs to assess the effects of climatic change on the environment

Soil Mapping

Future global change programs will benefit considerably from accurate information on soil type. The TM sensor includes two bands of interest for soil mapping: TM5 (1.55-1.75 micrometres) and TM7 (2.08-2.35 micrometres). In 1984 the CCRS and Agriculture Canada carried out an evaluation of the information content of TM data for soil mapping in western Canada.

Figure 7.8 is a TM image of an area near the town of Outlook, Saskatchewan where TM bands 1, 5, and 7 are displayed as blue, green, and red respectively. It can be seen in this image that there is considerable separation between the clay, loam and sandy areas. TM5 and TM7 band reflectances increase in progressing from heavy clay, to clay, to loam, and to sand, indicating a correlation with texture. This relationship may be due to the greater water holding capacity of the finer textured soils but can, nevertheless, be used to identify the different soil types.

Figure 7.8: Landsat TM image of the area near the town of Outlook, Saskatchewan acquired on October, 1984. This illustrates the ability of a TM band combination of 1,5, and 7 to distinguish between clay, loam, and sandy areas.

Soil Erosion

Actual soil erosion, manifested as rills and gullies on bare fields, can be mapped with aerial photography using soil and topographical maps as auxiliary information. Once this initial erosion survey has been carried out, TM or SPOT imagery, along with the Universal Soil Loss Equation, can be used to assess the effects of crop rotation and environmental factors on erosion (Stephens and Cihlar, 1981; Cihlar, 1987; Cihlar et al.,1987)).

AGRICULTURAL INFORMATION SYSTEM

The beginnings of an agricultural information system were founded with the establishment of a Crop Information System (CIS) in Winnipeg. The detailed functional requirements for such a system have been specified in a report of a Technical Study Group of an Interdepartmental Crop Information System Steering Committee. This technical study group had representatives from the Canadian Wheat Board, Agriculture Canada, Statistics Canada, the Atmospheric Environment Service and the Canada Centre for Remote Sensing (CCRS). It should be noted that the user agencies, represented by the Canadian Wheat Board, Agriculture Canada, and Statistics Canada, have been involved in the specification of the research requirements and resulting system. This is an essential input for the development of any successful system to operationally use remotely sensed data. This study emphasized the need for a crop information system to bridge the technology gap between the satellite receiving stations and the user agencies and the need to develop and maintain a historical data base. This data base is essential for direct comparison between current data and that of other years or regions. This study also helped specify the data processing procedures of such a system. Specifically, the system was designed to carry out radiometric and geometric corrections to raw satellite data so that the user agencies would not have to apply these preprocessing operations themselves and invest in sophisticated image analysis equipment. This would allow the end user to focus attention on the analysis and information content of the imagery.

The system, which is being operated by the Manitoba Remote Sensing Centre (MRSC) of the Manitoba Department of Natural Resources, produces weekly composite images from the AVHRR data (Brown et al., 1990a). This processed imagery is distributed to users within 3 working days following the acquisition of the last image that goes into the generation of the weekly composite image.

Although this system was initially set up to handle AVHRR data, it has been designed in such a manner that the functionality of the system may be expanded to handle SAR data when these become available from satellites in the 1990s.

FUTURE RESEARCH AND DEVELOPMENT NEEDS

Remotely sensed imagery records biological indicators of ecosystem change. To effectively use these data and to extend the analysis beyond what can be done presently there is a need to carry out the following research and development.

- For remotely sensed data to be used as input to various models such as soil moisture, or crop yield models, there is a need for better data calibration. This involves calibration of sensors operating in all regions of the electromagnetic spectrum, extending from the visible and near-infrared to the microwave.

- Since microwave imagery holds such potential for use within agricultural applications because of its all-weather capabilities, it is important that substantial resources be devoted to the evaluation of the capabilities and limitations of sensors operating in this region of the electromagnetic spectrum. To this end, research should be devoted to the development of radar backscatter models relating the magnitude of the backscatter to parameters such as soil moisture, crop biomass, and crop development stage. In order to use these data effectively within operational programs it is essential that the radar backscatter process from vegetation be fully understood.

- There is a requirement for a system to integrate the various data bases that are available and make these available to the diverse groups monitoring different aspects of agricultural data needs. This involves not only the requirement for these data to be placed on-line so that they may be accessed by electronic means but also that the formats be compatible and there be substantial improvements in the user interface. Such data bases could include soils type, water bodies including both quality and quantity, administrative boundaries, land use, and meteorological readings from as many stations as are available.

- There is a requirement to develop net biomass models to evaluate the effect of the conversion of forested areas on agricultural production and the subsequent changes in the fluxes of carbon dioxide. Similarly, there is a need for models to evaluate the effect of conversion of agricultural land to rangeland and vice versa.

- There is a need to have effective and up-to-date management plans to deal with what could be rapid changes in the environment such that marginal agricultural land can be diverted to the best use.m The very nature of research and development programs requires investigations to be carried out over limited areas where there is adequate and extensive characterization of the ground. This particular aspect of the work has been done well in the past, but what is required now is to develop a better methodology to scale upward from the research and development programs to regional and national scales.

- There must be a commitment to archive remotely sensed data which can be used for global change activities now and in the future. The archive of the Landsat imagery has been of tremendous importance in assessing changes that have occurred over the last two decades and this must be continued. Not only must there be a commitment to archive these data, but there must be a commitment to maintain this archive, catalog the contents, update the archive and catalog, and make these data available on-line to those needing the information. This archive should include, in addition to the original data, any derived products from the data such as biomass, crop type, land use, etc.

- More development must go into more effective integration of Geographic Information Systems and Image Analysis Systems. There has been some progress in this area but these are usually specific to two particular systems. There is a need for a system to handle both the raster and vector data within one environment and for the development of data base standards which would allow for easy transport of data between systems.

- Expert system development needs to be encouraged. There is vast store of information and knowledge available which are not being used within the present information and image analysis systems. For example, such simple things as recommended crop rotation practices should be incorporated into the crop identification programs. This will require the development of new classification algorithms which use these data more effectively than the *a priori* probabilities used within the present most popular classification algorithm (maximum likelihood algorithm).

- Yield models which incorporate the strengths of meteorological and remotely sensed data need to be developed. Point meteorological measurements give an accurate reading at a particular location. The methodology needs to be developed to use these with the regional coverage of the remotely sensed data to interpolate between these point values. In addition, remotely sensed data give a direct observation of the effects of such factors as precipitation, hours of sunlight, etc. Procedures must be involved to use these within the yield model. That is, to use factors such as Normalized Difference Vegetation Index as derived from the remotely sensed data as a surrogate for leaf area index, and to use information on crop development as derived from the remotely sensed data, to reset the time scale of the yield models. There is a requirement to have models which operate with various inputs from the low resolution AVHRR and RADARSAT SCANSAR mode data to the higher resolution TM, SPOT, and 20-30 m resolution data of the SAR sensors.

- Soil moisture information is an important input to crop development models to set the initial conditions in the spring. The procedures to reliably relate radar backscatter to soil moisture at the surface and subsequently relate this information to the lower layers of the soil need to be refined.

- Techniques need to be defined to use remotely sensed data in conjunction with GIS data bases for the local (could be at a farm level) management of land use and soil conservation.

CHAPTER 8

REMOTE SENSING FOR DEMOGRAPHIC STUDIES RELATED TO GLOBAL CHANGE

R.A. Ryerson and C-P. Lo

INTRODUCTION

The Brundtland Commission notes that growing population is one of a number of global level problems (World Commission on Environment and Development, 1987) and a key factor contributing to environmental degradation around the world. Some suggest that environmental degradation is also responsible for slowing down the growth in world food output (Brown and Young, 1990). Compounding the problem is the question of global climate change which will further adversely affect food production. By 1990, the annual increment of global population passed 90 million, most of which has been concentrated in the third world. More specifically, in the less developed world, population growth contributes to poverty, starvation and drought. For many developing nations, the population explosion is manifest in urban centres, as well as in the squatter settlements surrounding such centres. This is not a new phenomenon (Lo, 1979).

While the impact of such population change is most dramatic in and around urban areas, it also can take a toll on the land that is used for agricultural production to support the additional population. Such land is often in marginal areas unsuited to sustained production. Therefore the mapping of land use change in these areas is here considered to be related to the problem of demographic change and global monitoring. An additional consideration is that an additional 50,000 people added to certain parts of the world will have less impact than 50,000 added elsewhere.

To estimate population, predict future population, and model future impacts, a number of strategies have been employed in Canada and elsewhere. These strategies can be characterized as: direct census; less direct methods based on building assessment from either the ground or from some form of remote sensing imagery; or, completely indirect methods that rely on surrogates such as land use information. This paper reviews the non-census remote sensing based methods, with an emphasis on Canadian work and capabilities, in the context of large area studies of use for global scale monitoring.

Although the use of remote sensing as the basis for population census in developed countries has been discounted for a number of valid reasons related to cost and accuracy, its use for intercensal updates of small areas and for spot checks of census enumeration accuracy is deemed appropriate (Clayton and Estes, 1980; Morrow-Jones and Watkins, 1984; Watkins and Morrow-Jones,1985. It is also less likely subjected to a systematic bias against illegal residents and other people who avoid the census enumerations. In so far as population estimation is concerned, the remainder of this paper deals with the developing world, although relevant methods related to land use mapping are drawn from North American work.

The paper closes with suggestions for future research and recommendations for a large scale operational project that builds on the Canadian experience.

BUILDING-RELATED DEMOGRAPHIC MODELS USING REMOTE SENSING

The most direct approach to population estimation using remote sensing is to count the number of dwelling units from aerial photographs. This dwelling count is then multiplied by an occupants-per-dwelling unit factor obtained either by ground survey or from existing census data. This method is best applied to detached single story houses in rural and urban areas, and the population estimate is usually very accurate (Binsell, 1967; Henderson, 1979).

However, when this method is applied to an urban area where high-rise residential structures are intermixed with detached houses, the counting of dwelling units becomes difficult. The number of stories of a building has to be estimated by stereoscopically viewing the aerial photographs. To obtain a more accurate count of dwelling units, an initial classification of buildings must be done so that the number of dwelling units associated with each building type is known (Lo, 1986). The typology of residential buildings developed also allows type-specific occupants-per-dwelling unit factors to be derived. A high degree of variability in the accuracy of the dwelling unit count can occur if small spatial units are used to aggregate data. Most of the difficulty is caused by multiple dwelling-unit structures and the occurrence of vacant dwelling units (Lo and Chan, 1980; Watkins, 1984). The error in the dwelling-unit count has been found to be random, and can be compensated for or reduced by aggregating the smaller spatial units into larger spatial units. The census tract is a particularly suitable spatial unit for this purpose (Lo, 1986).

The accuracy of the dwelling-unit count method of population estimation obviously depends on two factors: (1) the completeness of the dwelling-unit count, and (2) the representativeness of the occupants-per-dwelling count factors. To improve the dwelling-unit recognition accuracy, large scale aerial photographs (1:10,000 or larger) are normally used. The use of colour and colour-infrared photographs has also been evaluated, allowing smaller scale imagery to be used (Binsell, 1967; Lindgren, 1971; Clayton and Estes, 1980). Lindgren (1971) reported accuracies of 99.5 percent in the identification of residential structures using 1:20,000 scale colour-infrared photography for the metropolitan area of Boston.

The occupant-per-dwelling unit factor is normally derived from existing census data which are not necessarily synchronous with the date of photography. A more desirable approach would be to conduct a sample field survey to determine the average household size for each type of dwelling unit. This should yield a more realistic occupants-per-dwelling unit factor for each dwelling type. The use of large-scale aerial photographs and the dwelling-unit count method coupled with census data can produce population estimates at census tract levels with a mean accuracy of 90 percent (Lo, 1986).

Instead of simply counting the dwelling units, a variant of the method that yields highly accurate results is to measure the strip lengths of residential structures from aerial photographs, as demonstrated by Collins and El-Beik (1971) for the city of Leeds in the United Kingdom. The three most common types of houses reported in that city are back-to-back, terraced, and semi-detached. The strip lengths for back-to-back and terraced houses are measured. For terraced houses with three stories, the strip lengths are multiplied by a factor of 1.5. The semi-detached houses are counted. A photo-factor is derived for each enumeration district from census data and the population is related to the amount of housing. On the basis of ten enumeration districts for each type of housing, an average photo factor is derived for each. This average photo-factor is multiplied by the number of houses of the appropriate housing type to yield a population estimate. Although this approach produces a population estimate at the enumeration district level with an accuracy of 98 percent, it is even more laborious and time consuming than the pure dwelling count method.

In an effort to automate the dwelling unit count method of population estimation, a raster approach has been attempted to relate residential building density with total density of the buildings. This leads to an estimate of dwelling-units on a grid-cell basis (Lo, 1989). A Geographic Information System (GIS) can then be applied to estimate the populatio,n grid-cell by grid-cell, using average occupant-per-dwelling factors derived from existing census data for each grid cell. The grid cells can be aggregated into census tracts or any other desirable spatial units.

Unfortunately the estimates from this method fail to differentiate between high-rise and single-story buildings, and has to be mathematically adjusted by a double logarithmic function. Further research in improving this method of dwelling-unit count is required, particularly in the direction of an artificial intelligence and expert system approach which may offer a method to recognize multiple unit structures, detached, or semi-detached houses. Such a method may be automated for use with SPOT digital satellite data. At this point, the building-related demographic models converge with the land-use-related models.

LAND-USE-RELATED DEMOGRAPHIC MODELS USING REMOTE SENSING

Land use information has long been suggested as a component in models to provide an indirect means of estimating population (Hsu, 1971), especially in less developed countries where an accurate census is not generally possible (Olorunfemi, 1985). An indication of the importance attached to land use information for demographic studies using remote sensing can be seen from the fact that of 72 papers on demography held in the Canada Centre for Remote Sensing (CCRS) RESORS collection, 15 are equally concerned with land use mapping, while 21 are equally concerned with demography and aerial photography (CCRS RESORS Search conducted February 1990). In the context of population studies, a number of models and approaches have been applied with varying success, using aerial photographs and satellite imagery (Hsu, 1971; Kraus et al, 1974; Ogrosky, 1975; Yunus, 1978; Adeniyi, 1983; Olorunfemi, 1984; Han, 1985).

The basic approachto using imagery to make land use maps from which to estimate population assumes that the built-up areas of a settlement should be proportional to the population raised to some power (Nordbeck, 1965; Lo and Welch, 1977). Tobler (1969) used satellite data to demonstrate that there is a strong correlation between built-up area and population. More sophisticated models have typically assumed that a certain population density is associated with a particular land use class. In effect, the approach is similar to those noted above with buildings, albeit with less accurate and a more generalized result (Iisaka and Hegedus, 1982; Lambin and Lamy, 1986).

For population to be estimated from land use requires a clear understanding of how the region's land use is related to its population. For example, Adeniyi (1983) has identified different residential land use classes that relate to certain population densities in Nigeria. Others have used empirical observations (Han, 1985), regressed against independent population estimates. One must also take into consideration factors such as geomancy - local customs that dictate where a residential location would be propitious. For example, in Korea, Han (1985) noted that local custom and weather, in the form of cold winter winds from the north, dictate that the best location for a house is south of a hill, north of a river. Lambin and Lamy (1986), working in Burkina Faso, have noted that one can also use the appearance of agrarian systems on satellite imagery to determine, at the village level, zones that are agricultural, inhabited, forested, or used for water supply or pasture. These, along with their particular characteristics, could play a role in population estimation. In other societie,s other factors, including some which are random, apply. Such factors and local social organization and agrarian systems should play a key role in deciding how one would design any population study, be it rural or urban. It should suffice to say for this discussion that whatever approach is adopted with remote sensing, it is absolutely essential that local conditions be thoroughly understood. These conditions, including social organization and the resulting impact on housing location and density, should be taken into consideration when designing an indirect census.

In spite of these difficulties, the information derived from land use has been successfully applied to a variety of demographic problems - from urban planning to the projection of population to assist in the estimation of future pollution loadings of lakes. Obviously, as the maps become more generalized and less accurate with regard to residential information, the accuracy of any population estimate will likely decrease. In general, the accuracy of the land use approach to population estimation with satellite imagery has largely been limited by the accuracy of the land use maps one could make with the imagery. Where land use has been interpreted from aerial photography , the accuracy of population estimates derived from the land-use information has proven to be satisfactory. This is especially the case in developing countries where alternate sources of population statistics tend to be less accurate. For example, Adeniyi (1983) found that population estimates from aerial photography compared with those from other sources within several percentage points. Olorunfemi (1985) found that remote sensing methods using house counting and land-use models obtained estimates of 317,470 and 317, 549 respectively for the city of Ilorin, Nigeria. Other remote sensing methods resulted in estimates that ranged from about 323,000 to 342,000. The State Government estimate was 299,000, while another independent estimate was 300,000.

Discrepancies of from five to fifteen percent appear to be common, with some uncertainty about which methods yield the most accurate results. In summary, results based on remote sensing appear to be encouraging.

In the future, data which are comparable to aerial photography will come from more sophisticated and more reliable space borne sensors, as well as from sophisticated airborne sensors. As such data become more widely available, more accurate land use maps should result, with an attendant increase in the accuracy of population estimates derived from such maps. The following paragraphs review the current status and findings with regard to land use mapping in Canada relevant to population estimation and associated monitoring of land use change. The review closes with a look to the capability of new sensors.

Satellite remote sensing was first used in the Great Lakes Basin in North America for large-area land use mapping in an operational context related to population. (Thie et al, 1973; Gierman et al, 1975). The objective of the study was to provide land use maps and information from which population could be projected and pollution loadings estimated for the Great Lakes system at the watershed level. The accuracies of the land use maps were found to be high where aerial photography was used, but considerably lower where satellite imagery was used. This and other Canadian studies using Landsat Multispectral Scanner (MSS) reviewed before the advent of higher resolution satellite imagery (Ryerson et al, 1982) did not meet the generally accepted standard of 95 percent accuracy for land use mapping set out by Clawson (1965), or even the more relaxed standard of 85 percent set out by Jensen et al (1983).

A number of other studies done in Canada since 1982 have used a variety of techniques with higher resolution Landsat Thematic Mapper (TM) and SPOT imagery. Two separate but related problems have been addressed: the mapping of land use; and, the identification of changes in land use. While the accuracies have not been consistently high, there have been encouraging results. The primary finding has been that methods based on visual interpretation (often of images which have been subjected to sophisticated pre-processing using a variety of algorithms) have tended to perform better for both land use and change mapping than those based on image classification methods alone. These finding are consistent with what one would expect given the characteristics of the sensors systems and the nature of image interpretation (see the discussion in Ryerson (1989), and the literature review in Seguin and Ryerson 1987).

In one of the most exhaustive assessments of Landsat MSS imagery for land use change, Martin (1989) found that changes at the rural urban fringe could be detected with accuracies approaching or exceeding 85 percent. He used a variety of methods based on visual inspection of digitally merged or treated Landsat Multispectral Scanner image data sets from different dates. Seguin and Ryerson (1987) described methods using aerial photographic sampling and visually based image interpretation using the PROCOM-2 (use of trade names is for information only and does not necessarily imply an endorsement by the Canada Centre for Remote Sensing or the Government of Canada). Changes were accurately mapped over a large area using the TM imagery. Carignan et al (1989) were also able to derive useful information for Montreal from TM imagery. In a study of changing wetlands and adjacent land uses/land covers Tomlins (1986) concluded that "there is no single best method of using TM data...(but)...visual interpretation is less prone to error". Thomas (1988) reached a similar conclusion with regard to wetland monitoring in southern Ontario.

In an evaluation of SPOT imagery, Howarth et al (1988) found that rural-urban land conversion was readily identifiable. Similar findings were reported by Wilson et al (1988) who concluded that visual interpretation of stereoscopic panchromatic transparencies was useful for large-area urban and agricultural change mapping.

A common thread running through much of the successful work on land use mapping in Canada and elsewhere is the use of visual inspection to identify change. This finding is consistent with what one would expect given the nature of the images and the interpretation algorithms available for digital image analysis. The digital methods cannot yet use elements such as context, shape, pattern and texture in interpretation (Ryerson, 1989). Such elements, when used with ancillary data (such as topographic maps or old land use maps), are particularly important for land use mapping.

Visually-based methods were used in the work described by Rivard et al (1990). They reviewed work in rural-urban land conversion mapping in Canada done for the Canada Land Use Monitoring Program. The accuracies were not generally acceptable compared to those realized with aerial photography - the primary data source used for land use mapping in the past. However, the errors were "understandable and correctable". A central problem in the Canadian context is oneof confusion between urban and non-urban uses. For example, bare, unvegetated ground (cropland or land in transition) often surrounds new urban areas and is confused with them. In other cases, new housing is built within treed areas without greatly changing the appearance to the TM sensor. However, Turner (1990) has estimated that 19 urban-centered regions in Canada, corresponding to 62 percent of the rural-to-urban land conversion in 1986, could be mapped with >85 percent accuracy with visually interpreted TM imagery.

For application outside of Canada, the visually-based approach to land use/land cover mapping proved to be more successful for several reasons. Competing sources of information are fewer, the urban areas usually stand in sharper contrast (except in drier environments) to their surroundings, and the nature of transportation systems leads to denser and more centralized urban concentrations usually surrounded by cropland or plantations. The second application described by Rivard et al (1990) was land cover mapping of 85 percent of Cameroun's 475,422 square kilometres. Twenty-one full scenes and five quarter scenes of TM imagery were interpreted with the PROCOM. An average of twelve classes were identified on each of 43 maps at 1:200,000 scale. A total of eight major classes and fifty-five sub-classes were identifiable.

A key problem in the Cameroun study was availability of data. Only 85 percent of the country was covered by cloud free TM imagery. Non-ocean areas of the Earth cover a total of 135.7 million square kilometres. We estimate that of this total as much as 15 percent is sufficiently cloud covered to prevent the routine use of conventional optical sensors for land cover mapping. Unfortunately, these same areas of Earth often coincide with the most rapidly growing population centers. For this reason, the cloud penetrating capabilities of radar seem necessary.

To date there has been little work done on population estimation with radar imagery. Lo (1986) evaluated Shuttle Imaging Radar-A (SIR-A) for human settlement analysis in the United States and China. He found that the detectability of settlements varied dramatically. Detectability was much easier on the north China plain, even for small villages, than was the case for larger towns in the United States. Lo assumed that this was related to the flat terrain against which the often walled and very compact villages stood. The fact that significant radar backscatter occurs from buildings has been noted by others as well (Henderson and Anuta, 1980). Lo found that there was very high correlation (0.92 at 0.01 significance) between settlement-area measured from the radar images and maps of the same settlements. However, all of the measured areas were 1.5 times the true area as a result of the glare from the intense radar backscatter associated with urban areas. Residential areas could be separated from industrial areas and airports, largely as a result of their large, smooth surfaces. Population was closely related to the area measured from the imagery. However, shape was not always identified correctly as a result of the glare. This was particularly the case for larger and less compact cities in the United States.

Harris (1985) reported correlations between population and settlement area in Tunisia almost identical to those of Lo, with a correlation of 0.91 at 0.01 significance. Harris, who did not use settlements with less than 1000 population, also suggested that in larger centres there were likely to be buildings with more than one story and thus settlement area would become less reliable as an indicator of population. For the purpose of studying rapid growth, particularly of squatter settlements, this concern may not be important. Where it is important, the findings of Olorunfemi (1984 and 1985) and Adeniyi (1983), with aerial photography, suggest that one may be able to apply models that link residential characteristics, as they appear on radar imagery, to building type and, thence, to population. It is significant that Harris found that the higher incidence angles of the SIR-A ($50\pm3^\circ$) yielded better results than did the SEASAT SAR with a lower angle of $23\pm3^\circ$. The planned RADARSAT will have incidence angles as high as 49-50° in the high incidence scan SAR mode with 4 looks and range x azimuth of 20x28 metres (Luscombe, 1987). Radarsat will also have extended modes to 59°.

These findings lead one to cautious optimism about the efficacy of using radar imagery from aircraft or spacecraft for demographic purposes, as well as land use information from sensors such as SPOT and TM.

From the literature it appears that accurate population estimates are obtained when known populations for sample areas of a certain land use class are used to generate models of population over larger areas. Given the types of land use information available, and the land information required to estimate population, it would also appear that accuracies of residential mapping on the order of at least 85 to 95 percent are required to generate population estimates that are acceptable in the developing world. These are much lower than accuracies obtained with the Census and associated estimation procedures in Canada where provincial level estimation accuracies vary from the Census by percentages like 1.34 (for Quebec) and 0.8 (for Alberta). At the national level such errors amounted to a total of 240,900 people, or 0.95 percent (Statistics Canada, 1991).

TOWARDS AN APPROACH TO LAND USE MAPPING FOR DEMOGRAPHIC AND GLOBAL CHANGE STUDIES

Land use information and land cover have been noted above as important elements in the understanding and estimating of demographic changes related to environmental and global change. In addition, it has been argued that global level changes may be manifested in changes to the land use and land cover information that may be interpreted from remotely sensed data. To this end, a variety of remote sensing systems have been discussed as data sources for global change assessment (see the review by Cihlar et al (1989)). Sampling methods have also been reviewed or put forward to monitor land cover and land use change at the global level. Some rely on sampling and various higher resolution imagery sources (Cihlar et al, 1989; Mace, 1990), while others rely on low resolution NOAA (National Oceans and Atmospheric

Administration) AVHRR (Advanced Very High Resolution Radiometer) imagery at 1 kilometre resolution (Cihlar et al, 1989).

A key concern is whether the imagery source used can actually capture the changes of interest. An early study of the usefulness of several different approaches to mapping land use in the Great Lakes basin found that visual interpretation of 80 metre Landsat MSS imagery yielded generalized land use maps that were less accurate than ten year old maps prepared from aerial photographic interpretation (Thie et al, 1973). Furthermore, such generalized maps from the Landsat MSS did not yield information believed to be of direct use for pollution studies related to the carrying capacity of the Great Lakes basin. As well, the changes found near urban areas could not be captured effectively with such a coarse resolution.

NOAA AVHRR data may be useful to identify vegetation condition trends and potential zones of change in which to sample with higher resolution imagery. It may also provide snapshots at nearly the same time and with the same calibration for widely separated areas of the globe. However, the findings cited here leave one with questions concerning the potential usefulness of both MSS and the even coarser resolution NOAA AVHRR data for more than their demonstrated use to identify gross changes in vegetation greenness (Prout et al, 1986).

When discussing possible sensors and data collection strategies, the concept of land use should be clearly differentiated from that of land cover. From remotely sensed imagery one usually maps land cover from which one in turn infers land use. Cover can be either natural or man made, while land use usually implies some form of human activity. It is this activity component that helps make visual interpretation of high resolution imagery essential. A thorough review of the land use concept is given by Clawson (1965), while Ryerson and Gierman (1975) present the concepts as they relate to image interpretation.

Will NOAA AVHRR imagery have the spatial resolution and information content to provide useful information with respect to land use and demographic change? The weight of evidence and our experience leads to our conclusion that it will not.

It would appear that Landsat TM and SPOT imagery will be the preferred sources of land use and related information for the minimum 114 million square kilometres of Earth that are here estimated to be sufficiently cloud free to permit regular imaging with the Landsat TM sensor. For the remaining areas totalling as much as 21 million square kilometres, radar imagers on either airborne (Lowry et al, 1986) or spaceborne platforms (Luscombe, 1987) may well prove to be the only reliable imagery sources to ensure that coverage is at relatively the same date for the areas being monitored.

RESEARCH REQUIRED

From the literature review above and the discussion following, more research is needed. First, as noted elsewhere, there must be some agreement on the types of land use changes that are important. At the same time, one must assess the nature of the changes that can be detected from the various sensor systems available and planned. To each feature one wishes to monitor, there must also be attached accuracy limits in terms of both the original mapping and the changes that are detectable. Much of this assessment may be based on existing, published work. In any case, some of the required work is being planned as part of the Canadian Global Change Program (Cihlar et al, 1989).

In terms of population estimation, there must be further assessments of radar imagery from both airborne and spaceborne synthetic aperture radar (SAR) systems. Given that most work to date has been done in dryland or North American environments, future work should concentrate on the evaluation of SAR for population estimation in the humid tropics. Of special importance are those areas characterized by rapid population growth in squatter villages on the urban fringe. The dearth of published results in this area leads us to conclude that new work must be done, likely in co-operation with demographers from the developing world, using airborne radar specifically acquired for the research. It would also be useful to explore the nature of population estimation models that can be driven using the types of land use and related information available from SPOT and Landsat TM imagery.

Finally, improvements in both building-related and land-use-related demographic modelling through the use of a GIS / Artificial Intelligence approach to image interpretation should be explored. More land-use-related variables sensitive to population change must be identified to formulate a more accurate model for population estimation using remote sensing.

A GLOBAL LAND USE MAPPING PROGRAM

A basic question one comes to is how can population, land use and other associated changes be monitored on a global scale? Several guidelines become apparent from the review and discussion above. The approach would likely use TM imagery, visually interpreted for the non-cloudy regions of the world. For the cloudy regions the approach would depend, to a certain extent, on the results of the research on radar outlined above. In any case, Lowry et al (1986) suggest that most basic land use information can be interpreted from airborne X-band SAR.

On the matter of costs, the work reported by Rivard et al (1990) is instructive. In Cameroun a commercial organization mapped a complex area relatively inaccessible from Canada. To cover an area of approximately 400,000 square kilometres required the equivalent of 23 full scenes of Landsat TM imagery. The number of images was larger than might be expected given the nominal coverage of TM imagery. The additional images were required to avoid cloud, and to cover coastal and border areas. For many of the images, only part scenes were used. The time required for interpretation was six person-months, with a further $10,000 for travel related to training and field verification. Of the total of six person-months required for interpretation, three were provided by an experienced Canadian consulting interpreter, while three person-months of a Cameroun citizen were required (Rivard et al, 1990). To input the entire data set into a GIS would have cost about 0.75 times as much again as the interpretation. (Vincent, 1990.)

Expanded to the cloud-free area of the world, such a mapping would require a minimum of about 4,000 and maximum of about 6,600 TM full scene images. To do the interpretation would require no more than

143 person-years, with an additional 107 person-years for the input into a GIS. Direct project related travel costs would be no more than $2.5 million (this assumes that even the largely uninhabited areas of the globe would be mapped in the same fashion).

Spread over a five year period and accounting for management, the annual budget for the mapping of the non-cloudy regions of the world would be in the vicinity of 55 person-years per year, 1,400 images per year, and $500,000 for project travel. Supplies, maps, office space, GIS and PROCOM-2 systems and support would be extra. While the initial interpretations would likely be done in Canada, those working in less developed countries could be trained as well. It is quite likely that 50 percent or more of all interpretation and GIS inputs could be done by developing countries after technology transfer to these countries. Such an approach would yield substantial benefit to them, while at the same time greatly reducing the overall cost of the project.

RECOMMENDATIONS

From the literature review and the preliminary costs outlined above, six recommendations may be made:

- a project should be initiated to evaluate the usefulness and cost of both spaceborne and airborne operational SARs for land use/land cover mapping and population estimation using both land use models and, if feasible, direct building assessments;

- a project should be initiated that assesses the usefulness and accuracy of land use/land cover information derived from visual interpretation of Landsat TM imagery for population estimation and the studies related to global and environmental change monitoring;

- an accurate assessment should be made of the timely coverage of the world by non-cloudy, useful TM images. Included should be an estimate of the number of images required, and the area of Earth not covered by such imagery;

- it should be established what the global interest would be in a consistent world-wide land use/cover mapping program that would yield GIS compatible data at a map scale of 1:250,000;

- Canada should seek the support of appropriate international agencies to proceed with a global inventory. As a first step, Canada should develop a further demonstration and pilot test of the concept in co-operation with those agencies in Canada as well as in other countries interested in such activities; and,

- depending upon the findings from the five recommendations noted above, a global baseline project should be undertaken to generate accurate land use/land cover maps of the entire world using available TM technology and radar data.

CHAPTER 9

REMOTE SENSING FOR WILDLIFE HABITAT: PAST ACHIEVEMENTS AND FUTURE CHALLENGES

A.M. Turner, J.D. Heyland and H. Epp

INTRODUCTION

Wildlife and wildlife habitat are very important to Canadians. In 1987, more than 18,000,000 Canadians spent a total of over $5 billion on wildlife related activities (Environment Canada, 1989). Our national affinity for wildlife and wilderness is being undermined because of climatic and anthropogenic changes to the environment. Under the influence of global changes, wildlife habitat will be altered in space, time, quality and quantity. Because remote sensing is a technology that can measure many aspects of the terrestrial and marine environments in a repetitive, synoptic fashion, it could become an essential component for measuring global changes as they affect wildlife.

This paper will review anticipated impacts of global changes on wildlife habitat, look at selected achievements of remote sensing in this area, present national requirements regarding wildlife habitat and suggest a few directions where remote sensing can play a significant role in contributing to the understanding wildlife habitat through the systematic monitoring of key global change variables.

IMPACT OF GLOBAL CHANGE ON WILDLIFE HABITAT

The last major disruption of global climate occurred during the Pleistocene ice age. During that period, at least 32 genera of mammals became extinct (Pain, 1988). Current models indicate climatic changes are occurring 10 to 40 times faster than those during the last ice age. The impact of these climatic changes coupled with increased anthropogenic pressures of the past several hundred years, does not bode well for maintaining the genetic and species diversity and wildlife populations we now enjoy.

Several studies have reviewed the impacts of global changes on wildlife. Most analyses of impacts are steeped in speculation due to two reasons: the sparsity of hard information on the effects global changes on the natural environment; and secondly, the better understood, but still incomplete knowledge of the relationships between habitat and species population, especially under the influence of changing environmental conditions.

A comprehensive summary of climate change impacts on a variety of resources has been prepared by the U.S. Environmental Protection Agency (Smith and Tirpak, 1988). They conclude that the net impact of climate change, particularly global warming, on species diversity, individual species, and inter-species dynamics is difficult to assess. However, they suggest that:

- climate change will destabilize natural ecosystems and alter competition in, as yet, unpredictable ways;

- indirect changes to habitat may have greater impact than direct physiological effects;

- natural and anthropogenic features will act as barriers to species response and movement;

- areas thought to be the most sensitive to climate change also have a large proportion of threatened species, species sensitive to heat and drought and species that inhabiting coastal areas will be the most threatened;

- sea level rise will cause a loss of coastal habitats thereby affecting all of their inhabitants; and

    - migratory birds will experience mixed effects depending
    upon their particular habitat requirements.

Most of these forecasts will also apply to Canada. Specific global change impacts can be gleaned from the literature and are summarized in Table 9.1. The chart illustrates that many types of global changes will affect wildlife and wildlife habitat in both direct and indirect ways. For example, the melting of a significant proportion of polar ice not only has the direct effects mentioned in the chart by will also influence sea level changes which in turn affect various coastal wetland habitats.

A common belief regarding species response to climate change is that an increase in CO_2 will cause an increase in growth of some plants at the expense of others (Peters, 1988). Furthermore, plant and animal species will respond by different means and rates to climate change. Since animals depend upon plant life for food and cover, the dispersal rates of some animals will be determined by the dispersal of the plants that they use. It is widely believed that vegetation belts and the wildlife they support will tend to move poleward. If natural or man-made barriers cannot be overcome, both plant and animal species will be threatened with extinction.

Under this changing habitat scenario, species with small populations and small geographic ranges will suffer the most and may not be able to adapt or move to new areas. To exacerbate this situation, the range presently occupied by a species may be less than the optimum habitat because of habitat destruction or isolation caused by human activities.

ACHIEVEMENTS OF REMOTE SENSING FOR WILDLIFE HABITAT

In the late 1970s, an extensive overview of remote sensing use for wildlife habitat studies in Canada was conducted (Adams, 1978). These applications ranged from biophysical inventories to monitoring of habitats using both aerial photography and satellite imagery. Since then, developments of new sensors have allowed more detailed and more extensive analyses to be done. For example, launchings of Landsats 4 and

Table 9.1

Selection of some major anticipated impacts of global
changes on wildlife habitat. Summarized from Peters, 1988,
Pain, 1988, Smith and Tirpack, 1988, Topping and Bond, 1988,
and internal documents of the Canadian Wildlife Service

SEA LEVEL RISE
- coastal wetland flooding causing habitat loss for waterfowl
- islands disappear affecting waterfowl
- salt marsh nesting sites affected
- salt water intrusion affects fish, mollusks, and waterfowl

OCEAN CURRENTS
- changes in distribution and salinity of currents causing shifts in seabird and marine mammal populations

TEMPERATURE RISE
- mammals may forego breeding; birds may lay smaller clutches
- BIOME SHIFTS
  - vegetation belts move northward; tundra and alpine biomes reduce in area
  - present nature reserves are "islands" from which plants and animals may be trapped from dispersing to better areas
  - fragmentation of disturbed habitat may reduce species and genetic diversity

PRECIPITATION INCREASE
- affects breeding success of some wildlife

PRAIRIE DROUGHTS
- reduction in wetlands; loss of breeding areas for waterfowl
- possible increases in insectivores

SNOW INCREASE
- mobility of wolf, caribou and deer impaired; can cause dramatic population declines
- foraging ability of caribou impeded

SNOW MELT
- late snow melt affects nesting success of arctic geese
- rapid snow melt can cause acid shock to some waterbodies

POLAR ICE MELT
- larger and more polynyas; birds, fish and mammals associated with ice edge affected
- open water between arctic islands will impede migration
- algae and phytoplankton distribution affected; affects marine mammals

MELTING PERMAFROST
- pooling and greater mineralization in ponds may increase waterfowl habitat

Table 9 continued ...

-    may provide increased carbon source for atmospheric exchange

ACID RAIN
-    acidic lakes can cause loss/reduction of fish species; therefore waterfowl that rely on fish are adversely affected
-    acid soil affects vegetation and hence food and cover for many wildlife species

OZONE DEPLETION
-    possible increase in tumours in some animals
-    damage to phytoplankton will have adverse effects in food chain

ANTHROPOGENIC CHANGES
-    oil spills cause catastrophic loses of marine birds and mammals
-    agricultural use of wetlands reduces waterfowl and ungulate habitat
-    some pesticides have toxic effects on wildlife
-    forestry, agriculture, utility and transportation corridors cause loss or fragmenting of various habitats
-    agriculture, transportation routes and built up areas prevent mobility of species adapting to climate change

5, and SPOT have given scientists the tools to conduct detailed inventories of wetlands which could not have been done with sensors of lesser resolving capability.

At the other end of the spectrum and perhaps more relevant to global scales, the advancement in imaging technology from meteorological satellites has enabled large areas to be surveyed and monitored. Specifically, the Coastal Zone Color Scanner (CZCS) of the Nimbus group of satellites and the Advanced Very High Resolution Radiometer (AVHRR) aboard the National Oceanic and Atmospheric Administration (NOAA) satellites provide coverage swaths of about 1600 and 2700 kilometers respectively. Moreover, the daily repeat cycle of the NOAA satellites is significantly more frequent than satellites with higher resolving capabilities.

A variety of remote sensing applications have shown promise for mapping or monitoring the effects of global changes for various types of wildlife habitat. The studies cited below are not an exhaustive list of remote sensing research on wildlife habitat but rather are selected examples of the types of studies that have been attempted. The potential of either the technique or imagery type for ongoing global change monitoring were factors in the choice of examples. In addition, the development of a strong relationship between the measured variable and a particular wildlife habitat characteristic was an important selection criteria.

Wetland Habitat

Wetlands are important for a variety of reasons. They have many functional characteristics related to hydrology such as nutrient export, buffering of hydrologic events, and the trapping and transformation of sediments, toxic substances and nutrients (Environment Canada, 1986). The direct and indirect economic importance of wetlands, as outlined by Maltby (1986), are numerous and include fuel, fishing, textiles and recreation. Furthermore, wetlands are important in global exchange of carbon and other trace gases (Bartlett, 1984). However, it is primarily because of their high biological productivity and use as breeding and rearing areas for many of Canada's waterfowl, shorebirds and other wildlife species that wetlands are important to wildlife biologists.

Remote sensing studies of wetlands have ranged from detailed studies of specific wetlands to attempts at large area inventories. The most extensive inventory of wetlands undertaken in Canada using satellite imagery is the wetland inventory by Ducks Unlimited Canada (Koeln et al., 1986). A 900,000 km^2 area of the prairies has been digitally classified using Landsat Thematic Mapper (TM) imagery. This area represents about 10 percent of the breeding habitat area of North American ducks yet 50 percent of North American ducks nest there. Three wetland types have been classified: open water, deep marsh and shallow marsh. Accuracy assessments have determined that Thematic Mapper imagery is most successful for classifying individual wetlands greater than two hectares (Jacobson et al., 1987). Although there are a great number of wetlands less than 2 ha, an inventory over such a large area could only be practically achieved using digital satellite imagery. The inventory has been useful as a management tool for the conservation and restoration of wetlands. In the long term, Ducks Unlimited foresees expanding its inventory to other regions, classifying uplands of the entire prairies and parkland pothole region and conducting repeat coverage for both wetland and upland areas (Konrad et al.,1989). The monitoring aspect of the program may be critical in a Canadian context since ecoclimatic models of climate change show particularly high temperature increases and dry conditions in the prairies as a result of increased atmospheric CO_2 (Rizzo and Wiken, 1990).

Because of the small individual size of the vast majority of wetlands, it is likely that regular monitoring of high resolution satellite imagery such as TM coupled with selected airborne and ground data may be the best way to assess both anthropogenic and climate induced changes to wetlands in the prairie environment.

While agriculture may be the largest cause of wetland loss in Canada, other agents can be responsible. For example, damming of the Peace River in British Columbia has caused extensive vegetative and hydrologic changes to the Peace-Athabasca delta in northeastern Alberta. These changes have been documented through the use of Landsat multispectral scanner (MSS) imagery (Wickware and Howarth, 1981). These authors developed a five stage, multi-date change detection approach resulting in a quantitative picture of vegetation and water changes in this fragile ecosystem.

From a methodological perspective, inventories and classifications can produce successful results. However, from a wildlife habitat viewpoint, it is often necessary to establish relationships between changes in habitat and corresponding changes in other wildlife variables. By establishing these relationships, a more complete understanding of the ecosystem can be achieved. This understanding can, in turn, lead to more informed management of changing environments.

These functional linkages are being used in a study of changes to waterfowl habitat resulting from acid precipitation. An extensive inventory of the location, area and perimeters of lakes for most of eastern Canada has been derived from digital analysis of Landsat Thematic Mapper imagery (Helie and Wickware, in progress). These lake counts and measures have been compared with acid loading data plus soil and geological data in order to estimate the number and sizes of lakes at moderate and high risk to acidification. In a separate application, this information is being used in a northern Ontario setting (McNicol et al.,1989). Population figures, habitat requirements and feeding characteristics of certain indicator species of waterfowl are being used to infer acidification in lake habitat. The lake counts and measure information can therefore be used to extrapolate the lakes vulnerable to acidification and to estimate waterfowl affected over a much larger area than would otherwise be possible.

Remote sensing of wetlands and related vegetation is currently being used in arctic settings to define the habitats of arctic shorebirds. Classifications of vegetation on Roley and Prince Charles islands using Thematic Mapper imagery have been used to define the ecosystem occupied by arctic shorebirds (Morrison, pers. comm.,1990). Similar work has been done in the Mackenzie delta area (Dickson and Smith, 1989). In this study, over 350 nesting and staging sites were identified using both digital and visual interpretations of Landsat MSS and TM. These applications will provideuseful baseline data when potential impacts of global changes such as sea level rise are superimposed on these environments.

While many useful studies of selected coastal wetlands have been undertaken, a national picture of these resources has not been attempted in Canada. Because of the proximity of these wetlands to sea level and their role in trace gas exchange with the atmosphere, it would be useful to have a more complete knowledge of the coastal wetland resources for global change studies. A review of remote sensing for coastal wetlands concluded that various trade-offs are involved when choosing airborne and satellite sensors (Hardisky et al., 1986). While AVHRR imagery is suitable for continent-wide studies, it is not useful for resolving typical wetland features. Imaging spectrometers from airborne platforms offer a wide range of utility for species discrimination, biomass estimation and vegetative stress. A summary of the performance of various sensors for coastal wetland applications is found in Table 9.2.

Because of the variety of wetland types, sizes and distribution in Canada, different techniques will be suitable in different circumstances. For

Table 9.2

Performance rating of remote sensors for studying wetlands (after Hardisky et al., 1986)

3 = reliable, 2 = needs additional development,
1 = limited value, 0 = n/a

	Salt Marsh Mapping	Brackish Marsh Mapping	Coastal Land Use	Vegetative Stress	Wetland Biomass
Aircraft					
color film	3	3	3	2	2
color IR film	3	3	3	3	2
MSS	3	3	3	3	3
AVIRIS	3	3	3	3	3
Spacecraft					
NOAA AVHRR	1	0	2	1	1
Landsat MSS	2	1	2	1	2
Landsat TM	3	2	3	2	3
SPOT	3	2	3	2	3

	Tidal Inundation	Water Properties	Submerged Aquatic Vegetation	Coastline Erosion
Aircraft				
color film	2	2	2	3
color IR film	3	1	1	3
MSS	3	3	3	3
AVIRIS	3	3	3	3
Spacecraft				
NOAA AVHRR	2	2	1	0
Landsat MSS	2	2	2	1
Landsat TM	3	3	3	2
SPOT	3	3	2	2

example, Landsat Thematic Mapper imagery has been evaluated for estuarine, riverine and palustrine environments (Tomlins, 1984). Some general findings are that both digital and visual classification techniques and different band combinations have advantages and drawbacks. Digital techniques are suitable for rapid mapping of large areas, image to image change detection, and image to digital map overlays. On the other hand, visual interpretation of enhanced imagery is less prone to error because of the use of textural and contextual aspects of wetlands.

Biogeochemical Aspects of Wetlands

Besides being of interest as habitat for waterfowl, wetlands also play an important role in the global cycling of carbon and other elements. Because this relationship is not fully understood, it offers an opportunity for remote sensing, wetland and atmospheric experts to help quantify this relationship. In the United States, a three part measurement of wetlands in global biogeochemical cycling has been suggested (Bartlett, 1984). The three recommendations are:

- development of a geographic wetlands data base (an inventory based on remotely sensed and other data);

- research into wetland-atmosphere exchange processes (development of technology and expertise to assess the fluxes of carbon, sulphur, and nitrogen compounds across the wetland-atmosphere interface); and,

- research in establishing transfer functions (a hybrid approach making extensive use of GIS and modelling, whereby various measured components of the wetland system are integrated and extrapolated from the local to the global scale).

In Canada, an attempt to more fully understand the role of wetlands as a system is being made through a multi-agency program coordinated by the Canadian Institute for Research in Atmospheric Chemistry (CIRAC News, 1989). The program is making use of ground-based, aircraft and satellite observations of the wetlands in the Hudson Bay Lowlands and northern Quebec. The measurements are focused on the greenhouse gas exchange between wetlands and the atmosphere. A gas exchange model will be developed from the data which will aid in the estimates of methane source strength for northern wetlands as well as assess the response of wetlands to climate change.

Biogeochemical studies of wetlands do not have an immediate payback to wildlife investigations. However, because these studies will enable scientists to more fully understand the role wetlands play in atmospheric exchanges of gases, they may help refine models of climate change. This achievement would enable habitat specialists to more fully appreciate climatic impacts on wildlife through their habitat.

Terrestrial (Non-Wetland) Habitats

Other ecological relationships of wildlife in terrestrial (non-wetland) environments have been explored using remotely sensed imagery. In one example, moose habitat affected by hydro dams in north-central Manitoba was defined using Landsat imagery and surveyed population survey data (Bowles et al.,1984). Digitally classified Landsat MSS data were used as a tool to ease the time and costs required to locate areas where moose were likely to be found. Six cover types were classified including deciduous vegetation which was strongly correlated with moose population data gathered from airborne surveys. The project produced four thematic maps at a scale of 1:150,000.

In another application, the ecological association between old growth coniferous forest and northern spotted owls in northern Oregon has been used as the basis of a classification of Landsat MSS imagery to define the extent of this habitat (Hewitt et al., 1986). Using remote sensing in this manner can be an extremely useful component in the application of habitat suitability models which have been created for the spotted owl (Laymon et al., 1985). Such an integrated system has been developed for elk habitat suitability (Eby and Bright, 1985). The "effectiveness index" created through the GIS could also be useful for developing scenarios of habitat changes brought about by various global changes.

Land Use and Land Cover

General land use and land cover information can be of important use for habitat applications, particularly for impact studies. Most habitat related studies of land use have focused on areas that are undergoing or threatened with change, primarily of anthropogenic origin. For example, several regional studies of Environment Canada have used aerial photographs, land use maps and soils information over several years to identify changes to wetlands near rapidly expanding urban centres such as Vancouver (Pilon and Kerr, 1984), and southern Ontario (Snell, 1987). These studies identified trends in the land uses patterns and showed that agricultural and urban development contributed to the loss of wetlands in these areas. Some of these studies relied on ancillary information obtained from the Canada Geographic Information System (CGIS). They also illustrated that the level of detail provided by photography is needed for characterizing the patterns in these actively changing environments. Using satellite remote sensing for these types of applications would have to demonstrate a similar level of detail and the ability to integrate the results with relevant data bases.

An area where satellite remote sensing of land use has been applied successfully is habitat fragmentation. Fragmentation of habitats such as boreal forest is known to impact on wildlife, particularly interior forest bird species (Freemark and Merriam, 1986). Knowledge of this can be used to avoid unnecessary destruction of large forests when planning for energy corridors.

Ontario Hydro has developed a technique using digital analysis of Landsat Thematic Mapper to map the land cover types in broad areas where hydro lines are to be built (Pierce, 1989). The land cover information was fed into an Arc/Info GIS where area and edge measurements of each forest stand were calculated and combined with information on breeding birds (Wagner et al.,1989). Subsequently, a habitat impact model was constructed.

Since the threshold between large and small woodlots is in the order of a few hectares, the spatial resolution of AVHRR imagery would probably be too coarse for detailed analysis of habitat fragmentation. However, a similar approach using coarser resolution data could be used to identify broad areas of forest which might be more vulnerable to fragmentation. This would have importance in a national context and for scoping more specific studies of fragmentation.

In another application of land use and land cover information, a broad area of Alberta undergoing agricultural expansion has been mapped for change, also using Thematic Mapper imagery (Thomas and Turner, 1990). A visual interpretation technique was used to update 25 year old land use maps at a scale of 1:50,000. The change maps were automatically digitized, stored and analyzed with the aid of both mainframe and micro-computer based GIS. Comparison with wildlife capability information enabled quantification of the location and amount of high potential waterfowl and ungulate habitat lost primarily to agricultural expansion. The technique showed that consistent standards in land use interpretation can be applied to a large area producing acceptable results in a cost effective manner.

Vegetation Indices

Vegetation indices for continental-sized areas are now possible using remote sensing data. However, vegetation parameters such as biomass, Leaf Area Index (LAI) and Absorbed Photosynthetically Active Radiation (APAR) are the important measurements of biological productivity. The relationship between vegetation indices and these other vegetation parameters would be extremely useful for models of global primary productivity and biogeochemical cycling. Remote sensing alone is insufficient to quantify the functional role of vegetation in controlling energy and mass exchange from land surfaces. A new generation of global ecological models is required to quantify the activity of terrestrial vegetation and provide a means of predicting the consequences of the anthropogenic perturbations.

The Net Primary Productivity (NPP) of terrestrial vegetation is probably the most fundamental measure of global habitability. Previous attempts to estimate the NPP of large areas have developed correlations with one of three variables: actual evapo-transpiration, leaf area index (LAI), and absorbed photosynthetically active radiation. It has been suggested, however, that integrating the three variables for estimating NPP of large areas may now be possible (Running, 1986). Of the three key variables needed, LAI, intercepted shortwave radiation and surface temperature are all measurable by current satellites. Consequently, a first dynamic estimate of global terrestrial NPP may now be possible by integrating satellite measurements with simple ecosystem models of carbon conversion efficiency.

Using AVHRR to develop vegetation indices may be a viable method for consistent mapping and monitoring of the main cover types of continental areas. In one example, continental-scale effects of fragmentation have been identified (Tucker et al.,1985). They developed a technique using 4 km resolution, geographically referenced AVHRR imagery to create vegetation indices for the entire continent of Africa. A spectral vegetation index was calculated to allow the green-leaf dynamics of the African surface to be monitored for the whole of the continent. The authors observed seasonal variations in the spectral vegetation index for almost all vegetated areas of Africa including tropical rain forest, tropical seasonal forests and savanna. Deserts and semi-deserts were the only areas observed to be temporally invariant.

Continental-scale vegetation variations can be related to the patterns in bird speciation response to fluctuations in climate and vegetation. This has been demonstrated in the shrinkage of African tropical rainforest and the isolation of forest bird species into a few refuges since the last ice age (Haffer, 1982). More recent expansion of these rainforests due to increased moisture conditions has brought about the coalescence of some these refuges and subsequent hybridization of the bird species in these contact zones.

Assuming that measurable climate-vegetation-wildlife relationships exist in most parts of the world, the global mapping and monitoring of land cover, land use and biological productivity would be critical variables to measure. This would be necessary to understand how changes in land cover affect phenomena as diverse as atmospheric CO_2 concentrations, terrestrial primary productivity, the hydrologic cycle, and the energy balance at the surface-atmosphere interface. Vegetative cover information is required in order to determine the rates of change of the earth's biotic resources and the ways in which land use is adjusting to increasing demands on these resources.

Using spectral indices as an estimate of biomass has been shown to vary depending on the morphology of the plants. For example, salt marsh cordgrass has been shown to have different shape over a 17° latitudinal range, creating widely varying infrared reflectances despite identical live biomass (Bartlett et al., 1988). The authors conclude, however, that LAI and hence APAR measurements may be correlated with spectral indices over large areas.

In Canada, the use of the Normalized Difference Vegetation Index (NDVI) values produced from AVHRR imagery has become a common measure to estimate changes in terrestrial productivity over time. These estimates have been successfully applied to studies of prairie drought (Allison et al., 1989). Integration of NDVI estimates with temperature and precipitation variables has met with some success (D'Iorio et al., 1989) although precipitation appears to be more highly correlated (Houghham, 1987; Gallo and Heddinghaus, 1989). These findings indicate that NDVI estimates may have a role to play in monitoring and modelling seasonal and yearly vegetation responses to changing climatic variables over very large areas. An inferred relationship between NDVI and waterfowl habitat quality or quantity has yet to be developed but would be a natural extension of work already completed.

NDVI measurements from simulated AVHRR imagery have been found to be highly correlated with those obtained from simulated TM, SPOT and, especially, MSS imagery (Gallo and Daughtry, 1987). Although this relationship was developed in an agricultural setting, it may be applicable to vegetation types associated with various habitats. As such, the use of multiple remotely sensed data sets could be an important technique for surveys and sample stratification.

Snow Cover

From a wildlife perspective, snow cover changes over time have been linked to the several habitats. Snow depth and extent can affect the winter mobility of wolves and elk and the foraging ability of caribou. In addition, the timing of snowmelt from the nesting areas of arctic geese is a major factor affecting reproductive success (Reeves et al.,1976). Based on arctic nesting geese population information since the 1950s, it appears that poor breeding years are becoming more frequent, perhaps indicating long term changes in snow conditions (Cooch, 1990). These ecological relationships of snow and wildlife coupled with global modelling scenarios pointing to changes in the distribution, amount and duration of snow cover are sufficient reasons for wildlife habitat specialists to be interested inglobal changes in snow.

Remote sensing has been used with reasonable success to map snow extent. In the 1970s several studies were undertaken to map the presence of snow cover in the critical spring period for several colonies of snow geese (Heyland, 1975; Reeves et al.,1976). In these studies, visual interpretation of Very High Resolution Radiometer (VHRR) data from the NOAA satellites was used. The satellite observations of snow cover agreed with the ground studies of both snow cover and, later, with observations of numbers of young geese.

At present there is no operational use of satellite imagery to monitor national snow cover in support of habitat requirements. Research is continuing into the use of Nimbus passive microwave data (Goodison et al., 1987). The passive microwave sensor shows the greatest promise for operational monitoring of snow cover extent and depth, snow water equivalent and melt. In anticipation of the launch of Radarsat, CCRS is developing algorithms of snow water equivalent which integrate active microwave and other visible-infrared imagery (Leconte, 1990).

Marine Habitat

Projected climate changes will have great impact on the oceans in terms of shifting currents and temperature changes, as well as rising sea levels. These changes will have secondary impacts on the distribution and amount of the primary productivity of the oceans. In addition to indirect effects of climate, the thinning of stratospheric ozone is thought to have a direct negative impact on phytoplankton viability (Topping and

Bond, 1988). Phytoplankton dominates marine primary productivity and therefore influences the marine food chain. In addition, phytoplankton contributes to the interchange of CO_2 between the ocean and atmosphere (Perry, 1986).

It has been demonstrated in various studies that the phytoplankton component of primary productivity can be measured using remote sensing tools, particularly the Coastal Zone Color Scanner (CZCS) of the Nimbus satellites and airborne Fluorescence Line Scanner (FLI) imagery (Gower 1987). In particular, the work of Sullivan et al., (1988), in the Antarctic, has shown a strong correlation between the retreating ice-edge margin and the production of phytoplankton blooms as identified from ocean colour CZCS and SMMR passive microwave imagery. Furthermore, the relationship appears to be due to the increase in meltwater created by the retreating ice margin.

In addition to ice edge, phytoplankton distribution has been related to oceanographic discontinuities and ocean currents (Borstad and Gower, 1984). They found that surface phytoplankton closely followed the core of the Baffin current in the northeast Arctic. They also were able to correlate the distribution as measured from ship collection and airborne surveys with the thermal patterns found on AVHRR imagery.

In a study in the Beaufort Sea, remote sensing of water colour and temperature have helped define the locations of Bowhead whales which often congregate near oceanographic fronts (Borstad, 1986). Other physical factors influencing the distribution of Bowhead whales include the Mackenzie River plume and the edge of pack ice. Airborne spectrometer measurements of ocean colour and water temperature were combined with AVHRR thermal and visible imagery. This study demonstrated that remote sensing can aid in the understanding of relationships between oceanographic phenomena and Bowhead whale location. Given changing arctic ocean conditions in the future, these relationships will be useful for impact studies of arctic wildlife.

Clearly, these sorts of relationships would be of interest to explore the use of remote sensing imagery given the scenario of reduced pack ice conditions in Canada's Arctic due to climatic warming. Changes in ice conditions, phytoplankton distribution and currents can be related to the habitats of a number of species of wildlife including polar bears, whales and many species of Arctic waterfowl.

In more recent studies off the coast of Africa, the relationship between surface and space estimates of chlorophyll has been more rigorously defined (Lohrenz et al., 1988). There is hope, with the launch of ocean colour sensor aboard Landsat 6, that the measurements of chlorophyll can be more accurately measured. This development, coupled with the improvements in moored surface measurements using variable fluorescence (Falkowski, 1988), should enable algorithms of primary productivity to be developed with more accuracy. These developments should not only help in estimates of primary productivity in the oceans but also, by extension, aid in the studies of total carbon flux within the oceans.

FUTURE CHALLENGES OF REMOTE SENSING FOR WILDLIFE HABITAT

In order to put in place a strategy for using remote sensing for understanding global changes that affect wildlife habitat, it is important to have a overall working goal. A proposed goal is put forward below:

> To develop a greater understanding of global change impacts on wildlife and their habitat by assessing current wildlife resources in a spatial context through ecologically relevant and quantitative means and over a significantly long period, with the objective to inform and influence decision makers and managers with a wildlife habitat interest.

Because this goal encompasses both scientific and non-scientific domains, to achieve it will require the meeting of challenges for both groups.

Technical Challenges

Technical challenges of remote sensing research for habitat can fall into three categories:

- the development of ecologically valid relationships;

- the effective use of the "multi" concept; and,

- the effective use of GIS technology.

Remote sensing research has a history of exploring relationships of reflected, emitted or absorbed radiation of various ground phenomena. While initial research demands such studies, there has perhaps been a lack of understanding of the ecological or functional significance of these measurements. The importance of global change issues will dictate that remote sensing be used in ways that these relationships are clearly defined. This will be particularly true for studies of habitat and biological productivity because of the inherent interdependence of wildlife and various other natural resources.

As noted previously, the resolution of imagery most conveniently used for national or global studies (e.g., AVHRR) will not always achieve the detail necessary for detecting variables appropriate for wildlife habitat. This is not necessarily a drawback since global coverage does not always imply global significance. In order to achieve "global significance" for habitat studies it will be necessary to make effective use of multistage sampling, multisensor research strategies and multitemporal measurements, particularly for terrestrial and wetland habitats where small-scale changes may have profound implications for wildlife. For example, in prairie pothole mapping, selective use of detailed airborne remote sensing data, much of which exists, should be correlated with satellite data such as TM and AVHRR. Establishing relationships between these varied data sets will be needed in order to a obtain a quantifiable national or regional picture of habitat changes and impacts.

To meet technical challenges, it must be recognized that remote sensing data cannot supply all the essential spatial data on habitat. Because of the indirect impacts of global changes on wildlife resources, other information on wildlife will be essential to complete the assessments. Much useful information has been gathered on wildlife populations, harvest data, interactions of animals and their environment, and wildlife capability, as well as biophysical variables such as soils and climate. These varied data sources will need to be integrated using GIS systems which are now capable of performing complex analysis functions such as multi-variate relation and modelling.

As part of the proposed research strategy for the United States, experimentation, modelling and monitoring have been suggested as stages (Smith and Tirpak, 1988). Specific to monitoring applications, three general roles have been proposed. These are: 1) the resolution of ecological patterns at different temporal and spatial scales; 2) regional detection of trends; and, 3) the calibration and validation of models. Although remote sensing may have a role in all of these stages, a particular niche could be found in large-area analyses of recent-past variability of resources such as habitat, due to various global changes, and monitoring biomass productivity patterns.

Modelling using GIS technology has been employed to predict shifts of ecosystems in response to climate change (Rizzo and Wiken, 1989). They used the Goddard Institute for Space Studies (GISS) model of atmospheric circulation to show how the locations of ecodistricts of Canada would be altered with a doubling of atmospheric CO_2. Because of the important vegetation influences and responses to climatic changes, measures of biological productivity as derived from remotely sensed imagery could be a component in the refinement of ecological models. Remote sensing could contribute to the development of other models in areas such as coastal wetland response to rising sea levels, vegetation growth and decay and vegetation succession (Cihlar et al.,1989).

National Interests and Requirements

The Canadian Wildlife Service (CWS) has a long history of monitoring wildlife and their habitat for numerous priority areas. To set a goal of monitoring all habitats at risk from global changes is presently unrealistic. Priorities should be based upon a set of criteria developed by those with a nationally or strong regionally legislated responsibility for wildlife. The spatial framework for their areas of interest may not necessarily be the optimum for remote sensing of global changes. Yet there is a wealth of wildlife information that could aid remote sensing analyses of global changes.

Below are spatial frameworks and issues of interest to CWS that might be used to focus the efforts of a long term monitoring strategy for global change:

Spatial Frameworks
- Migratory Bird Sanctuaries
- National Wildlife Areas
- other protected ecological areas
- ecodistricts, ecoregions
- prairie wetlands monitoring sites
- flyways
- existing long term, large scale monitoring sites
- prairie pond counts
- known nesting colonies (e.g., snow geese)

National Wildlife Issues and Interests
- migratory birds and mammals
- vulnerable, threatened and endangered species
- wetlands
- climate change impacts on wildlife habitat
- habitat loss (e.g.,conversion of wetlands to agriculture and urban uses)
- hunting and trapping
- effects of toxic substances such as pesticides on wildlife -
  - sustainable use of wildlife resources
  - non-consumptive uses of wildlife

Currently the Canadian Wildlife Service is developing a federal wildlife habitat strategy. The primary objective of this strategy will be to maintain or enhance wildlife habitat in order to sustain all species indigenous to Canada. Within this broad objective is the requirement for scientific expertise to measure and improve the technical basis for habitat conservation. The focus of this technical requirement will be directed at the impacts of climate change and the development of monitoring and evaluation techniques. How remote sensing can be harnessed to contribute to this task remains to be determined. However, it is certain that remote sensing will not be used in isolation from other interests and data available on wildlife and habitat.

The example cited earlier of using indicator waterfowl in conjunction with lake counts and measures derived from Thematic Mapper imagery has been used to infer lake acidification over a very large area (McNicol, 1989). Other relationships are in need of exploring such as eider populations and open arctic water, marine mammals, ice edge and phytoplankton concentrations. Some relationships will be more complex than others, requiring further research in order to quantify.

Giving priority to global change remote sensing programs for wildlife habitat should take into account the following:

- the immediacy of the global change impact on habitat,

- the gaps in essential resource data, and

- the need to understand critical ecological relationships.

Destruction of habitat from anthropogenic influences (e.g. agriculture, forestry, urban growth) continues to be the prime threat to wildlife habitat. This threat was a major reason for the development of the remote sensing program of Ducks Unlimited Canada. Acid rain destruction of lake productivity is perhaps the next most immediate threat to wildlife habitat. Large-scale impacts of global warming and sea level and arctic ice changes will not likely be measurable from satellites before the turn of the century. However, it will be important to establish a solid base of resource and ecological information now that can be used to measure vulnerability, determine impacts and influence courses of remedial action.

A growing requirement recognized by CWS and other Environment Canada services concerned with global change is that scientific activities must have significance beyond the immediate scientific interest. Specifically, scientific knowledge of global change must be related back to public awareness, socio-economic issues, government policy and action. In a wildlife context, this means that the impacts on habitat that are capable of measurement with remotely sensed imagery should be shown to have benefit to the management or regulation of those resources.

Interdisciplinary Co-operation

If remote sensing is to contribute to the understanding of global processes affecting wildlife habitat or to measuring the habitats themselves, it must done through enhanced cooperation between those responsible for wildlife habitat and the remote sensing community. Within the wildlife management hierarchy itself, regional, national and non-government organizations will need to work together, since their individual interests vary considerably. As with all joint endeavours, cooperation should be based on a mutual appreciation of the requirements and constraints operating within each area of interest.

Although wildlife and wildlife habitat are resources that will be greatly affected by global change, theirs is but one of many such sectors that will be impacted. Linking several of these sectors will likely be required to justify a national remote sensing program that can help meet their needs. For example, a national land use/land cover mapping program could be of interest not only for habitat uses but for a variety of other resource sectors such as forestry and agriculture. Multidisciplinary cooperation through joint projects and data sharing will help ease the financial burden of individual stakeholders. Current global change programs such as the Boreal Forest Experiment, the AVHRR National Land Cover Mapping Project (Cihlar et al., 1989) and the Northern Wetlands Study (CIRAC News, 1989) are examples of programs that are being conducted by others but are of significant interest to wildlife specialists. Other global programs originating outside of Canada, such as proposed sea level monitoring, will be of great interest to Canadian coastal habitat interests.

PROPOSED REMOTE SENSING PROGRAM FOR WILDLIFE HABITAT

Despite the useful remote sensing initiatives of other groups, there will be a role for remote sensing oriented programs specific to the requirements of Canadian wildlife habitat. The following is a sample of three proposed initiatives.

National Assessment of Vulnerable Habitats

As an initial effort to estimate climate change impacts and prioritize other studies, data on land use and land cover derived from remotely sensed imagery would be used to measure the potential vulnerability of selected species or habitats to global change. The objective of this study would be to identify and map habitats at risk according to selected criteria such as these examples suggested by Smith and Tirpak (1988):

- habitats with a small geographic distribution,

- habitats of species with small populations,

- habitats that are adjacent to physical and anthropogenic barriers that would impede the dispersal of the species, and

- species that would be adversely affected by fragmentation of its existing habitat.

Initially, the entire country should be examined with detailed assessments done on environmentally protected areas and other special areas of interest. The CCRS/IGBP project to create a national land use/land cover map from AVHRR imagery could be used to identify and measure features such as barriers to dispersal. It would be necessary to integrate this land cover information with ecological data, locations and attributes of existing protected areas and areas of potential change as derived from climate change models. Measurements, including sizes of land parcels and proximity analyses, as well as more complex modelling scenarios, would be developed using GIS.

This proposed study would help identify vulnerability of most of the threatened and endangered species in Canada, but other habitats vulnerable to impacts from environmental stresses would also surface. Furthermore, such a study would help focus more detailed vulnerability projects or direct further research on specific impacts.

It would be most beneficial if habitat requirements of particular species or species complexes continued to be investigated parallel to remote sensing investigations. This would be vital to improving the confidence placed in establishing causal links between species population or movement and the remotely sensed classifications.

National Wetland Mapping

Wetlands are of long standing interest to Canadian wildlife specialists. As described earlier, remotely sensed imagery from satellites have been used to map open wetlands. However, there is a lack of a national data base of sufficient resolution to provide a solid base from which to compare future changes. Some detailed information does exists for several actively changing wetland areas in urban and agriculturally dominated regions.

At the present time an inventory of wooded and coastal wetlands is particularly lacking. Coastal wetlands will be especially vulnerable because of sea level changes. An inventory of wetlands could be based on Landsat Thematic Mapper imagery and would probably require supporting data bases (e.g. topographical, soils and tidal information for coastal wetlands), in order to obtain a complete and accurate inventory of the resource. The inventory could initially focus on known coastal wetland concentrations and estuaries where various anthropogenic pressures have already diminished wetland resources. Eventually, the inventory might include most of the coastline of Canada. Some research will be necessary in order to define an appropriate technique that will extract functional wetland classes, rather than conveniently classifiable units. The use of Thematic Mapper imagery supplemented with airborne spectrometer data for calibration might be the optimum remotely sensed data sets currently available to meet this mapping challenge.

A second phase of investigation for wetlands applies particularly to the prairies. It is widely acknowledged that the prairies will probably suffer some of the most severe effects from climatic change, more than any other area in Canada. Global warming may significantly increase the mean annual temperature by several degrees by the middle of the 21st century. The prairies are also home to a disproportionate number of vulnerable, threatened and endangered species which will be affected by these changes. This relatively short-term response to climate change that will take place in the core of the prairies will have an impact on the waterbodies, wetlands, vegetation, agriculture and wildlife.

Although Thematic Mapper has been used to map wetlands, there are technical gaps in information for wetlands less than 2 hectares (Jacobson et al., 1987). Some estimates show that 90 percent of wetlands are under 1/2 hectares in some areas of the prairies (Adams, 1987). Financial difficulties arise when systematically monitoring these small areas using conventional data sources. Nevertheless, there is a need to investigate to what extent satellite remote sensing of wetland changes can be correlated with detailed ground measurements and perhaps serve as a surrogate or indicator of changes in wetland abundance and change over a large area. Several detailed ground and aerial data sets currently exists which could be used in this research (e.g. Adams, 1987). Establishing such relationships will enable habitat biologists to make use of remotely sensed data for estimating losses and gains and population levels in waterfowl habitat for a large area. Expanding the lake counts and measures program (Helie and Wickware, in progress) to the prairies may be one avenue by which remotely sensed imagery could be obtained for this region.

As a counterpart to a national wetland inventory, it would be beneficial for ecological experts to follow and perhaps become more involved in studies of wetlands-atmosphere exchange processes. In this regard, the results of the Northern Wetlands Study and Boreal Forest Experiment will be useful. The establishment of transfer functions between the various inventoried spatial parameters and rates of material exchange will require considerable research. The results will be most useful if ecological relationships can be established as well.

Vegetation Indices and Modelling Research

Because of the influence of vegetation in numerous processes such as global radiation balance, geochemical cycles, habitat and drought, there exists a requirement to more completely understand this important earth resource. In this regard, the objectives put forward by Cihlar et al.,1988 should be implemented. These include the development of appropriate techniques to locate and measure vegetation change; to develop methods to measure total phytomass, net primary productivity, carbon storage and any temporal changes therein; and thirdly, to develop and apply models of vegetation succession as derived from remotely sensed imagery to climate change scenarios. Presently, the AVHRR sensor appears most suited to these applications, although sensors planned for the Earth Observing System (Eos) will be useful towards the end of the decade.

Although these objectives could satisfy many applications, it will be useful to conduct parallel studies which relate vegetation measurements to specific habitat requirements. For example, in Canada's prairies the Normalized Difference Vegetation Index (NDVI) technique which uses AVHRR data has shown promise for measuring drought conditions (Allison et al., 1989). This type of analysis could be related to stress levels of prairie habitats, particularly for waterfowl. In its simplest form, the NDVI could help identify areas of chronic stress from drought. A more sophisticated approach would be to relate NDVI measurements with detailed measurements of habitat quality, quantity and breeding success of waterfowl obtained from other sources. More research needs to be undertaken, particularly in the prairies, that will help establish these relationships. Over a sufficiently long period, a model of vegetation stress - species response could be developed for use as a predictive tool for habitat impact or for planning remedial action in altered habitats. These investigations will strengthen the ecological significance of broader studies of vegetation.

CONCLUSIONS

It seems clear that remote sensing can play an important role in assessing and monitoring wildlife habitat and biological productivity in both direct and indirect ways. This paper has summarized some of many uses that have been made for wetland, terrestrial and marine environment studies. In addition, the ingredients of a successful program have been put forward based on the use of a variety of sensors, ecological spatial frameworks, GIS techniques, co-operative and interdisciplinary involvement in projects, and a clear understanding of national goals and reporting structures related to wildlife habitat. Finally, a few global change research initiatives have been suggested which would be of particular benefit to Canada's wildlife interests from a national perspective.

How well Canadians cope with global climatic changes over the next century will be determined, in part, by how well we are able to integrate, analyze and derive significance from the wide range of information available to us on resources such as wildlife habitat.

CHAPTER 10

MONITORING THE GLOBAL CHANGE OF WATER RESOURCES USING REMOTE SENSING

J. Whiting and R.P. Bukata

INTRODUCTION

The extent to which the climatic response to the gradual increases in greenhouse gases will impact hydrological processes in general, and water resources in particular, is far from fully understood. The coming decade will see large scale multinational programs dedicated to both the monitoring and modelling of global climate change and its proactive and responsive interactions with anthropogenic activity. The results of such human/climatic interactions will be direct impacts on the atmospheric and terrestrial environments. Such impacts will be multidisciplinary in nature and will display large variations in both response times and spatial extent. Some aspects of the relationships among climate change and water resources and the possible roles of remote sensing (perhaps the single most unifying activity of the global climate programs) in contributing to the understanding of such relationships will be examined. Evaluating the implications of climate change to water resources is generally considered to be a three-step process:

- using Global Climate Models (GCM) along with existing paleoclimate or proxy data, develop quantitative scenarios of changes in major climatic variables;

- using these scenarios, simulate the hydrologic cycle for the region of interest; and,

- assess the impact of these hydrologic variations on the natural basin parameters (such as groundwater flow, surface run-off, basin storage capacity, etc.) and the water resource management practices (such as dams, aqueducts, reservoirs, etc.).

Figure 10.1 illustrates these interrelated activities in schematic form. As suggested by Figure 10.1, the problem of climate change and its relationships to water resources and management practices can be stated as two fundamental questions:

- how susceptible are water resources to climate change; and,

- how adaptable are water resource management practices to changes in water resources?

These two fundamental questions immediately suggest three more specific questions:

- what are the basic parameters that must be available to convincingly estimate the susceptibility of water resources to climate change and the adaptability of water resource management practices to those water resources changes;

- what techniques, methodologies, and sampling strategies are required to directly monitor or theoretically infer those basic parameters; and,

- what is the nature and impact (along with the progression rate and spatial scope) of the feedback loops?

The general questions concerning the adaptability of water management practices to water resources, while of paramount importance, particularly on the municipal and regional levels, will not be dealt with in the ensuing discussions. Rather, attention will be focused on the climate change and water resources change interactive components of Figure 10.1.

Germane to the entire issue, of course, is the need to define a sensible region upon which to evaluate the hydrological implications of climate change. Canada may be conveniently divided into five basin regions

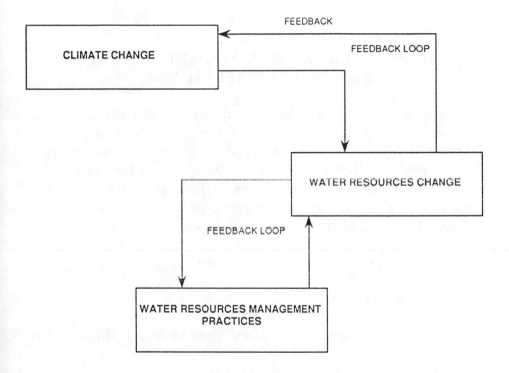

Figure 10.1: The Three-Step Interactive Components Relating Climate Change and Water Resources.

each draining into an ocean. These five ocean basin regions (Pacific, Arctic, Gulf of Mexico, Hudson Bay, Atlantic), illustrated in Figure 10.2, should logically be considered as Canadian targets for hydrological study. As listed in Figure 10.2, these ocean basins may be further subdivided into principal river basin regions. Local water resources issues should first be considered within the interactive setting of their principal river basin. Continuity within the interactive setting of its basic ocean basin and continuity within the interactive setting of the five ocean basins must logically follow.

THE ESSENTIAL VARIABLES OF HYDROLOGY AND REGIONAL CLIMATE CHANGE

It is certainly realized that the dynamic nature of a basin's aquatic environment is a convoluted consequence of a myriad of physical, chemical, biological, socio-economic, and anthropogenic parameters that are inescapably interlinked. However, assuming that precipitation inputs to a basin are controlled by conservation laws, the parameter precipitation at time t, $P(t)$, may be expressed in terms of five essential hydrographic variables, viz:

$$P(t) = Q(t) + E_T(t) + S(t) + W_G(t) + W_S(t)$$

.... (1),

where: $Q(t)$ = runoff at time t;
$E_T(t)$ = evapotranspiration at time t;
$S(t)$ = storage of water (lakes, rivers, snow, ice, plants, etc.) at time t;
$W_G(t)$ = groundwater at time t; and,
$W_S(t)$ = soil moisture at time t.

$P(t)$ in equation (1) refers to the total precipitation input to the region of interest. As such it is not necessarily pure rainwater or pure snow. Rather, $P(t)$ includes all of the downwelling material at time t, such as atmospheric particles, acid rain, greenhouse gases, carbon concentrations, etc. Differentiating equation (1) yields the governing hydrologic cycle equation:

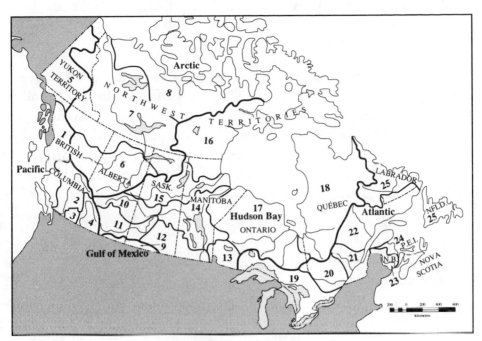

OCEAN BASIN REGION	RIVER BASIN REGION	AREA IN 000's km²	POPULATION IN 000's 1981
Pacific	1 Pacific Coastal	352	616
	2 Frazer-Lower Mainland	234	1 722
	3 Okanagan-Similkameenª	14	189
	4 Columbiaª	90	161
	5 Yukonª	328	23
Arctic	6 Peace-Athabasca	487	286
	7 Lower Mackenzie	1 300	43
	8 Arctic Coast-Islands	2 025	13
Gulf of Mexico	9 Missouriª	26	14
Hudson Bay	10 North Saskatchewan	146	1 084
	11 South Saskatchewanª	170	1 282
	12 Assiniboine-Redª	190	1 300
	13 Winnipegª	107	77
	14 Lower Saskatchewan-Nelson	363	224
	15 Churchill	298	68
	16 Keewatin	689	5
	17 Northern Ontario	694	157
	18 Northern Quebec	950	109
Atlantic	19 Great Lakesª	319	7 579
	20 Ottawa	146	1 270
	21 St. Lawrence	116	5 193
	22 North Shore-Gaspé	403	653
	23 St. John-St. Croixª	37	393
	24 Maritime Coastal	114	1 314
	25 Newfoundland-Labrador	376	568
CANADA		9 974	24 343

ªCanadian portion only; area and population on U.S. side of international basin regions are excluded from totals

Figure 10.2: Ocean basin regions subdivided into principal river basin regions.

$$\frac{dP(t)}{dt} = \frac{dQ(t)}{dt} + \frac{dE_T(t)}{dt} + \frac{dS(t)}{dt} + \frac{dW_G t)}{dt} + \frac{dW_S(t)}{dt}$$

..... (2)

The hydrologic processes defined in equations (1) and (2) are schematically illustrated in Figure 10.3 for surface, subsurface, and above-surface water. It must be stressed that while we have conveniently reduced P(t) to five terms, each of these terms require directly measured values, theoretically inferred values, or mathematical definitions involving other variables. A particularly difficult term appears to be S(t). Further, it is not always possible to directly measure the parameter:

$$\frac{dP(t)}{dt} \quad .$$

It is often necessary to infer:

$$\frac{dP(t)}{dt} \quad ,$$

in terms of surrogate variables such as cloud cover, cloud water content, etc.

The term "climate" is currently in widespread use, and while the term is intuitively understood to represent a general convolution of weather-related environmental conditions, a specific mathematical expression for "climate" is an elusive commodity. The term "climate change" is intuitively understood to represent the time-derivative of this elusive commodity. Adding further complexity to such a "climate change" time-derivative expression is the need to distinguish natural climate change progression (seasonal variations, impacts of both predictable and non-predictable natural phenomena) and climate change progression resulting from anthropogenic activities. These difficulties notwithstanding, however, it would indeed be convenient to discuss a mathematical definition of climate change in terms of its principal variables. Further, since the climate most readily observable (and most directly intimate with local water resources) is the regional climate, we suggest that a mathematical expression for regional climate be considered as a second hydrologic parameter.

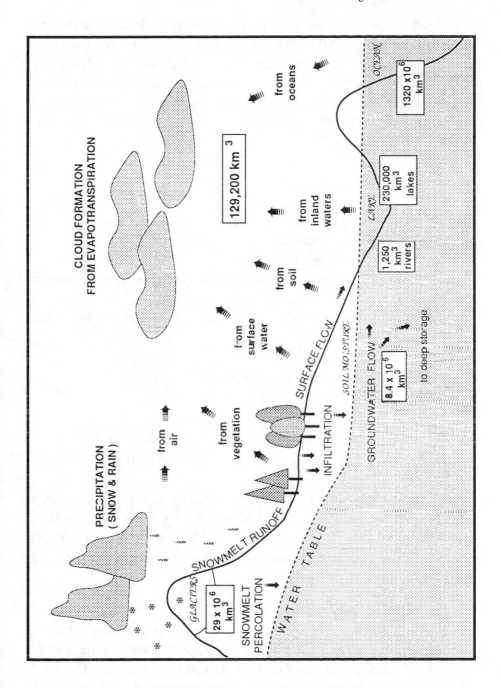

Figure 10.3: Schematic illustration of hydrologic processes for surface, subsurface and above surface water.

In a manner similar to the precipitation, we now determine that the time-dependent regional climate parameter, C_R, may be adequately defined in terms of four variables. Again it must be realized that obtaining numerical values for these four basic variables may necessitate the invoking of mathematical expressions, introducing further variables or surrogates or statistical expressions. We functionally define regional climate C_R as:

$$C_R = f\{T, P, V, R\},$$

where:
- T = near surface air temperature,
- P = precipitation,
- V = surface wind velocity,
- R = removal of matter to "end point" or "storage" status (i.e., to a state in the time-frame of the analysis after which no further transport or transformation will occur).

Then, regional climate change $\dfrac{dC_R}{dt}$ is given by:

$$\frac{dC_R}{dt} = \frac{\partial C_R}{\partial T}\frac{\partial T}{\partial t} + \frac{\partial C_R}{\partial P}\frac{\partial P}{\partial t} + \frac{\partial C_R}{\partial V}\frac{\partial V}{\partial t} + \frac{\partial C_R}{\partial R}\frac{\partial R}{\partial t} \quad ...(3)$$

Notice that while equation (3) defines a change in regional climate, it does not define C_R as a distinct single entity with an associated parametric unit. It is, rather, an index of changing conditions within a regional climate and as such will be defined as the Index of Regional Climate Change.

The time derivatives of equation (3) are relatively well- defined and estimable. $\partial T / \partial t$ may be readily obtained from temperature; $\partial P / \partial T$ is as defined by equation (2); and $\partial V / \partial t$ is the acceleration of surface wind. Both $\partial P / \partial T$ and $\partial V / \partial t$ can also be obtained from records. The "end point" or "storage" removal term R is more controversially defined. Since equation (3) defines regional climate change (as opposed to global climate change) it is not restrained to the same conservation of matter laws that dictate the behaviour of global climate change. Consequently, matter may accumulate or diminish from a region depending upon the conditions existing at any particular time. R, then, may be confidently taken to represent the difference between input and output matter, i.e., R is essentially a positive or negative residual for the basin under consideration: R = Input - Output as a function of time.

From equation (1), R(t) may be written as:

$$R(t) \quad = \quad P(t) - E_T(t) - Q(t)$$

$$= \quad W_G(t) + W_s(t) + S(t)$$

$$= \quad \text{groundwater + soil moisture + surface water storage} \quad ...(4).$$

Thus, R(t) is the sum of all surface and subsurface water present in the basin at a particular time. $\partial R/\partial t$ is the time rate of change of the entire non-atmospheric water content of the basin, since at any time the basin may be far removed from total saturation. However, R(t) may be regarded as a percentage basin saturation term, i.e. a non-atmospheric equivalent of relative humidity for a particular basin. $\partial R/\partial t$ may thus be considered as a hydrologic regional change in non-atmospheric relative humidity. This is a direct analogy to global aquatic fate wherein aquatic transports occur from groundwater to rivers to oceans to great ocean depths (the ultimate "endpoint"). The regional counterpart of great ocean depths is subsurface water. Further, it is interesting to note that precipitation which is the governing parameter for the hydrologic cycle is, quite appropriately, a variable in the regional climate expression.

While the time derivatives of equation (3) do not present insurmountable problems to scientific philosophy or direct numerical estimations, the partial derivative terms of equation (3) do accentuate the inherent difficulties in successfully relating regional climate change to even a reduced number of hydrologically significant environmental variables. The index of regional climate change, dC_R/dt, is dependent upon the climatic impact of each of near-surface air temperature, precipitation, surface wind speed, and subsurface residual storage capacity, in the absence of the other hydrological driving forces. Setting up the required controlled research experiments or establishing verifiable environmental models to obtain such partial derivatives as a function of both space and time, is not necessarily a simple task. Nevertheless, such determinations of multivariate dependencies must be made if impacts of regional climate change are to be not only understood and predicted, but also responsibly acted upon.

Table 10.1 reviews the recommended hydrological and climatic variables discussed to this point, along with surrogate and other dependent variables which could be required to obtain the basic variables of equations (2) and (3). Some of these sub-variables emerge from recommendations given in such sources as the GEWEX Workshop held in Saskatoon, October 26-29, 1989, and various 1980's NASA documentation on EOS (Earth Observing System), NASA Advisory Council (1988), Goodison et al. (1983); and standard hydrological textbooks. These variables represent a rather broad cross-section of what traditional hydrological studies have found to be desirable model parameters, climate change indicators, and variables which lend themselves to direct measurement. Some of these variables have been collected routinely as a matter of monitoring protocol, others to satisfy particular regional or local needs. Also included within Table 10.1 are suggestions for what would be the minimal restrictions on the desirability of spatial resolution, accuracy, and frequency of measurement.

DATA COLLECTION PRACTICES

The interrelationships of global climate change, regional climate change, hydrologic cycle change, water resources change, and water resources management practices requires simultaneous numerical information on a large number of socio-economic atmospheric, terrestrial, and solar properties (variables which have been neglected in the current discussions, but which should definitely be incorporated into more sophisticated refinements of the current discussions). Even the intentionally abbreviated nature of Table 10.1 illustrates this point

TABLE 10.1

Hydrologic and Climatic Variables

Parameter	Variables	Spatial Resolution	Accuracy	Frequency
Rate of Precipitation	Precipitation	1 km	10%	1 per day
	Rate of Precip.	100 km(h) x 5 km(v)		
	Snow Cover	1 km	10%	1 per day
	Cloud Cover	1 km	5%	4 per day
	Cloud Water Content	50 km	$0.1\ kg\ m^{-2}$	4 per day
	Cloud Top Height	1 km (v)	0.5 km	4 per day
	Columnar Water Vapour Pressure	100 km (h) x 100 km (v)	0.002 ppm	2 per day
	CO_2	1 km	10%	1 per day
	CO	1 km	10%	1 per day
	N_2O	1 km	10%	1 per day
	CH_4	1 km	10%	1 per day
	CFM	1 km	10%	1 per day
	Aerosols	(10x10x1) km	5%	1 per day
	Runoff	100 m	10%	1 per day
	Area (Lakes)	30 m	2%	1 per day
	Height (sfc)	100 m	5 m	1 / 10 yrs
	Evaporation			
	Area (soil thermal)	30 m	10%	1 per yr
	Wind Speed	$50\ km^2$	$1\ ms^{-1}$	1 per day
	Temp (lake sfc)	30 m	$0.5°$	2 per day
	Area (biomass index)	30 m	10%	1 per mon
	Biomass Density	1 km	5%	1 per wk

Parameter	Variables	Spatial Resolution	Accuracy	Frequency
	Production Rate	30 m	20%	1 /3 days
	Vegetation Condition	30 m	15%	/3 days
	Land Use	30 m	10%	1 per mon

TABLE 10.1 (continued)

Storage

Snow Cover	1 km	10%	1 /3 days
Area (snow, ice)	1 km	10%	1 per wk
Temp (snow sfc)	1 km	1°K	1 /3 days
Albedo (snow)	?	?	?
Ice Height	30 m	1 m	1 /5 yrs
Volume (lake,river)	?	?	?

Groundwater

Area (discharge, recharge)	30 m	5%	1 /2 mon
Vegetation vigor	30 m	10%	1 per mon
Irrigation Practices	30 m	10%	1 per yr

Soil Water Content	1 km	10%	6 per yr
Surface characteristics	30 m	20%	1 /50 yr
Terrain Slopes (DEM)	30 m	20%	once
Frozen Ground boundaries	1 km	10%	1 per day

CLIMATE

Temp.(Troposphere)	100 km(h)x5km(v)	1°K	1 per day
Temp.(Surface)	1 km	1°K	2 per day
Temp.(Cloud emission)	1 km	1°K	4 per day
Cloud Albedo	50 km	5%	4 per day
Precipitation	(see above)		
Surface Wind	50 km^2	1 MS^{-1}	1 per day
Storage	(see above)		
Groundwater Content	(see above)		
Soil Moisture Content	(see above)		

note: sfc - surface

dramatically. Such information is generally accumulated through direct monitoring/sampling strategies, estimated through models or retrieval algorithms, adopted from prior research activities, or simply avoided (such as considering only steady-state solutions or instances when an unattainable variable can be considered as having a negligible impact). Clearly, therefore, existing data collection and data interpretation practices currently in widespread use can severely restrict the ability to use climatic or hydrologic cycle change to predict water resources changes. Data collection issues include non-directly comparable monitoring systems, calibration inaccuracies, station inconsistencies, socioeconomic skewing influences, non-representative data sets, data inaccessibility, and inappropriate temporal and spatial sampling strategies. Data interpretation problems include shortcomings in retrieval algorithms, relatively short data records, deficient cause/effect climate models, incompatibilities among existing data records and analyses schemes, the exorbitant time and cost factors involved in computer analyses of climate models for regional resolution, and onerous volumes of existing and future satellite data.

MONITORING THE
HYDROLOGIC AND CLIMATIC VARIABLES

The anthropogenic influences to the evolution of the earth's biosphere and geosphere have resulted in a world wide collaboration of environmental monitoring of unprecedented multidisciplinary complexity. Central to such global environmental monitoring is the role of spectra-radiometric optical sensing devices mounted on earth-orbiting satellite platforms. In addition, *in situ* airborne and shuttle environmental missions have been established to supplement such remote sensing programs. Such low to zero altitude measurement techniques are particularly essential for studies of the aquatic environment in which dynamical time scales and optical complexities (particularly of inland waters) render space monitoring quite uncertain in many instances.

Unarguably, what environmental satellites do, they do very well. Satellites offer an enormous potential for improving the temporal and spatial coverage of hydrometeorological data to meet the real-time needs of Canadian user agencies. They are essential for monitoring regions of the Canadian terrain inaccessible to appropriate ground-based monitoring protocols. They provide a singularly valuable snapshot in time of the spatial arena in which physical, chemical, and biological forces and targets interact with fluctuations in the terrestrial ecosystem. They are excellent for monitoring change, both in space and time (the very essence of the hydrological cycle and climate variables monitoring requirements discussed above), and they are invaluable to such geometric applications as delineating landforms, coastlines, and land-use boundaries.

Remote sensing devices directly record the spectro-optical emanations (either passive or active) from some combination of the organic and/or inorganic components of the biosphere. No *per se* parametric information is collected. Consequently, the spectro-optical information must be converted, through appropriate multidisciplinary modelling activities into <u>inferred</u> estimates of the chemical, physical, or biological variables being sought. With this realization of the strong dependency of remotely sensed data upon reliable inference techniques, Table 10.2 illustrates the parameters and variables of Table 10.1 alongside techniques and platforms that are and will be available for inferring those variables as part of the coordinated efforts of global monitoring. Table 10.2, while emphasizing available space vehicles, does not restrict itself to such satellite monitoring methodologies, particularly when such variables are best determined via ground-based measurement techniques. Also included in Table 10.2 are our best estimates of the degree of difficulty in obtaining reliable inferences of the variable in question: A, refers to those determinations which are feasible and relatively simple; B, refers to those determinations which are feasible but are complex and/or difficult; and C, refers to those determinations that cannot be confidently considered to be feasible. In some instances, a Feasibility of B is assigned to a variable because a planned satellite has yet to be launched. In other instances a Feasibility of B is assigned because the accuracies, spatial resolution, or retrieval algorithms, while of some value, are either non-optimal or as yet unverified. A Feasibility of C is assigned to those variables which, if required, should be determined using other methods

TABLE 10.2

Techniques, Satellite, Feasibility Factor
and Importance of the Variable.

Variable (location)	Technique	Platform	Feasibility Factor	Importance Factor
Aerosols	lidar (sfc)	—	B	1
Albedo (snow)	VIS,IR	AVHRR/POES, LANDSAT	C	3
	microwave	SMMR/SPOT/NIMBUS 3	C	
	SAR	RADARSAT	C	3
(cloud)	VIS,IR	AVHRR/POES	B	3
	microwave	VHS/GOES,SMM/I/DMSP C		3
Area (lake)	near IR	LANDSAT TM4	A	3
(soil thermal)	IR	HIRS,HSU, AVHRR/POES	B	1
	microwave	VAS/GOES	C	1
(biomass index)	colour, IR	AVHRR/POES	A	1
	SAR	RADARSAT	C	1
(snow)	VIS,IR	AVHRR/POES	A	2
	microwave	SMM/I/DMSP	B	1
(groundwater)	IR thermal	LANDSAT TM6	B	1
	microwave	SMM/I/DSMP, AMSR	C	1
Biomass (density & production)	VIS,IR spectrometry	BIOME	C	1
Cloud (amount, type,height)	observation	ground	A	1
	VIS	AVHRR/POES, VISSR /GOES	B	1
CO_2	ground	—	A	1
CO	IR spectrometry IR emission	ISAMS/UARS	C	1
CH_4	IR spectrometry	ATMOS/shuttle	B	1
CFM_5	ground	—	A	1
	IR spectrometry	ATMOS/shuttle	B	1
Frozen ground	ground	—	A	1
Height (lake)	ground	COHMAP	A	3
(ice)	radar sounding	airborne	C	3
Landuse	VIS IR	AVHRR/POES	A	2
	microwave	SSM/I/DMSP	B	2
N_2O	ground	—	A	1

TABLE 10.2 (continued)

	IR emission	UARS	C	1
	IR occultation		C	1
	IR interferometry	ATMOS/shuttle	B	1
Precipitation	rain gauge, radar	ground	A	1
	IR	GOES-J	B	2
	microwave	SMM/I/DMSP	B	2
	radar	TREM	C	1
Rate (precipitation)	radar	TREM	C	1
Runoff	IR-thermal,	VIS GOES	C	1
	microwave	DMSP	C	1
Snow water	microwave	SMMR/NMBUS	B	2
equivalent		SMM/I/DMSP	B	1
Soil water content	microwave	SMM/I/DMSP	C	1
		AMSR		
Surface	VIS,IR	SSM/I/DMSP	C	3
characteristics	AMSR			
Temperature (cloud)	IR	TOVS/POES	C	3
	microwave	VAS/POES	C	3
(lake)	IR thermal	AVHRR/POES	A	1
(snow)	IR thermal	AVHRR/POES	A	3
	LANDSAT(TM6)	SPOT	C	3
(surface)	IR thermal	HIRS,AVHRR/POES	B	1
	microwave	VAS/GOES	C	1
(troposphere)	radiosonde	ground	A	3
	IR	TOVS/POES	B	3
	microwave	VAS/GOES,AMSU	C	3
Terrain slope	DEM	SPOT	B	2
Vegetation-	VIR,IR	AVHRR/POES	A	2
condition				
	SAR	RADARSAT	A	2
Water vapour	radiosonde,LIDAR	ground	A	1
content	microwave	SSM/I/DMSP	C	2
	AMSU	C	1	
	IR	VAS/GOES	B	1
Windspeed	radiosonde,	ground	A	1
	observation			
	Doppler radar	ground	A	1
	Scatterometer	VAS/GOES	A	1

Notes:

VIS	visible
IR	infra-red
SAR	synthetic Aperture Radar
sfc	surface
A	easy
B	difficult

TABLE 10.2 (continued)

C	not possible	
1	essential	
2	desirable	
3	non-essential	
Satellite	available	
AMSU	Advanced Microwave Sounding Unit	1994
ATMOS	Atm. Trace Molecules Obs. by Spectroscopy	1990-4
BIOME	Biological Imaging & Observational Mission to Earth	1989 (1996)
(EOS)		
COHMAP	Cooperative Holocene Mapping Project	1990
DMSP	Defense Met. Sat. Program-Special Sensor	1989
	-Microwave Imagery	
	-Microwave Temperature Sounder	
GOES-SSM/I	GCO stationery Obs. Env. Sat.	1990
-SSM/T		
-J		
-VAS	Atmospheric Sounder	1988-1995
-VISSR	Visible Infrared Spin-Scan Radione	1988-1995
HIRS	High Resolution IR Radiation Sounder	1988-1995
ISAMS	Improved Stratospheric & Mesospheric Sounder	1990
LANDSAT	Land Remote Sensing Satellite	1972-
MSU	Microwave Sounding Unit	
NOAA	National Oceanic & Atmospheric Admin.	1975-1990
POES-AVHRR	Polar-orbiting Operation Satellite	
	Advantaged Very High Resolution Radionide	
-TOVS	Tiros Operational Vertical Sounder	
RADARSAT	Radar Satellite	1994
SPOT	Systeme Pour l'Observation de la Terre	1986
TREM	Tropical Rainfall Explorer Missura	1993
UARS	Upper Atmosphere Research Satellite	1991

or techniques. We have also included our best estimates of the relative importance of the selected variables to the overall problems of climate and water resources interactions. We have used a somewhat arbitrary set of criteria for prioritizing the relative importance of the variables of Tables 10.1 and 10.2. We have ascribed an Importance Index of 1 to those variables without which we see very little hope of evaluating the hydrological impacts of global or regional climate change. An Importance Index of 2 is ascribed to those parameters that we deem essential for the intercomparison and refinement of predictive climate change models and for resolving ambiguities that may arise from interpretative methodologies. An Importance Index of 3 is ascribed to those parameters whose value may be of great importance to isolated situations of environmental issues or model development, but which we feel do not necessarily display sufficient universality to be included within the regional climate change responses considered here.

The variable "albedo" refers to the radiation return (usually irradiance) from a target normalized to the radiation impinging upon that target. Albedo is essentially an irradiance reflectance plus a volume reflectance from optically penetrable targets such as clouds, water, and snow. Technically, therefore, every data bit recorded by environmental satellites, once normalized to the downwelling radiation at the target, is albedo, whether that albedo be associated with land, air or water. Certainly, recording all such albedo is important, and it may, therefore, appear incongruous to note albedo with any Importance Factor other than 1. Table 10.2 specifically considers only albedo from snow and cloud. While the ability to detect and delineate the presence and extent of clouds and snowcover is undeniably essential to the hydrological assessments of a region, such detections and geometric estimations may be acceptably performed without precise determinations of the snow and cloud albedo. The Importance Factor of 3 assigned to the albedo entries of Table 10.2 arise not from the need to locate the snow and cloud cover in a scene, but to utilize precise measurements of cloud and snow albedo to estimate values of precipitation concentrations. It is our opinion that direct monitoring of downwelling precipitation from the operational rain gauge and radar network throughout the Canadian terrain provides a considerably more effective means of obtaining reliable precipitation data. Only part of the Feasibility Factor of C ascribed to snow and cloud albedo in Table 10.2 arises from perceived shortcomings in albedo retrieval algorithms and methodologies. The largest concern arises from the "target-of-opportunity" scenario imposed upon such satellite determinations by distinct limitations on frequency of observations. Satellite orbits are very often at variance with the periodicities of regional precipitation patterns.

Further, the Importance factor of 3 has been ascribed to snow and ice albedo only as far as the hydrologic cycle/regional climate is concerned. Despite the obvious difficulties in obtaining precise estimates of snow and ice albedo, these variables would be considerably more important to other areas such as atmospheric interactions and high-altitude long-range transport of air pollutants. These variables would likewise assume more prominence in target basins for which reliable ground-based precipitation networks cannot be established. In such cases, however, the "target-of-opportunity" scenario of satellite overpasses might be, at least partially, compensated by a controlled airborne remote sensing program.

Figure 10.4 tabulates the number of variables in each of the priority, feasibility classifications expressed as a percentage of all the variables listed in Table 10.2. Figure 10.4(a) considers all the techniques (ground-based and remote) that are available for estimating or directly monitoring the hydrological variables. Figure 10.4(b) considers only the remote sensing methods. Clearly the feasible and important variables (i.e., A1, B1) must heavily rely on ground-based monitoring techniques. The harsh reality of Figure 10.4 is that over half of the hydrological variables of priority 1 cannot be obtained via the remote sensing techniques available during the upcoming decade.

The results of such importance feasibility analyses suggest:

- when remote sensing is considered as an independent
  entity, less than 6% of all its monitoring activities
  generates readily obtainable information on a top-
  priority hydrologic variable;

A. TOTAL (%): ALL TECHNIQUES

IMPORTANCE INDICES FEASIBILITY FACTORS	1	2	3
C	21.9	1.6	17.2
B	17.2	7.8	3.1
A	18.8	6.2	6.2

TOTAL = 62

B. REMOTE SENSING ALONE (%)

IMPORTANCE INDICES FEASIBILITY FACTORS	1	2	3
C	26.4	1.9	20.7
B	19.0	9.5	3.7
A	5.6	7.6	5.6

TOTAL = 48

Figure 10.4: Percentage of hydrological variables according to Feasibility Factors [A, B, & C] and Importance Indices [1, 2, & 3].

- with additional interpretative efforts and skills, over 25% of the remote monitoring activities can generate information on a top priority hydrologic variable;

- remote sensing methodologies employed to evaluate hydrologic cycle impacts are strongly dependent upon direct ground-based monitoring activities proceeding in tandem with the remote sensing;

- about 50% of the satellite and ground-based monitoring effort appears to be directed either towards readily obtaining information on variables of lesser hydrological consequence or attempting to obtain reliable information on parameters that would best be monitored by some other technique; and,

- even when ground-based activities supplement the satellite data, approximately 37% of the top priority variables cannot be appropriately determined for global hydrological monitoring.

At the moment, remote sensing techniques can play a significant role in obtaining some A1 and B1 variables. Perhaps with additional algorithms and model development over the next decade the feasibility of remote sensing techniques can further improve.

Figure 10.5 illustrates the space and time scales of water resources processes given in NASA (1986). Superimposed on these event scales are the desirable spatial and temporal scales of the monitoring activities of Table 10.1. It is immediately evident that events and processes which proceed in large dimension over extended time periods require monitoring over considerably smaller spatial scales and shorter time frames. Consistent with our equations (2) and (3), the events of Figure 10.5 could appropriately be defined by climatic change indices (such as dC_R/dt) while the monitoring activities of Figure 10.5 must be obtained as a function of both space and time. If one could sensibly estimate

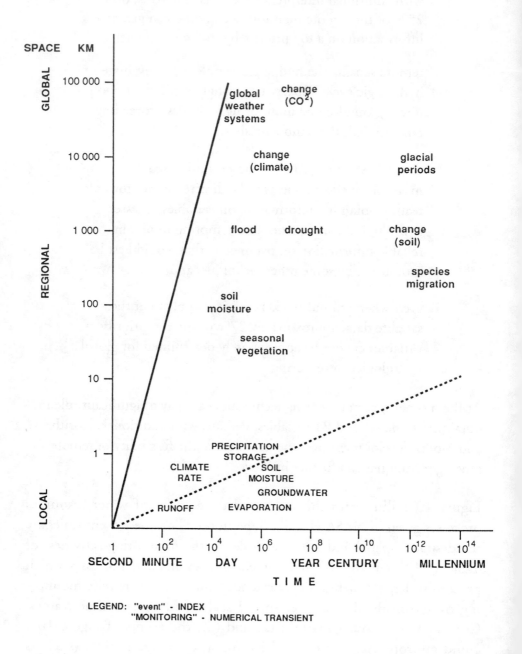

Figure 10.5: Space and time scales of water resources processes given in NASA (1986) showing the desirable spatial and temporal scales of monitoring activities.

suitable upper and lower spatial and temporal limits on each of the events and monitoring requirements of Figure 10.5, such d{space}/d{time} values associated with the events and monitoring activities could be cautiously incorporated into regional climate change and regional hydrology model equations such as equations (2) and (3).

IMPLICATIONS OF THE ABOVE ANALYSES

The rationale that generated the Feasibility and Importance analyses of Figure 10.4 was based upon an attempt to dispassionately cull such prioritization from not only our past experiences, but also from our awareness of the experiences of other workers in the general areas of hydrology and remote sensing. Dispassionate intentions not withstanding, however, personal biases regarding the degrees of Feasibility and Importance categorizations of the hydrological variables may be inadvertently present. Categorization criteria were also based upon the ability to satisfy the spatial resolution, accuracy and frequency requirements listed in Table 10.1 (criteria which themselves rely upon judgment calls in both the need for compliance to such data acquisition requirements as well as the ability for measurement techniques to comply to such requirements). Here too is an opportunity for inadvertent personal bias. It is hoped, however, that such inadvertent biases, if indeed present, are self-cancelling in terms of over-and-under estimations, and that the basic conclusions of Figure 10.4 will remain realistic. We do not anticipate that the reader will necessarily agree with every one of our classifications. In fact, we genuinely hope that readers desire to prove that our criticisms of some of the remote sensing techniques are unfounded. We more fervently hope that by clever, innovative thought and action with regard to satellite sensor development, orbit parametrics, algorithm generation, etc., they can prove our caution to be unfounded.

Figure 10.4(a) suggests that 50% of the monitoring activities (remote and direct) listed in Table 10.2 and scheduled for the upcoming global climate change program are of little consequence to the general objective of evaluating climate change impacts on the regional hydrologic cycle and water resources. Considering almost solely the satellite monitoring activities (Figure 10.4(b)), this percentage increased to ~58%.

This situation is somewhat analogous to the optimist-versus-pessimist philosophical argument as to whether the contents of a glass qualifies it as being half-full or half-empty. Adopting the optimist's view logically dictates, therefore, that the maximum benefit to hydrological impact studies would result from nurturing the A1, A2, B1 and B2 activities of Figure 10.4 and Table 10.2. Because of the monopoly of satellite methodologies and techniques in the B1 category, this might be one of the most fruitful targets for not only current hydrological operational applications, but for future research and development considerations. Perhaps with both theoretical and experimental efforts directed towards additional algorithm and model development over the next decade, the feasibility of remote sensing techniques can further improve.

The most disturbing consequence of this analysis is the substantial number of monitoring activities that are classified C1. This refers to those essential hydrologic parameters which cannot be feasibly determined by the techniques (ground-based or space-based) listed in Table 10.2. Approximately 37% of the top-priority hydrological variables lie within this category. It would be tempting to recommend that these areas constitute serious targets for immediate research and development activity. And, indeed, such a suggestion must be made. It could, however, be extremely hazardous to recommend that such research strategies be directed towards developing retrieval algorithms for satellite-acquired data in these areas unless such problems as inappropriate satellite sensor characteristics, unfortunate orbit characteristics, insufficient ground-scale resolution, atmospheric obfuscation, and albedo deconvolution can be simultaneously solved. It is considerably less hazardous, however, to recommend that such research strategies be directed towards developing retrieval algorithms for airborne remote sensing missions for regional climate studies in which the frequency of observation, environmental status of the observation interval, spatial resolution of the target, sensor characteristics, and essential auxiliary atmospheric and/or biospheric data are under direct control of the investigative team.

The variables whose monitoring category is C1 are certainly essential to the hydrology/climate change objectives of the upcoming decades. It may be possible that clever theoretical model and algorithm development could promote a satellite technique from C to B status. However, these parameters had best be obtained via other means. Direct ground-based measurement techniques may, in fact, already exist for determining some of these variables since the direct measurement techniques listed in Table 10.2 are certainly not exhaustive.

It must again be emphasized that the percentages presented in Figure 10.4 have been determined solely for the monitoring of hydrological parameters required for global climate change impacts on regional aquatic resources. Further, we have only considered Feasibility and Importance Factors in terms of hydrological cycle/water resources issues appropriate to the Canadian terrain. Other locations on the globe will, of course, be defined by different atmospheric conditions and surface cover, and consequently, would generate different feasibility figures for remote monitoring. Certainly a more complex basin terrain could demote some variables from the A to B to C categories, and a less complex basin terrain could improve a C to B or B to A. However, it seems highly unlikely that an environmental simplicity could be globally encountered that would dramatically remove the existing obstacles to monitoring the essential hydrology/climate change variables.

Canada is fortunate in possessing operational networks of ground stations dedicated to the routine data base collection, crisis-contingency, and continuous and periodic monitoring of climate-related and hydrologically significant variables. While such operation networks are not without their own shortcomings (as briefly discussed earlier), they do, however, provide a very comfortable alternative for obtaining reliable data that may be unattainable from satellite overpasses. Ground-based monitoring techniques, understandably, are of minimal consequence to the physically inaccessible regions of Canada (just as they are for the regions of other countries for which reliable ground-based networks do not exist as a consequence of particular physical, financial, or socio-economic constraints). In order to obtain essential information for such areas, research activity into remote sensing algorithm development for C1 variables might become a necessity.

In this communication, we recommend that ground-based networks provide, where possible, input variables into regional climate models dedicated towards an analysis on a Canadian basis. Such a philosophy, however, cannot be implemented on a global basis if one intends to utilize remote sensing (particularly satellites) as an integral component in the interweaving of regional climate monitoring and/or modelling into global climate monitoring and/or modelling. To achieve such an objective, sensitivity analyses directed towards assessing regional climate model tolerances to the inherent inaccuracies in remote sensing algorithms (as well as tolerances to the logistical limitations of satellite monitoring) assumes paramount importance. The results of such sensitivity analyses can ultimately dictate which input variables should comprise obligatory ground-based collection and what the quantified consequences actually would be if remote estimates of C1 variables were allowed to be used as inputs to either regional or global climate change studies. Sensitivity analyses <u>need also to be made of the equations themselves</u>. Such sensitivity analyses are far from simple and themselves form the subject for independent future expanded discussions.

BIOLOGY AS AN INTEGRAL COMPONENT OF GLOBAL MONITORING

The hydrologic cycle is primarily driven by physical forces occurring within and transported by the atmospheric and aquatic environments. Consequently, the majority of the variables listed in Table 10.1 are physical in nature. The hydrologic cycle, however, does not act in a vacuum. As schematically shown in Figure 10.6, the unperturbed terrestrial universe can be logically represented by the forces of physics, chemistry, and biology co-existing in a state of dynamic equilibrium. Perturbations to such a terrestrial equilibrium, however, are represented in Figure 10.6 as a step-function generator and would include human, mammals, insects, solar eruptions, comets, asteroids, anthropogenic activities associated with the advances of civilization, earthquakes, orbital perturbations, etc. It is suggested that such step-function generation directly inputs the chemistry portion of the terrestrial equilibrium cycle, and as the equilibrium attempts to re-establish, impacts to terrestrial biology are to be logically expected.

Since oceans, lakes, and rivers act as carbon reservoirs and contain an abundance of biological life, step-function impacts on the hydrological

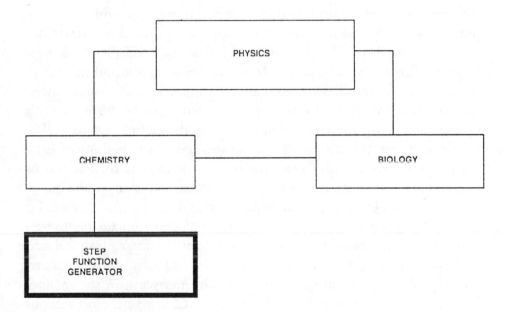

Figure 10.6: The Terrestrial Universe.

cycle cannot ignore associated biological consequences. Global biogenic monitoring must, therefore, provide information on the carbon reservoir. However, there has been a surprising lack of literature concerning changes in the aquatic biological regime. An integral component of water resources monitoring programs must be the cataloguing of reliable chlorophyll concentration measurements. Chlorophyll-retrieving algorithms currently in widespread use have been derived for deep-ocean waters and neglect the optical complexities of inland and coastal waters. In such optically complex waters chlorophyll concentrations must be inferred from an environment of competing organic and inorganic populations. Optical modelling techniques are required to extract not only chlorophyll but also the competing suspended and dissolved components of inland water masses. To extract such organic and inorganic component concentrations from remote measurements of inland waters, the subsurface volume reflectance spectrum must first be related to such organic and inorganic concentrations. The direct linkages to such a relationship are the scattering and absorption cross sections of each aquatic component. Such cross sections are defined as the amount of scattering and absorption that a single unit concentration of an aquatic component would experience at a particular wavelength. Such a model is discussed in great detail in Bukata et al. (1985). To obtain the optical cross sections of chlorophyll requires coordinated efforts of optical and water quality collection, multiple regression, radiative transfer theory, and optimization technique analyses which interweave in the manner illustrated in the flow diagram of Figure 10.7. Chlorophyll cross sections are subject to variability directly associated with spatial location, seasonal phytoplankton growth cycles, and species definition. They may even, through some proactive feedback loop, be a function of the very climate changes they are being used to monitor (Bukata et al., 1989). These variabilities notwithstanding, we strongly recommend that such chlorophyll cross sections be determined and catalogued for every major inland (and possibly even oceanic) water body on a global scale. Certainly such optical cross sections are mandatory for the Canadian lakes as large as those shown in Figure 10.8.

The mapping of biomass on a routine basis is already well established. The weekly world crop assessment index (biomass area, production rate,

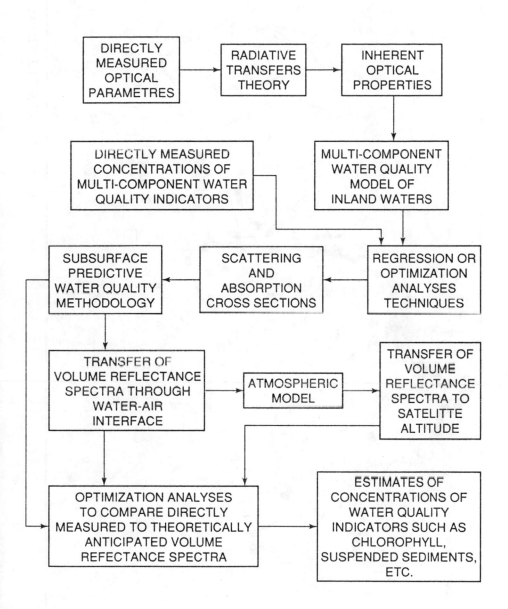

Figure 10.7: Flow diagram showing requirements to obtain optical cross sections of chlorophyl.

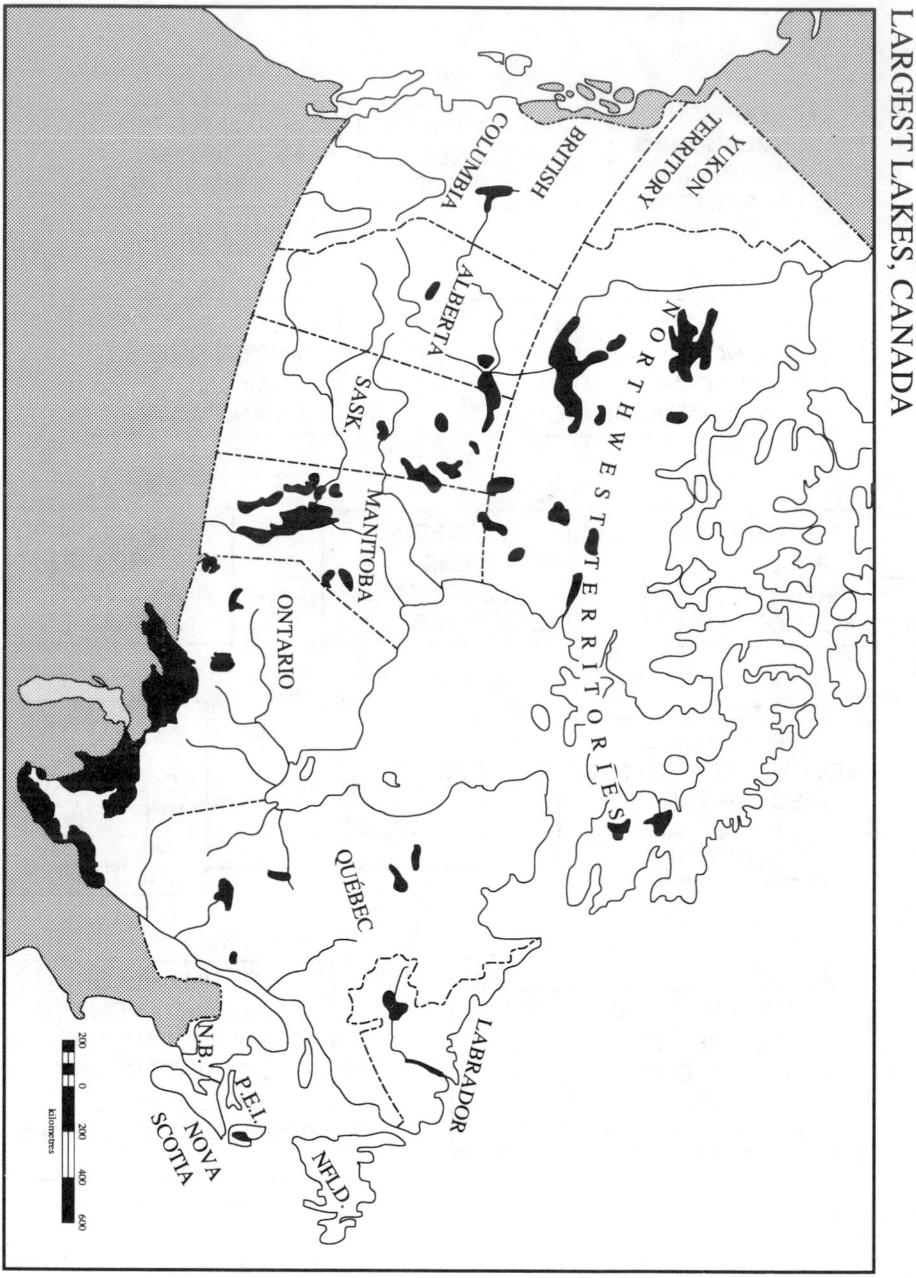

Figure 10.8: Canadian lakes requiring optical cross sections.

vegetation condition) derived from the NOAA satellite (Whiting, 1989) for the northern hemisphere in July 1988 is shown in Figure 10.9. Clearly, such large scale satellite mapping is inappropriate for the regional climatology issues stressed in the current discussions. However, such biomass assessment indices may be readily generated on a regional basis. Figure 10.10 illustrates such a yield assessment map (also derived from NOAA satellite) for Saskatchewan during severe drought conditions in June 1988.

SUMMARY

As illustrated in the flow diagram of Figure 10.1, outputs of Global Climate Models (GCM) are generally taken as inputs to hydrology models that describe changes in water resources. Due to the discrepancies in both the spatial and temporal scales between those suitable for global climate concerns and those suitable for regional climate concerns, we have suggested that Regional Climate Models (RCM) be developed. RCMs are not subjected to the same conservation of matter laws that constrain the GCMs, and in such a manner we have defined a Regional Climate Change Index (dC_R/dt) in terms of four basic variables: near surface air temperature, T; precipitation, P; surface wind velocity, V; and, a non-atmospheric water storage term, R. We have also defined the driving force of the hydrologic cycle as being the rate of total precipitation ($dP(t)/dt$) in terms of five basic variables: runoff, Q; evapotranspiration, E_T; storage, S; groundwater, W_G; and, soil moisture, W_S.

The mathematical expressions for both the Regional Climate Model and the regional hydrology cycle contain time derivatives of the principal variables (in addition to multivariate interdependencies), and as such represent the most convenient format for remote sensing monitoring systems. Since all variables must be inferred from optical radiation fluxes, absolute values of such variables are estimated with considerably less reliability than changes occurring in that variable with the passage of time.

Figure 10.9: Weekly world crop assessment index derived from the NOAA satellite (Whitig 1989) for the northern hemisphere in July 1988.

Figure 10.10: Yield assessment map (derived from NOAA satellite) for Saskatchewan during severe drought conditions in June 1988.

By reducing the hydrological and regional climate change expression to a finite set of variables, sub-variables and surrogates, we have estimated the degree of difficulties and the parametric priorities associated with the use of remote sensing and ground monitoring techniques to relate climate change and water resources. As Figure 10.4 illustrates, considerable effort and modelling development will be required in this decade to maximize the contribution of remote sensing to the general questions of the hydrologic cycle. It is also eminently clear that regional climate and water resource issues will be very dependent upon ground based monitoring being used, where possible, to supplement remote observations.

The hydrology cycle should not be considered in isolation from the biological component of climate change due to the interactive nature of physics, chemistry, and biology in the terrestrial universe. And while we have not derived appropriate expressions for the regional carbon cycle, we realize that such expressions must be established and we have strongly recommended that regional biomass indices (area, production rate, vegetation status), as recorded from satellite altitudes over basin land, be an integral part of hydrological monitoring (Figures 10.9 and 10.10). To enable chlorophyll mapping over optically complex inland waters, it is necessary to catalog the absorption and scattering cross sections of chlorophyll for every principal global water mass (Figure 10.7).

We have suggested that the five ocean basin regions of the Canadian terrain be the principal targets for the hydrological and water resources assessments of climatic change. The subdivided component river basins serve as ideal secondary targets. From the material discussed herein, a successful global monitoring program for hydrological assessment must include four elements:

- a focus on time scales of days or weeks, rather than annual or even monthly averages (time and spatial scales of events and monitoring activities shown in Figure 10.5);

- the ability to collect or infer information on unam-biguously-defined hydrologically significant variables (items listed in Table 10.2 as Importance Factor of 1);

- the ability to incorporate GCMs into regional studies (or develop RCMs as we suggest in equations (2) and (3)); and,

- the ability to incorporate into analyses schemes data such as snowfall and snowmelt, foliage growth cycles, drainage patterns, soil dynamics, regional storage capacities, and other sub-variables listed in Tables 10.1 and 10.2. Considerable work is required in establishing the functional relationships among the variables and sub-variables at the appropriate regional spatial and temporal scales.

RECOMMENDATIONS

The overall problem of assessing the hydrological impact of global climate change is logically reduced to three components: A) appropriate theoretical scientific model development; B) appropriate data gathering and monitoring activities; and, C) appropriate selection of environmental sites. Our recommendations in each of these areas are as follows:

Theoretical Model Development

Regional Climate Models (RCMs) must be developed due to the disparities in temporal and spatial resolution requirements that separate global climate analyses from regional climate analyses. Mathematical expressions relating sets of hydrological and aquatic parameters must be obtained. Techniques must be established and verified that enable monitored data values to be transformed into the required model parameter and variables.

Data Gathering and Monitoring

A focus on time scales of days or weeks rather than yearly or even monthly is essential for regional hydrology and water resources.

Information is required on unambiguously defined hydrologically significant parameters and variables. Quite simply this translates into monitor what you <u>need</u>, not just what you <u>can</u>.

The hydrology cycle must be considered in concert with the carbon cycle. In this regard biomass indices over land and water should be incorporated into global and regional hydrologic monitoring activities. Satellite estimations of biomass area and production must be determined over the land. Satellite estimations of primary production occurring in inland waters must be attempted. To facilitate such primary production estimations, it is essential to catalog the optical cross sections of chlorophyll for all major Canadian lakes.

Target Sites

The Canadian terrain is hydrologically divided into five principal ocean basins. These ocean basins (Pacific, Arctic, Gulf of Mexico, Hudson Bay, and Atlantic) are the recommended targets for the hydrological impact studies based on regional and global climate changes.

COST ANALYSIS FOR HYDROLOGICAL MONITORING

The cost breakdown for the monitoring activities related to estimating the impact on regional hydrology and water resources of global climate change will follow the importance and feasibility pairing diagram of Figure 10.4. A yearly cost for each of these pairings has been determined from knowledge of the present cost of image and future costs of future satellites.

Factors considered in cost estimations include:

- present availability of ground, airborne, or satellite data gathering platforms,

- data reduction requirements,

- frequency of observations,

- humanpower to produce desired results,

- model design, development, verification and application,

- design, fabrication, launching and operational activities of planned satellite missions (amortized into an annual cost).

The Cost Table (Figure 10.11) lists yearly values in millions of dollars. Each of the A, B, C, 1, 2, 3 combinations has been separately itemized. Remote Sensing has been considered both separate from and incorporated into a hydrological monitoring program. Two cost estimates have been recommended:

- a minimum program comprising only the feasible and essential hydrological monitoring activities (Table 10.2-A1, A2, and A3); and,

- a desirable program comprising the feasible, essential, and desirable hydrological monitoring activities (Table 10.2-A1, A2, B1 and B2). The yearly cost of the remote sensing and ground programs would be:

- 18 million dollars for the minimum program and 204 million dollars for the desired program. The yearly cost for the remote sensing component alone would be 5 million dollars for the minimum program and 146 million dollars for the desired program.

A. TOTAL ($MILLIONS): ALL TECHNIQUES

IMPORTANCE INDICES / FEASIBILITY FACTORS	1	2	3
C	1400	100	900
B	140	50	20
A	11	3	4

B. REMOTE SENSING ALONE ($MILLION):

IMPORTANCE INDICES / FEASIBILITY FACTORS	1	2	3
C	29	2	25
B	19	10	4
A	6	6	4

Figure 10.11: Cost Table ($ millions) for Annual Costs of Hydrological Monitoring. Refer to Table 10.2 for Explanation of Column and Row Headings.

CHAPTER 11

BOREAS
(BOREAL ECOSYSTEMS-ATMOSPHERE STUDY):
GLOBAL CHANGE AND BIOSPHERE-ATMOSPHERE INTERACTIONS IN THE BOREAL FOREST

BOREAS Science Steering Committee

INTRODUCTION

To a large extent, the Earth Sciences of meteorology, oceanography, atmospheric chemistry, bioclimatology and ecology grew up independently of each other. Observational methods, theories and numerical models were developed separately within each discipline. This situation began to change about 20 years ago as it become obvious that an interdisciplinary approach was required in order to understand the Earth System as a whole.

Two forces have favored the growth of the new interdiscipline called "Earth System Science". One is the unified perspective on Earth provided through satellite remote sensing that has been one of the most important cultural impacts of space technology. The second is a growing awareness of and/or apprehension about global change which encompasses the so-called greenhouse effect (Rotty, 1983; Trabalka, 1985; Ramanathan, 1988; Hansen et al., 1981); stratospheric ozone depletion (Antarctic Ozone Hole Special Issue,1987; WMO, 1989); deforestation and other anthropogenic changes to the Earth's surface (Mooney et al., 1987; McElroy and Wofsey, 1986); and, the possibility of second-order biospheric feedbacks resulting from the above stresses due to changes in photosynthesis, respiration, transpiration and trace gas exchange (NRC, 1988). The next few years should see the emergence of a research strategy to explore the causes, impacts and likely future developments in global change which will doubtless include a focus on biosphere-atmosphere interactions and their response to perturbation. The planned study, BOREAS, described in this paper represents a significant contribution to the broader effort concerned with global change.

The Boreal Forest biome (dominated by coniferous species, but containing deciduous species) is composed of upland forests, extensive wetlands and bogs, and many lakes. It is one of the largest biomes on the Earth's surface and is a major storehouse of organic carbon, mostly in its soils. Its sensitivity to changes in the physical climate system (PCS) and the nature and severity of the possible consequences of such changes, in terms of ecological perturbations and the release of organic emissions into the lower atmosphere, are the subjects of much scientific conjecture and debate (Tans et al., 1990).

Various modelling studies have indicated that changes in the climatology and ecological functioning of the biome could have significant implications for at least the circumpolar region. Consequently, the proposed study is aimed primarily at providing a research base for a range of related investigations into the biome's internal dynamics and its links to the global environment. Briefly, the goal of the Boreal Forest Study is to understand the interactions between the boreal forest biome and the atmosphere in order to clarify their roles in global change.

The scientific issues at stake are as follows.

Sensitivity of the Boreal Forest biome to changes in the physical climate system: A number of simulation studies have been carried out to assess the climatic impact of increasing atmospheric CO_2: see the reviews of Schlesinger and Mitchell (1987) and Harrington (1987). Many of these studies indicate that the greatest warming engendered by increasing CO_2 will occur at higher (45°N-65°N) latitudes with the most marked effects within the continental interiors; for example, the doubled-CO_2 experiment of Mitchell (1983) produced a difference of 3K to 10K in the mean winter surface temperature for much of the land surface area of this zone. If this, or anything like this, should actually come about, it would have a dramatic impact on the biophysical characteristics and ecological functioning of the biome (see Figure 11.1).

The Carbon Cycle and the boreal forest: The study of Tans et al. (1990) presents evidence for the existence of a large terrestrial sink of carbon in the temperate boreal zone. The exact mechanisms involved and the spatial contributions to this sink are as yet unknown, but the implication is that carbon is being stored in either living tissue or in the soil. However, any sustained increase in surface temperature, combined with changes in soil moisture climatology, could result in changes in the cycling of nutrients in the soil profile and bogs with associated releases of CO_2 and CH_4 from the surface. If this occurs on a large enough spatial scale, the oxidation capacity of the lower atmosphere could be significantly altered. As yet we do not know enough about important processes within the region to be able to predict or even simulate the carbon source/sink dynamics there.

Biophysical feedbacks on the physical climate system: Research work has indicated, above, that changes in the ecological functioning of the biome could be brought about by changes in the physical climate system. It is anticipated that these may be accompanied by alterations in the biophysical characteristics of the surface, namely albedo, surface roughness, and the biophysical control of evapotranspiration (surface resistance). Any such changes may have feedback effects on the near-surface climatology (temperature, humidity, precipitation and cloudiness fields) (see Sato et al., 1989).

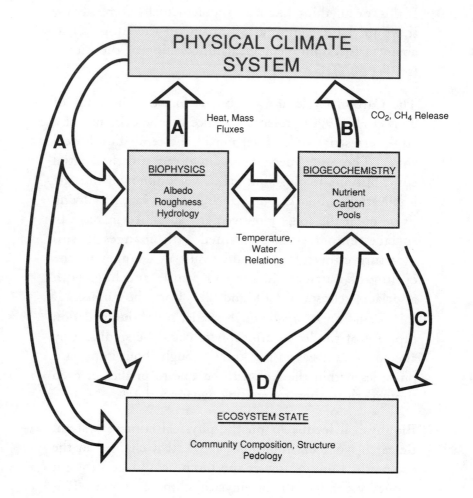

Figure 11.1:   Important interactions between the Boreal Forest and the atmosphere with respect to global change: (a)Influence of changes in the Physical Climate System on the biophysical characteristics and ecology of the biome; (b)Changes in nutrient cycling rates; release of CO_2 and CH_4 from soil carbon pool back to the atmosphere; (c)Ecological change in species composition results in changes in land surface characteristics of albedo, roughness and soil moisture availability with possible feedbacks on near-surface climatology.

In addition to the above scientific issues, there are important social and practical considerations. The Boreal Forest is a large, relatively unperturbed biome which is almost contiguous in the circumpolar region. Its borders fall entirely within many of the world's developed nations (Canada, European and Scandinavian Communities, USA and USSR), so its fate has social and economic significance. On the practical side, a complex experiment should be relatively easy to execute in the boreal region of North America due to good logistical and institutional support.

The focus of the proposed study is a cooperative field experiment involving land-surface climatology (LSC), tropospheric chemistry (TC) and terrestrial ecology (TE) components, with remote sensing playing a strong integrating role. A coordinated approach to the experiment design and execution will be adopted from the outset to ensure the maximum benefit from each discipline's participation.

OBJECTIVES

The overall goal of the study is to understand the interactions between the Boreal Forest biome and the atmosphere in order to clarify their roles in global change. This goal leads directly to the specification of detailed objectives to move toward the goal, some of which address short timescale processes (LSC, TC, TE) and some of which address longer timescale processes (TE) (see Figure 11.1).

The major objectives of BOREAS are as follows:

- develop an improved understanding of the processes and states governing the exchanges of energy, water, heat, carbon and trace gases between the Boreal Forest biome and the atmosphere with particular reference to those processes and states that may be sensitive to global change; and,

- develop the use of remote sensing techniques to transfer our understanding of the above processes from local scales to regional scales.

These objectives embrace contributions from all three disciplinary areas involved in BOREAS. A number of subsidiary objectives have also been specified:

- test the limits and sensitivity of different surface energy and mass (H_2O and CO_2) balance modelling approaches. (The models are to be forced by meteorological and remote sensing data). This involves the calculation of state variables (e.g. leaf area index, cover types, etc.) from remote sensing;

- quantify transfer processes between the land surface and the troposphere (includes use of planetary boundary layer studies for integration and scaling checks);

- define the trace gas climatology of the biome with reference to ecosystem state, diurnal and seasonal variability and long range transport;

- quantify the fluxes of radiatively important trace gases and those gases which could affect the oxidant balance of the atmosphere;

- investigate the relationship between trace gas fluxes and ecosystem nutrient dynamics, including the effects of possible feedbacks from the atmosphere to the surface; and,

- identify easily measured LSC and TE surrogates and remotely sensed variables which could be used to estimate trace gas fluxes.

EXPERIMENT DESIGN

Approach

The experimental approach is largely determined by the objectives as stated above. The most important characteristics are as follows.

Ecological Gradient: The overall goal of the project and some of the subsidiary objectives emphasize the need to study the biome's biophysical, chemical and ecological functioning under different conditions. The governing climatological variables determining these in the biome are temperature (associated with length of growing season, radiation budget, etc.) and moisture availability (associated with precipitation, snow hydrology and surface hydrological processes). Essentially, the northern ecotone of the forest is delineated by temperature (growing degree days) while the southern boundary is determined by moisture stress and fire frequency in central and western Canada, and by ecological competition with temperate forests to the east of the Great Lakes. A minimum of two sites is therefore required - one near the northern boundary and one near the southern boundary where moisture relations could play an important limiting role. Most global change scenarios predict warming and drying in the mid-continent. The proposed two-site strategy would therefore allow observations of processes associated with those limiting stress factors (temperature in the north, moisture in the south) that are most likely to undergo significant change within the biome as a whole.

Concentration of Effort: The measurement of fluxes at or near the surface and of radiances and emittances above the surface necessitates the use of sophisticated airborne and surface equipment. The operation of this equipment is expensive in terms of personpower and money and cannot be sustained for long periods. Additionally, there is a strong need to obtain contemporaneous observations of all the appropriate parameters. These facts favor concentrating the intensive observational effort at as few sites as possible and conducting a series of intensive field campaigns, each of about 20 days duration, with time in between for rest and for refurbishing equipment. These campaigns should be embedded in a longer term monitoring effort carried out using satellites and automatic instrumentation.

Scale: One of the objectives is to integrate models and observations of processes and states operating at small scales (<100 m²) with scales appropriate to regional remote sensing and airborne flux measurement. These two factors argue for sites of roughly 20 x 20 km in size, with stratified sampling and measurements within their borders.

Experimental Framework

The size, duration and scope of the experiment are constrained by the experimental approach and some practical considerations.

Size: The objectives require an explicit study of the effects of temperature and moisture availability as they control ecosystem state and surface-atmosphere exchanges in the biome. At least two intensive sites are required to resolve these effects; their final selection will be predicated by the process rates (mass/energy exchange) associated with each site rather than just climatology. Each intensive site will be of 20 x 20 km dimension to allow the acquisition of useful airborne flux measurements and satellite observations while still allowing reasonable coverage with surface instruments. It is anticipated that almost all of the LSC and TC work will be conducted within these 20 x 20 km main sites. Spacing between these sites may have to be on the order of 500 km to resolve the ecological gradient. Ecological survey studies may also require some sampling within the whole domain along and normal to gradient isolines with particular concentration within and around the main sites. The definition and allocation of additional TE sampling sites should be directed at defining the heterogeneity of surface states and processes within and between the main sites.

Duration: A one-year concentrated observational effort is currently planned for 1994, sandwiched between monitoring, pilot and planning activities (before) and by monitoring activities and limited revisits (after). Observational efforts may follow the First ISCLSP Field Experiment (FIFE) (Sellers et al., 1988) strategy of 2 or 3 intensive field campaigns (IFCs), each of about 3 weeks duration, during the growing season, to capture a range of conditions. Additionally, some hydrological work should be conducted during the winter. The analysis phase of the project would continue for at least 2 years after the main experimental effort.

Scope: The scientific issues and environmental conditions make the project a challenging one. The environmental conditions (cloudiness, lake, wetland, forest mixtures, logistical problems) and other complicating factors will make the technical design and execution of the experiment moderately difficult (see below).

Complicating Factors

Meteorological: The boreal region is typified by extended periods of cloudiness and relatively low solar angles throughout the year. This limits the opportunities for optical and thermal remote sensing.

Structural: The shape and arrangement of trees in forest canopies give rise to fundamentally different observational problems than in grasslands. Specifically:

Optical properties: At least two scales of phytoelement clustering have to be considered: needles to shoots, in the case of conifers; and, shoots to crowns. Both have severe effects on the radiative transfer properties of the surface; anisotropy, shadowing and ambiguous surface-cover contributions to the total radiation field are particularly difficult problems to resolve. Ground cover optical properties also have to be considered: moss, lichens, litter, etc.

Exchange characteristics: The height and spatial heterogeneity of tree crowns ensure efficient exchange between foliage and atmosphere. Unlike grasslands, aerodynamic resistance (r_a) is not a major control on evaporation and photosynthesis; the bulk stomatal resistance, r_s, is typically one order of magnitude greater than ra (see Figure 11.2). Because of this, gradients above the forest are shallow (due to efficient mixing), so foliage-air temperature differences are small. These factors discourage the use of Bowen ratio techniques for flux measurement and the application of the (T_s - T_a) remote sensing method of estimating heat fluxes. The use of eddy correlation systems (the only accepted measurement alternative) requires fairly level sites with large fetch; this is also a requirement for flux aircraft measurements. Flows below the canopy are complex, which poses severe problems for eddy correlation measurements of soil respiration/understory photosynthesis.

Geographical: The sites will undoubtedly contain a mixture of surface types: forests, lakes, bare rock, slopes, etc.

Logistical: Each site must be close to (<100 km) a small airfield (4,000 feet, hard runway) and reasonable accommodation. One site must be near (<350 km) an airfield with a 7,000 feet, hard runway and hangar, and with access to remote communication facilities: satellite downlink, etc.

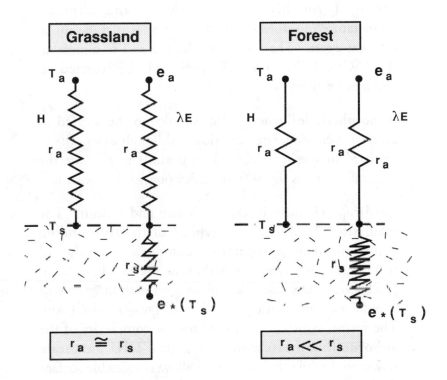

Figure 11.2: Roles of surface (r_s) and aerodynamic resistance (r_a) in energy/mass exchange over forests and grasslands. In grasslands, (r_a) (r_s), so that the T_s - T_a difference may be used to estimate the sensible heat flux, H. In forests $r_a < r_s$ so that T_s and T_a are nearly equal in which case accurate heat flux estimation must be based on a calculation of r_s, the dominant resistance term.

Site Selection

The main study sites were selected in the fall of 1990.

The essential characteristics of the BOREAS sites are as follows.

Site location: Two principal sites, each 20 x 20 km are arranged roughly north-south on the climatic temperature/moisture gradient. The sites may be up to 600 km apart. These sites will be the foci of almost all the LSC and TC work; TE studies will be centered on and around them.

Atmospheric influence: Sites should not be located in areas of even moderate pollution. Although exact criteria are hard to specify, it should be possible to separate the 'natural' trace gas signal from anthropogenic influences.

Landscape characteristics, patch size and terrain: The main sites should not be atypical of the surrounding region in terms of vegetation composition, soils and hydrology. The vegetation within the site should occur in patch sizes of less than 5 km dimension with three or four 'typical' elements with patch sizes of greater than 1 km. The former constraint is to reduce the complexity of the airborne flux measurement task (low-level mesoscale flows, etc.) while the latter is to allow sustainable surface flux measurements. The surface slopes in the flux measurement 'patches' should not exceed 1:20. There should be no large lakes in the sites and an upwind fetch of similar terrain and vegetation should be adequate.

Hydrology: It must be feasible to gauge the outflow of a reasonable proportion of the site area for hydrological and chemical studies.

Control: Acquire control or knowledge of near- and mid-term land use plans.

Logistics: Each site must be close (<100 km) to a small airfield with a 4,000 feet hard runway and reasonable accommodation. One site should be located within 350 km of a 7,000 feet hard runway and hangar, with access to remote communication facilities: satellite downlink, etc. Road access to the sites is essential.

Cloud climatology: The cloud climatology of the area should allow for a few clear days per month for optical remote sensing work.

Methodologies

The complicating factors discussed above mean that the optical remote sensing component of the study will be challenging (cloudiness, low solar angles, surface anisotropy, etc.) and that thermal remote sensing may be of limited value in calculating the surface energy budget (T_s - T_a). Additionally, surface validation efforts (flux measurement, biomass and leaf area index estimates, etc.) will be complex and labor intensive. These factors will probably impel us towards modelling and observing the physiological controls on energy/mass exchange instead of applying thermo/aerodynamic methods appropriate to short vegetation. This effort will necessitate investigations into methods for quantifying biological limits (photosynthetic capacity, minimum stomatal resistance) and stresses (soil moisture stress, saturation, soil nutrient status, constraints on mineralization, etc.) on surface atmosphere exchanges and nutrient cycling within the biome. There is obviously some potential for adapting existing methodologies to the science tasks but in some cases we will have to explore novel approaches. Additionally, the investigation of processes over a large spatial domain should be coupled with a mesoscale modelling effort at some level; as far as possible, this should make use of existing observational networks. The following methodological approaches will be explored within the experiment design.

Multiangle optical remote sensing: The surface anisotropy of forests dictates a multi-angle observational approach to allow effective interpretation of the existing satellite data and to explore future sensor designs.

Radar: Satellite and airborne radar remote sensing may offer opportunities to investigate canopy structure (which will help with optical data interpretation) and to conduct surveys of community composition and structure (CCS) under cloudy conditions.

Multispectral remote sensing: The requirement for better definition of the physiological state of the vegetation needs to be addressed, especially as thermal methods are less likely to be effective. The potential of high spectral resolution data for quantifying changes in leaf chemistry, and therefore photosynthetic capacity, etc., must be explored.

Flux measurement: Flux measurements of momentum, sensible heat, and mass (moisture, trace gases) will be carried out at the main sites. Surface and airborne eddy correlation, combined with light direction and ranging equipment (LIDAR), are the primary methods of choice for this study. Separation of the net CO_2 flux into photosynthetic and respiration components will probably require combined CO_2 surface flux/vertical divergence measurements conducted at night. (Horizontal flows may be a problem.) During the day, some of the airborne methods will rely on the grid/double-stack methods developed at FIFE, as simpler (one-level) methods are deemed unreliable.

Profiling: The need for semi-continuous atmospheric profiling represents a problem. Flux aircraft can be used up to a point; other non-labor intensive techniques should be investigated (radiosondes). LIDAR may be used during Intensive Field Campaigns.

Monitoring: As far as possible, automatic equipment should be used to monitor micrometeorological and soil moisture conditions.

Hydrology: Catchment water balance and sub-canopy raingauge methods (see Shuttleworth et al., 1984) should be used as additional means to determine the water balance, specifically the interception loss term. Snow interception and melt are clearly important to the hydrological processes within the biome and need special attention.

Data System: A data system with a central archive and active field nodes should be available to provide near real-time interactive access to data sets and in the field, quick-look analyses.

Simulation Modelling: A range of simulation models should be developed and run prior to the execution of the experiment. These should focus on the relationships between the forest ecosystem states/process rates and those parameters amenable to remote sensing. The requirement for model validation will help with the detailed design of the measurement network.

Climatology: Climatological data and synoptic meteorological data will be required for the region surrounding the sites.

EXPERIMENT EXECUTION

Schedule: 1990-1996

1990: Reconnaissance for sites using satellite, map data and airborne/surface surveys was performed. A list of strong candidates for the principal sites which satisfy the essential criteria listed above were provided at the end of 1990. During this year, preparatory work was initiated to resolve issues crucial to final site selection and detailed experimental planning.

1991: Candidate sites were instrumented with Portable Automatic Mesonet (PAM) devices. There were a preliminary satellite data collection effort, exploratory visits by flux teams and test runs with flux aircraft. The Experiment Information System were initiated.

1992-1993: Final site selection. Pilot efforts with flux measurement and airborne remote sensing and the monitoring effort will be intensified: soil moisture, stream gauging, satellite observations, etc are expected. The information system, investigator network and field nodes will be installed and tested. All preliminary monitoring data will be on-line.

1994: Main experiment execution (see next section).

1994-1996: Data analysis and monitoring work will continue.

1994 Experiment Execution

Timing:

The monitoring effort should continue throughout the year if practicable. The timing of Intensive Field Campaigns (2 to 3 during the year, each roughly 3 to 4 weeks long) may be set by the following events (Figure 11.3):

IFC-1 Thaw: Trace gas emission and anaerobic activity will probably peak with warming wet soil conditions. Wet soil may exert stress on trees. Recovery from winter state. (Second priority).

IFC-2 Growing season peak: This will be mid summer, with maximum radiation load and higher temperatures. (First priority).

IFC-3 Growing season decline: Effects of soil moisture and nutrient stress should be more apparent. (Third Priority).

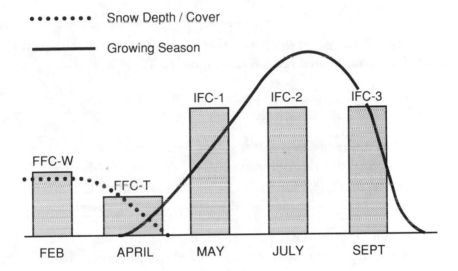

Figure 11.3: Timing of monitoring period and the Intensive Field Campaigns (IFC) in the experiment.

There currently seems to be no critical requirement for a substantial winter IFC although snow hydrology work should continue throughout the preceding winter. Some radiation measurements and remote sensing work might also be conducted during the winter.

Surface Observations:

Monitoring: The monitoring effort will include the soil moisture and catchment water balance studies, productivity measurements, biomass/species surveys, nutrient assays and micrometeorological observations.

Intensive Field Campaigns: A wide range of measurements will be executed in a coordinated fashion (see Figure 11.4).

Profiling: If possible, atmospheric soundings should be carried out at each site.

Surface fluxes: Two or three flux stations per site should be considered the minimum. CO_2 flux measurement is highly desirable. One tall (50 m) and two short (25 m) towers should provide a good range of sampling coverage.

Physiological: Leaf physiological properties should be measured: photosynthesis, stomatal conductance, leaf water potential, chlorophyll density, lignin/nitrogen, carboxylase, etc. Respiration components should be identified, if possible, using chambers, porometers, etc. Leaf optical properties should be measured and leaf extension data should be taken throughout the growing season. In general, a significant preparatory effort is required to improve our methods of making such *in situ* measurements.

Biogeochemical cycling and gas flux studies: Soil nutrient turnover rates and flux measurements of selected trace gases (N_2O, NO, CH_4, and CO_2) should be

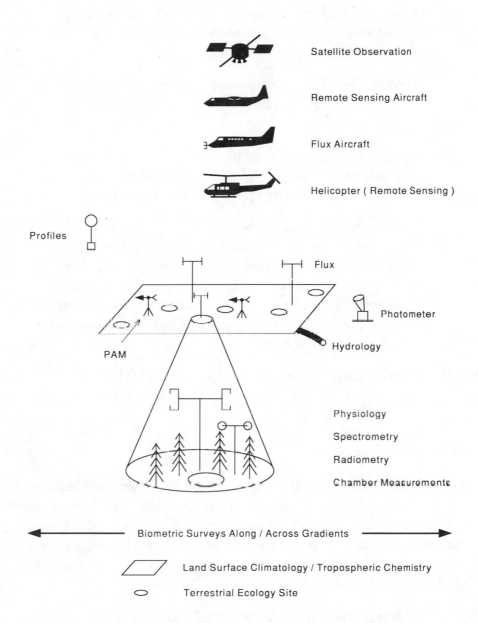

Satellite Observation

Remote Sensing Aircraft

Flux Aircraft

Helicopter (Remote Sensing)

Profiles

Flux

Photometer

PAM

Hydrology

Physiology

Spectrometry

Radiometry

Chamber Measurements

Biometric Surveys Along / Across Gradients

Land Surface Climatology / Tropospheric Chemistry

Terrestrial Ecology Site

Figure 11.4: Surface Observations at the 20 X 20 km sites.

measured and related to site and climatic conditions. The tropospheric chemistry equipment should be located at the upwind end of the site to prevent interference from the other experiment components.

Photometry: The optical state of the atmosphere should be monitored using photometers during aircraft and satellite overpasses.

Spectral properties: The spectral properties of phytoelements and ground surface should be surveyed and correlated with the physiological measurements.

Biometric surveys: More intensive assessments of biometric properties should be executed during IFC; some of these will be conducted outside the main sites. Overstory, understory, species mix, crown density, diameter at breast height (DBH), core samples (for net primary production), and branch and leaf angles, among others, should all be measured.

Calibration: Intercalibration of the experiment instruments should be built into the experiment design.

Airborne Observations

The airborne operations will be confined to IFCs for practical reasons. A number of aircraft equipped with remote sensing and airborne eddy correlation devices will be used in coordinated studies over and around the two main sites. These studies will provide data that will be used to bridge the gap between the surface measurements and the larger scale satellite and meteorological observations.

Airborne Remote Sensing: The reliance on physiological models rather than thermo/aerodynamic models displaces emphasis from a 'tracking' of the diurnal surface temperature wave, as was done in FIFE. An assessment of this approach will be made if possible, but it will not be the primary (energy balance) remote sensing hypothesis for the LSC component of the study. More effort will be dedicated to the remote sensing of canopy structural, biochemical and biophysical properties and surface soil moisture conditions.

Airborne Flux and gas concentration measurements: The requirement for understanding controls on surface-atmosphere exchanges in a one-dimensional framework defines our minimum size 20 X 20 km site design. The requirement for understanding the relationship between climate and ecosystem state implies more extensive surveys. It is anticipated that the main sites will be used as the foci for cross- and along-gradient airborne surveys of biophysical states coordinated with selected ground sampling efforts. Some of the airborne TC studies will also consist of regional transects or budget studies.

It is expected that several remote sensing aircraft equipped with optical, thermal, passive microwave and radar sensors will be committed to the experiment in addition to one or two helicopters equipped with radiometers and/or spectrometers. Two flux measurement aircraft should be available to measure the turbulent fluxes of water, heat, CO_2, momentum and some specified trace gases. One other aircraft may be used for extensive surveys of trace gas concentrations and gradients. The field campaign will be supported by ongoing monitoring for both sites from several satellite platforms.

SUMMARY

The Boreal Ecosystem-Atmosphere Study (BOREAS) has the goal of understanding the interactions between the boreal forest biome and the atmosphere in order to clarify their roles in global change. The field component of the experiment will consist of coordinated surface, airborne and satellite measurements over two 20 X 20 km study sites located near the northern and southern ecotones of the biome. The main experiment execution is planned for 1994, sandwiched between monitoring work and preliminary studies (before) and monitoring and analysis (after). The experiment will be an international collaborative effort involving scientists from the U.S., Canada and other countries and will consist of contributions from the fields of land surface climatology, terrestrial ecology, tropospheric chemistry and remote sensing.

BOREAS Science Steering Committee consists of: M. Apps, J. Cihlar, B. Goodison, F. Hall, B. Harriss, D. Leckie, E. LeDrew, P. Matson, S. Running, P. Sellers

REMOTE SENSING AND GEOGRAPHIC INFORMATION SYSTEMS (GIS) APPLICATIONS FOR MULTI-RESOURCE INVENTORIES IN CANADA

F. Hegyi

INTRODUCTION

Resource inventory techniques, such as the ones used in forestry, have improved considerably during the past 30 years. Methods documented by Spurr (1952) represent only a subset of the knowledge used in current inventory and monitoring projects. Computers, geographic information systems (GIS) and satellite image analysis systems, and knowledge based expert systems are key players in modern inventories throughout the world. Opportunities that exist for improving the efficiency and cost-effectiveness of forest inventory and monitoring projects depend largely on the willingness to accept new approaches, human expertise and the availability of financial resources. Each chosen strategy is associated with problems that are unique to the local conditions.

GLOBAL MULTI-RESOURCE INVENTORY TECHNIQUES

Prior to the 1940s, traditional resource inventory practices consisted mainly of ground surveys. During the late 1940s and early 1950s, the operational use of aerial photographs was introduced for the purposes of subdividing the forest into relatively homogenous strata and measuring their areas, as well as for controlling ground sampling (Spurr, 1948; Spurr, 1952). At the same time, the applications of statistically efficient sampling designs to forest inventory were receiving increased attention (Bruce and Schumacher, 1942; Bickford, 1952; Cochran, 1953; Dawkins, 1952; Spurr, 1952; Snedecor and Cochran, 1956). Forest inventory and monitoring techniques are well documented in books (Loetsch and Haller, 1973; Husch et al., 1972; Avery, 1975) and in the proceedings of the various symposia (Cunia, 1974; Lund, 1978; Frayer, 1979; Brann et al., 1981; Bell and Atterbury, 1983). In addition, publications focusing on statistical efficiency (Ware and Cunia, 1962; Freese, 1962), growth and yield projections (Fries, 1974), remote sensing techniques (Johannsen and Sanders, 1982) and geographic information systems (Weller, 1983; Anon, 1988; Anon, 1989; McPhalen, 1989), also contain relevant information for forest inventory under international conditions. While these references are not intended to be a complete review of the literature available on the subject, they provide a general background for the focus of this paper.

For decision making, forest planners and managers need current information which can be manipulated in a flexible way (Hegyi, 1985). The basic ingredients of such a land information system are: geo-referenced base, cadastral and thematic maps within the context of a geographic information system, cost-effective change detection procedures, and flexible data management algorithms. Examples of such systems are the forest inventory data base of British Columbia (Hegyi and Quenet, 1983; Hegyi, 1988) and New Zealand (Kirkland, 1985), the resource information management project in Thailand (Beaudoin, 1988), GIS strategic projects in the Nordic countries (Tveitdal and Hesjedal, 1989), remote sensing and GIS applications in Asean countries (Mok et al., 1988), and the forest change classification project in northern Florida (Hoffer and Lee, 1989).

Forest inventory and monitoring techniques have experienced some dramatic changes during the past 30 years, driven by technology, needs, local conditions and public pressure for information on resources other than forestry. The long standing leadership of the European practices have been challenged by the rapidly evolving technology. In particular, North American foresters, faced with extensive areas of unknown forests, have turned to remote sensing techniques, computers, and geographic information systems to aid in the design of forest inventory and monitoring projects. In recent years, considerable attention has been focused on global monitoring. The need for monitoring renewable resources on a global basis is well documented by Hildebrandt (1983) and Singh and Lanly (1983), and on a national basis by Schmid-Haas (1983), Lund (1983), Hagglund (1983) and Hegyi (1983). Geographic information systems have perhaps made the greatest impact on forest inventory and monitoring practices and their operational implementation has received considerable attention (Tomlinson, 1989; Hegyi, 1989).

RESOURCE INVENTORY AND
MONITORING TECHNIQUES IN CANADA

A review of resource inventory and monitoring techniques used in Canada indicates that numerous alternative methods are available, depending on needs and local conditions. However, there are a number of components that are common to most inventories, such as planimetric and cadastral maps, administrative boundaries, thematic forest cover and environmental sensitivity maps, road networks, and information on other resources and land use options. In addition, cartographic maps containing digital elevation data and change monitoring information are essential requirements of modern resource management.

Geographic information and satellite image analysis systems have become an integral part of resource inventories. The requirement of stand or area specific information further confirms the strong role of GIS in inventory practices. These new tools have a major effect on the statistical techniques that may be used for the inventory, as well as on data management and retrieval practices.

Given the available modern technology, resource inventory projects in Canada include the following components:

- Essential components of most resource inventory projects are the base maps. Starting with planimetric maps, ownership, cadastre and administrative boundaries are entered to form the base map. Automation of this process with GIS is cost-effective and provides the opportunity of storing the various sources of information as layers, facilitating further manipulations with thematic and topographic information. In cases where planimetric base maps are not available, geometrically corrected satellite imagery provide a practical alternative.

- Most management unit inventory projects, especially those in forestry, use vertical aerial photographs at 1:15,000 or 1:10,000 scale. These photographs are interpreted to provide descriptions of vegetative cover. For example, in areas where the number of species within homogeneous strata are less than five, individual species composition may be determined to the nearest 10%. Otherwise species groups or other relevant ecological units may have to form these descriptions. In addition, in forestry, the date of establishment or age, if available, and total height (e.g., average height of 100 largest stems per hectare) of the leading species, is estimated next. In order to improve the estimation of volumes of individual stands, some measure of stocking is important, such as crown closure to the nearest 10% or stems per hectare.

- Using ground control information and field samples, the interpretation of aerial photographs is confirmed. Photo-centres and the boundaries of homogeneous types are transferred onto base maps either photogrametrically or directly into the GIS. High quality forest cover maps can then be prepared with the aid of the computer.

- Sampling systems which are considered most cost-effective and efficient involve both large-scale photographs and ground samples. Experience indicates that 70 mm stereo photographs at 1:500 scale are highly suitable for the estimation of tree volumes. Random distribution of photograph samples is preferred, with the aim of representing adequately the major population groups. A sub-sample of the areas selected for photograph samples can then be chosen randomly and visited on the ground for detailed measurements. Ground and photograph samples are analyzed according to procedures outlined under multi-phase sampling. Alternatively, the selection of samples may follow the procedures defined under multi-stage sampling systems (Loetsch and Haller, 1973).

- In the case of forest inventory, tree volume equations may need to be derived from the sample data base, using independent variables which are compatible with the classification system. This approach allows volume estimation on an individual stand basis, a capability that is becoming increasingly important in multiple and integrated resource management.

- The major advantages of using a GIS for processing the inventory data are that the thematic forest cover and multi-resource levels can be combined with cadastre, administrative boundaries, and other relevant levels of information that are available in digital or georeferenced forms. Using either vector or raster based overlay procedures, areas of resultant polygons can be determined and the results displayed graphically, including colour enhanced thematic maps. As well, the statistical data may be manipulated in a flexible manner to provide a wide range of summaries.

- An integral part of any forest inventory is growth projections. In Canada several approaches are used, including deterministic volume equations with time as one of the independent variables, stochastic models, and simulation models. The use of expert systems in growth projections will likely pick up momentum and may replace conventional approaches to a large degree.

The above described procedure is enhanced by the use of satellite image data. For example, supervised classification of thematic mapper imagery can provide useful information for the planning of forest inventory projects, including both the classification and sampling. Furthermore, if funding for aerial photography is limited, or, due to weather conditions, parts of the area are not covered by conventional photography, satellite image analysis has the potential of providing a lower resolution alternative for implementing projects. For resource monitoring and change detection, satellite data provide perhaps the most cost-effective solution. Imagery obtained at two different times and subjected to multi-temporal analysis, provides opportunities far beyond the capabilities of any of the conventional techniques. Changes detected can be transferred to existing thematic maps, or entered directly into the GIS. A more sophisticated option is to use an integrated satellite image analysis and geographic information system to monitor and manage change data.

TECHNOLOGICAL CHALLENGES
FOR RESOURCE INVENTORIES

Traditionally, large field parties have been used to survey the land. Medium and small scale aerial photographs have provided opportunities to examine large areas in terms of such interest parameters as timber types, land forms, geological formations and agricultural uses. Extensive ground surveys have changed gradually to multi-phase and multi-stage sampling designs, and for quality control. As the resolution of airborne remote sensing products has improved, even more field work has been substituted with large scale aerial photographs and photo sampling has become a new challenge to statisticians. Information that could only be obtained in the past from ground surveys, can now be closely approximated with the combination of extensive photo and limited ground sampling, used within the context of double sampling, or even higher order multi-phase sampling designs. This was possible by correcting or "ground truthing" estimates from photographs from the sample measurements made on the ground.

Satellite imagery, such as the early versions of Landsat multispectral scanner data, has become fairly popular in a relatively short period of time, mainly because large areas can be covered frequently at lower cost than with conventional photographs. However, its low resolution has reduced its use mainly to monitoring changes, except in research and development environments, where claims have been made beyond its operational capabilities. With the advent of Thematic Mapper products, both spatial and spectral resolution have improved considerably, and the operational usefulness of spaceborne scanner products have increased. In addition, the release of SPOT data has shown resolution capabilities that can match conventional aerial photographs in many areas.

The major technological challenge of the 1990s will be, however, the replacement of conventional aerial photographs with high resolution airborne scanner data, such as MEIS. When analyzed and colour enhanced, MEIS products can appear as if they are large scale aerial photographs, but have the main advantage of being in digital form. Once a library of spectral signatures can be compiled for such applications as forestry, agriculture, geology, land use, land production capability and environmental sensitivity, high resolution airborne scanner imagery will challenge aerial photo interpretation in a manner similar to the replacement of manual drafting by GIS.

The development of remote sensing technology has, in the past, occurred as a joint effort between researchers and resource managers. This development has not progressed as fast as it could have, mainly because both the users and those who have had major control on funding the new technology, have learned their resource management skills in a more conventional and manual environment for data acquisition. Hence, remote sensing techniques, especially those involving satellites, have undergone some skepticism and even resistance.

However, with increasing concerns of the public about the environment and the changes that are being inflicted upon the land base, resource managers will be subject to scrutiny at a scale previously unimagined. Rightly or wrongly, practices previously considered acceptable and even cost effective, will be challenged. And the chances are that the challengers will have up-to-date information about the land base, using remote sensing technology, combined with powerful geographical information systems. In addition, in many cases the resource managers' own data will be used as the base, over which space and airborne scanner data will be displayed, showing the adverse effects on the environment. Entrepreneurs working with land information systems are just a few steps away from setting up data marts, where, on floppy disks, information may be purchased about most parts of the world. Conflicts between land use and resource management practices, whether involving forestry, mining, agriculture or rangeland, will be dealt with in the 1990s from a new power base of current information, which can be manipulated at ease to highlight areas of concern.

Availability of information about the natural resources of a region, province or country has created further problems or challenges. Surveillance of natural resources by competitors could become an active industry, creating both marketing and legal problems.

GIS AS THE INFORMATION SERVER

Information that is being accumulated about our resources and environment is constantly increasing. A large portion of the data are already in digital form and are geo-referenced. As new descriptive statistics are becoming available at frequent intervals, with remote sensing techniques, the size of the data base will create major information management problems. Geographic information systems have the functional capabilities of acting as information servers as well as data managers.

For example, in British Columbia, a relatively large number of GIS installations have been initiated, many of which are PC-based, using 386 machines with at least 80 megabytes of storage. Most of these systems have been acquired to carry out contract work for the expanded forest inventory program. However, some of the consultants and contractors involved in this program are seeking expansion to other disciplines, such as land use allocation, environmental monitoring and mining. As the momentum of the digital conversion of land information increases, PC-based systems could become limiting factors to production and throughput, and expansion of workstations and to more powerful processors, such as microVAX and VAX computers, will occur.

Alternatively, the PC industry will advance in response to this demand, and microcomputer systems will be available to address increasing processing needs.

The projected expansion of the GIS industry will result in further decreases in cost for digital conversion, as well as for the management and distribution of land-related information. In fact, this expansion will likely move to a situation where a few wholesale distributors of land-related information will feed the data to retailers, who will turn it into products that can be examined in a user friendly manner, perhaps even with home computers.

CONCLUSIONS

Public pressure on resource managers, to justify their decisions with respect to land use and environmental issues, will result in increased applications of remote sensing and GIS technologies. Demands for land-related information will increase and the data distribution industry will expand. A more informed public, and, in particular, special interest groups, will help to resolve some of the existing land use conflicts. At the same time, readily available data can become powerful weapons against decisions which are contrary to public interest.

Conventional aerial photographic products will be replaced by airborne multispectral scanner data in resource management, while the use of satellite imagery will expand in global environmental monitoring. Remote sensing technology will become the principal tool for data acquisition. GIS, on the other hand, will be used for the management and distribution of geo-referenced land information.

CHAPTER 13

RADARSAT:
A REVIEW AND DISCUSSION
OF POTENTIAL APPLICATIONS
TO GLOBAL MONITORING

J.K. Hornsby, H.W. MacKay, J.R. Harris
D.I.R. Low

INTRODUCTION

Radar systems were originally developed prior to World War II for the purpose of aerial reconnaissance navigation and ranging. The first imagery radar was developed in Britain as an aid in nighttime bombing (Simonett, 1983). These early systems were real aperture (RAR) systems in which resolution was dependent on antenna or aperture size. Advances in radar technologies led to the development of the synthetic aperture radar (SAR) which synthesis a long antenna resulting in a higher resolution than could be obtained from an RAR of equivalent antenna size.

After military declassification of radar, it began to be applied to resource monitoring activities. This in turn led to the eventual launching in 1978 of SEASAT I, the first satellite-based radar. It had an operational life of only 98 days but managed to acquire 100 million square miles of imagery. This amount of data was collected due to the all weather capability of radar. SEASAT I had range and azimuth resolutions of approximately 25 m at 4 looks. SEASAT I provided an opportunity for applications specialists to evaluate the contribution of satellite-based radar.

The next radar in space was the Shuttle Imaging Radars, SIR-A and SIR-B, launched in 1981 and 1984 respectively. These were primarily experimental sensors on-board the shuttle spacecraft and, therefore, the amount of data collected was minimal.

RADARSAT, which is due to be launched in 1995, will be the first Canadian remote sensing satellite. It is being constructed and launched in cooperation with the United States, Canadian Provincial Governments and the private sector. Canada is responsible for the design and integration of the overall system, for control and operation of the satellite in orbit and for operation of the data reception stations in Prince Albert, Saskatchewan and Gatineau, Quebec. NASA will provide launch services and will operate a data reception station in Alaska in exchange for radar data for its research programs.

The objectives of this paper are to review RADARSAT specifications and capabilities and discuss the application of RADARSAT data for monitoring resources on a global scale, and also to introduce the commercial arm of RADARSAT, Radarsat International Inc.

RADAR AND TERRAIN PARAMETERS

In order to appreciate the application of radar data for resource monitoring it is necessary to have some understanding of radar and terrain parameters which result in the formation of an image.

The following section briefly describes radar and terrain parameters and how these will affect the radar signal.

Radar System Parameters

To be able to understand the contribution of radar data for resource monitoring it is necessary to be familiar with basic system characteristics. These parameters include frequency, depression angle, polarization and look direction.

The radar frequency used will determine the strength of the radar return. A given surface normally appears rougher, resulting in higher backscatter, at higher frequencies (shorter wavelengths) than at lower frequencies. This is directly dependent, of course, on the surface roughness.

The depression angle, the angle at which the radar imagery is transmitted towards the surface, will affect the radar return based on the incident angle of the energy hitting the earth's surface.

Polarization describes the electric field vector of an electromagnetometer wave. The orientation of polarized SAR can be either horizontal or vertical. The radar energy can be transmitted and received in either horizontal or vertical mode. A depolarized return results when the average surface roughness is approximately equal to the radar wavelength.

The look direction is determined by the orbit pattern of the sensor and refers to the azimuthal direction of the radar energy. Topographic features, such as slopes, that are orthogonal to the radar look directions are preferentially enhanced. If a linear feature was trending parallel to the look direction, then return from this feature would be minimal.

Terrain Parameters

Terrain parameters affecting the radar return signal include surface geometry, surface roughness and dielectric properties.

The major surface geometry variables affecting the degree to which the signal is returned are slope and aspect. Since radar energy is transmitted at a particular depression angle and look direction, the topographic orientation of the earth's surface will highly influence the amount of radar return.

Surface roughness, which is defined by the surface cover such as vegetation and soil, significantly affects the backscatter of the radar signal, especially between the incidence angles of 25° and 60°. The information derived from the radar imagery for resource monitoring comes largely from this terrain parameter. The response due to surface roughness is also dependent on wavelength and incidence angle. A given surface may appear smooth at one wavelength (i.e. L-band - 23 cm) and rough at another (i.e. X-band - 3 cm).

The complex dielectric constant is a measure of the electrical properties of the surface and affects the reflective properties of the surface as well as the depth of penetration of the radar energy. Backscatter will increase from surface materials with a high dielectric constant and penetration will be proportionally less. Ground or vegetation that is moist will have a high dielectric constant resulting in stronger backscatter compared to dry ground and vegetation. Penetration is dependent on wavelength as well as dielectric constant. Depth of penetration increases with longer wavelengths and lower dielectric constants.

The RADARSAT sensor specifications, discussed in the following section, take account of these parameters and ensure that the information available from RADARSAT is useful for global monitoring and other Canadian and international applications.

RADARSAT SPECIFICATIONS

RADARSAT is scheduled for a five year life span following its anticipated 1995 launch. The launch, to be provided by NASA as part of the cooperative partnership with the United States, will be made using a medium-class, expendable launch vehicle.

The selected orbit for RADARSAT is a sun-synchronous, dawn-dusk polar orbit. The orbital altitude is scheduled to be 792 km and inclination is scheduled to be 98.6°. Orbital parameters are provided in Table 13.1.

Table 13.1

Orbital Parameters

Altitude:	792 km
Equatorial Crossing Time:	0600
Geometry:	Circular, sun-synchronous
Inclination:	98.6^{0}
Period:	100.7 minutes
Repeat Cycle:	24 days
Sub-cycle:	3 days

Data Acquisition

The RADARSAT SAR will operate at 5.3 GHz (C-band). The SAR will have a variety of beam selection modes providing various swath widths, resolutions and incidence angles. The operating modes were selected based on years of research into optimum requirements of a spaceborne SAR that would serve both research and operational users. These requirements led to critical features in the system design including elevation beam-forming capabilities in the antenna, so as to allow imaging of any of a set of defined swaths, and capability of the system to generate a choice of pulses, each covering a different band width so as to give the required ground range resolution. Operational flexibility allowing combinations of swath width and spatial resolution, as well as the capability of rapid switching between beams, has provided additional operational and experimental beam selection modes. These modes are summarized in Table 13.2.

Table 13.2

Beam Selection Modes

Mode	Swath Width	Incidence Angle	Resolution
Standard Beam	100 km	20° - 40°	28 m x 25 m (4 looks)
Wide Swath Beam	150 km	20° - 40°	28 m x 35 m (4 looks)
Fine Resolution Beam	45 km	37° - 49°	10 m x 10 m (1 look)
SCANSAR	300 or 500 km	49° - 59°	100 m x 50 m (8 looks) 100 m x 100 m
Experimental Beams	75 km	49° - 59°	28 m x 30 m

Basic characteristics of the RADARSAT are summarized in Table 13.3.

The data acquisition window for RADARSAT is a maximum of 28 minutes per orbit. Data may be downlinked in real time or stored on tape for subsequent downlink when the spacecraft is within view of a receiving station.

Table 13.3

Basic RADARSAT SAR Characteristics

Frequency:	5.3 GHz
RF Band width:	11.6, 17.3 or 30.0 MHz
Sampling Rate:	12.9, 18.5 or 32.3 MHz
Transmit Pulse Length:	42.0
Pulse Repetition Frequency:	1270 - 1390 Hz
Transmitter Peak Power:	5 kW
Transmitter Average Power: (nominal)	300 W
Average Radar Data Rate:	73.9 - 100.0 Mb/s
Sample Work Size:	4 bits each I and Q
Antenna Size:	15.0 x 1.6 m
Antenna Polarization:	HH
Antenna Elevation Phase Quantization	8 bits

Data Transmission, Storage and Reception

Data will be downlinked to receiving stations in Gatineau (Quebec), Prince Albert (Saskatchewan) and Fairbanks (Alaska). Radarsat International Inc., the private sector consortium, is negotiating the sale of reception rights to additional receiving station operators, other than Canada and the United States. The receiving stations will be ERS-1 compatible stations equipped with X-band antennae which will track the spacecraft above 5° elevation.

Data storage capability will be provided by two high-speed tape recorders. Each recorder will be capable of storing up to 10 minutes of data which would be downlinked when the spacecraft comes within view of an appropriate receiving station.

The data will be received at the receiving stations for storage and retransmission as required to a data processing centre.

Mission Management

A Canadian Mission Management Office (MMO) will be responsible for commanding the satellite, the ground reception and data processing facilities, and the data distribution systems.

RADARSAT APPLICATIONS TO GLOBAL MONITORING

The following section discusses the information which may be derived from radar imagery for specific resource areas. Emphasis is placed on renewable resource application areas.

Ice Applications

The ability of SAR to penetrate after dark and cloud covered skies in the northern latitudes will enable the collection of ice and weather information necessary to reduce navigational risks and make resource exploration safer and more effective. RADARSAT will provide the first routine surveillance of the Arctic region giving daily coverage and real time data transmission.

Oceans Applications

Radarsat data will provide information on ocean wave spectra, ship detection, ocean feature mapping and oil pollution detection.

Ocean wave spectra and ocean feature mapping may be used operationally in wave forecast models and ocean wave climatology. The spectra will also enable more efficient and safe offshore oil and gas operations, marine transportation and naval activities.

Ship detection will enable surveillance and monitoring of offshore economic zones, and the establishment of Arctic sovereignty. The surveillance and monitoring of environmental disasters such as oil slicks will also be possible.

Non-Renewable Resource Applications

Global stereo mapping and land use mapping activities will be greatly aided by the availability of RADARSAT data. Building a global stereo data set for mapping geomorphic features to assist mineral exploration and for topographic mapping are just two potential global monitoring applications. Land use mapping for such applications as resource inventory, coastal process studies and land use planning can also be aided through the interpolation of radar data.

Renewable Resources

Of perhaps most significance for global monitoring is the renewable resource areas, in particular agriculture/vegetation monitoring and forest monitoring.

Radar data has been demonstrated to provide useful information for the purposes of crop area and yield estimates and soil moisture determination (Brown, 1989, Cihlar et al., 1986, Dobson and Ulaby, 1986). The sensitivity of SAR to soil moisture is significant for environmental monitoring. The ability of different soils to retain moisture, such as clay versus sand, aids in the delineation of either problem areas or favourable areas for resource development. Evidence of hazardous waste leaking from containment areas into the surrounding terrain may be derived from the monitoring capabilities of regular SAR overpasses. Furthermore, soil moisture measurements by RADARSAT will allow the determination of global rainfall and contribute to a global climate model.

Agriculture Applications

Agriculture can be divided into four primary application areas:

- crop identification and area estimation;
- crop and foliage estimation and prediction;
- crop monitoring (i.e. change detection); and,
- monitoring and characteristics of catastrophic events (floods, severe storms, etc.).

From a remote sensing perspective, each application area has special requirements that, to be completely met, would require a diverse range of data including visible infrared (VIR) (i.e. Landsat, SPOT, NOAA, AVHRR), aerial photography (colour and black and white) and radar (SAR). Since the late 1970s, starting with the SURSAT (Canadian Surveillance Satellite Program) and the NASA SEASAT program, much emphasis has been placed on the use of radar for agricultural applications.

Key requirements for all four primary agricultural applications are timeliness of data acquisition and repeat coverage especially considering the day-to-day operational requirements for many agricultural programs. Although visible infrared is an excellent source of information the uncertainty of the data acquisition process which is dependent on atmospheric conditions (especially cloud cover), is a great hindrance to many operational programs. RADARSAT will provide guaranteed repetitive coverage due to SAR's all weather capability which is of the utmost importance in virtually all agricultural applications.

RADARSAT offers an innovative design characterized by C-band wavelength, HH polarization and five main operational modes outlined in Table 13.2. For crop identification, C-band has been found to be relatively insensitive to variations in incidence angle (Brown, 1989); therefore, data could be collected over the full 500 km range of the accessibility swath. Fairly high crop classification accuracies can be achieved with SAR depending on crop type and the particular site being investigated (Cihlar et al., 1986).

However, one particular advantage of SAR for crop identification is that research indicates that certain crops such as canola and possibly potatoes can be identified more easily earlier in the growing season on SAR than VIR data. Furthermore, the Wide Swath and Scansar modes would be useful for the large scale estimation of soil moisture, as Dobson and Ulaby (1986) have found a correlation between soil moisture and radar backscatter, especially at C-band and steep incidence angles (10-20°) while the Renewable-Resource Applications Group at CCRS have found that a similar correlation exists, using C-band data acquired by an airborne SAR, at incidence angles ranging from 45° to 60°. This suggests a high sensitivity of SAR to moisture, despite variations in incidence angles. Ulaby et al. (1984) have found that there is a correlation between radar backscatter and leaf area index, indicating that the Scansar mode may be a useful complement to AVHRR data for monitoring vegetation over large areas.

A combination of sensing modes, depending on the spatial resolution requirements, would be ideal for monitoring catastrophic events, such as floods, as the SAR shows distinct surface roughness contrast between flooded and non-flooded areas.

It is anticipated that RADARSAT, with its multiple modes of operations and range of spatial resolutions, will provide an extremely useful and timely data source for many agricultural applications both in an operational and research environment. The ability of RADARSAT to monitor large areas as well as conduct detailed studies of small areas should make it an extremely valuable source of data for agriculture applications.

Forestry Applications

The use of radar for forestry applications includes determining:

- the location and extent of clear cut forestry;
- state of regeneration;
- species composition; and,
- insect damage and disease.

SEASAT studies by Muller and Hoffer (1988), Rochon et al. (1986) and Werle et al (1986) demonstrate the use of spaceborne SAR data for the discrimination of forest cover types, and the identification of clear cut and regeneration sites.

The different operating modes of the RADARSAT SAR will allow broad monitoring programs to be conducted, as well as more detailed investigations using the fine resolution mode.

The all-weather capabilities of SAR make the sensor ideal for monitoring tropical rain forests. These areas are typically cloud covered making other types of remote sensing systems difficult to use. The importance of tropical rain forests in the global environment is recognized and currently under scrutiny by the scientific community. RADARSAT will be able to provide regular monitoring capabilities over large areas of inaccessible terrain.

The Scansar mode will be suitable for mapping large areas of tropical forest; the coarser resolution of 100 metres by 100 metres will reduce the difficulties of large data volumes when monitoring large areas. Areas of specific interest, such as regeneration, would be analyzed in more detail using either the standard beam or fine resolution beam. Variable incidence angles could be selected depending upon the topographic expression of the terrain. Using a steep incident angle it would be possible to enhance differences in relatively flat terrain.

RADARSAT International Inc.

RADARSAT International Inc. (RSI) has been established by the private sector to participate in the distribution of the RADARSAT data. RSI is a consortium of Canadian companies involved in space and remote sensing technologies. Each of the current consortium participants, Com Dev, Intera Technologies, MacDonald Dettwiler and Associates, and Spar Aerospace, is recognized as a world leader within its own technologies and disciplines.

RSI has the right to commercially distribute all RADARSAT data in excess of Canadian Government requirements and its commitments to provincial and international partners. RSI intends to maximize potential sales of data products and services worldwide through private sector entrepreneurship. It intends to develop commercial applications in cooperation with established firms in the value-added business, in both the domestic and export markets. It is expected that RSI's share of the total data acquired by RADARSAT will be approximately 35%. RSI will provide royalty payments to the Canadian Government and, in addition, has agreed to provide the upgrade of the ERS-1 (the European Space Agency's SAR satellite (launched in 1991) processor which is designated for processing RADARSAT data in Canada.

RSI represents an exciting new initiative in private and public sector cooperation. Traditionally, distribution of similar data would likely have been facilitated through a government agency or crown corporation. In the case of RADARSAT, the costs, risks and benefits are shared by the public sector and the private sector. The private sector, represented by the proven commercially successful consortium partners, is being given an opportunity to assist the RADARSAT program by doing what it does best - that is, develop, market and sell products and services.

CONCLUSIONS

With the launch of RADARSAT in 1995, the ability to monitor global environmental concerns and resource activities will be greatly enhanced. The unique ability of SAR technology to image at high resolution from space in all weather conditions, combined with the selectable operation modes of the RADARSAT, will make it a powerful tool for collecting information for such diverse applications as ice flow monitoring, ocean feature mapping, forest clear-cut and regeneration mapping and crop monitoring.

CHAPTER 14

RADARSAT, TROPICAL FORESTS, AND POLICY IMPERATIVES

R. Keith Raney

INTRODUCTION

With the launch of RADARSAT in the middle of this decade, Canada will move into a position of leadership in earth resource satellite remote sensing. This national initiative implies technical and policy issues of substance, both of which need focused attention in the years remaining before the start of the flight mission. This chapter provides an overview of RADARSAT in the opening section, and then moves into consideration of technical and policy issues. The key technical items considered in the second section arise from the potential importance of RADARSAT data products for large scale global environmental issues. The third section observes that data policy, rather than technical ability, is foreseen as the limiting factor that would preclude significant application of most satellite remote sensing information to the earth's pressing environmental problems. Assuming continued development of the required ground segment technologies, it would seem imperative to recognize and reconcile the policy issues so as to enable significant use of high resolution remote sensing data in the context of global environmental observation.

RADARSAT

The Government of Canada announced on 13 September, 1989 that RADARSAT, Canada's planned earth resources remote sensing Synthetic Aperture Radar (SAR) satellite, was fully approved for construction and operation, with a design lifetime of five years from its 1995 launch. The approved design, as outlined in this section (Langham, et al., 1989), is taken as the starting point and motivation for the issues considered in the remainder of the Chapter.

Mission Objectives

The mission objectives are based on Canadian national requirements for information on domestic resource management and environmental monitoring. Optical satellite remotely sensed data could theoretically give coverage at the scale and frequency required, but poor solar illumination much of the year at high latitudes and persistent cloud cover make SAR the only acceptable sensor technology for reliable and timely information (RADARSAT, 1982). Additional mission requirements for RADARSAT are based on domestic experience and bilateral studies with scientists from the United States. The results verify that SAR data have important land applications such as mapping of surface structure, soil moisture conditions, and crop and forestry monitoring in cloudy regions. Indeed, economic studies show that the expected benefits associated with domestic land applications are greater than those from sea and ice mapping (DTI Telecom-Econosult, 1987).

The SAR

The SAR is an advanced multi-mode instrument (see, for example, Luscombe, 1989) that operates at 5.3 GHz (C-Band) having a wavelength of about 5 cm. It has a choice of three transmitter pulse band widths and numerous beam selections (and thus incidence angles) to give images with a variety of swath widths and resolutions (see Table 13.2, Chapter 13). The beam positions and swath widths are electronically selectable, and each is rapidly accessible in response to a variety of user requirements during each orbit.

The various modes of the SAR each have applications for which they are best suited. Thus, for example, the wide swath mode will be that most used for wide-area data collection such as Arctic ice and large ocean features, while the standard mode will be preferred for crop monitoring. The high resolution mode will be used where most detail is required, most efficiently in site specific applications. Stereo images can be obtained by observing the same area at different incidence angles on two different opportunities. The experimental modes are a group of high incidence angle beams outside of the nominal SAR coverage envelope. These beams will be useful for extended access to scenes of interest, and for observation of shipping and icebergs, for example, and may be selected on user request when and where desired.

The SAR can be turned on several times per orbit to a maximum accumulation of 28 minutes. The radar coverage available using the 500 km swath mode over North America, both one day and three days of accessibility, is shown in Figure 14.1. Gaps in coverage could be filled in on subsequent days.

The Mission

The NASA launch of RADARSAT from Vandenburg is scheduled for 1995 using a medium-class expendable launch vehicle. The satellite payload will consist of SAR, described above, and its associated down-link transmitters, tape-recorders and command computer. The spacecraft will be supplied by Ball Aerospace, and SPAR Aerospace has prime system responsibility.

RADARSAT will use a sun synchronous dawn-dusk orbit. For a radar mission not needing scene sunlight, a dawn-dusk orbit offers several advantages because the satellite is rarely in the earth's shadow. Table 13.1 (Chapter 13) lists the pertinent orbit parameters for RADARSAT.

Perhaps the greatest operational advantage of the dawn-dusk orbit is that the SAR can be turned on at any time without consideration of conserving battery power, which means that there is no distinction between ascending and descending passes from an applications point of view. Another operational advantage is that the data reception periods for RADARSAT will not conflict with other remote sensing satellites, most of which use near mid-day orbit timing.

The nominal configuration of the spacecraft has the SAR pointing to the north so that there is almost complete coverage up to the North Pole. However, twice during the mission, for a period of about 2 weeks, the

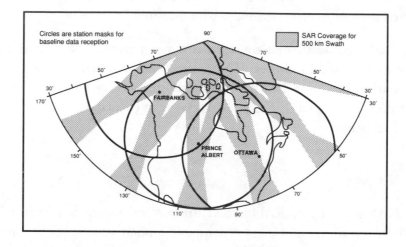

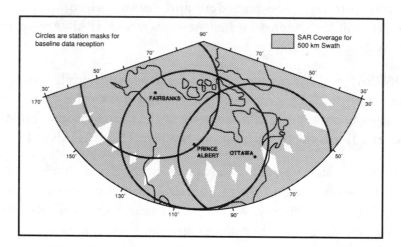

Figure 14.1: Typical Radarsat coverage available over North America for one day (upper) and three days (lower) of orbits.

satellite will be rotated 180 degrees about its yaw axis so as to direct the beam to the south. The purpose is to obtain a complete SAR map of Antarctica at the times of maximum and minimum ice cover.

RADARSAT will carry a tape recorder (with a spare back-up unit) with sufficient capacity for ten minutes of full quality SAR data. The X-band data down-link system is designed for handling simultaneously two channels of 100 MB/S data if needed, one recorded and one "live". With the data recorders, all areas of the world are able to be observed by RADARSAT, even those outside of the coverage circles of operational receiving stations. Figure 14.2 illustrates the three day coverage available from RADARSAT near the equator made possible through use of the data recorders. Full global access enabled through the on-board recorders is a major feature of RADARSAT, of particular relevance to global environmental monitoring.

Mission operations will be coordinated by a Mission Management Office (MMO) which will serve as the interface between the user community, the Mission Control Facility for commanding the satellite, and the ground reception and processing facilities. In Canada, the ERS-1 processing facility will be upgraded to handle the increased throughput of RADARSAT. In addition to coordinating and scheduling requests for SAR data acquisition, the MMO will monitor the entire data distribution system, and serve as the executive office for the mission.

Data processing is required to form images from the data delivered from the spacecraft. For SAR systems, this is often a lengthy, and always a complex, operation. Processing for RADARSAT has been designed to keep pace with the average rate of supply of raw data, a "zero back-log" approach. Users of highly perishable data, such as the Ice Information Centre, will be able to receive processed SAR data, integrate it with their on-line information systems, and relay it to operators in the field within three hours of SAR data collection.

Partnerships

Unique amongst remote sensing initiatives worldwide, the RADARSAT project is supported through partnerships with U.S. agencies, Canadian provincial governments and the private sector. Canada is responsible for

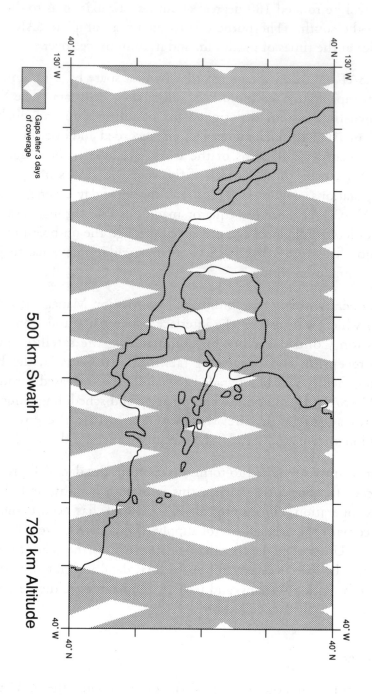

Figure 14.2: Example of Radarsat coverage available near the Equator (three days)

the design and integration of the overall system, for construction of the radar, for the provision of the satellite platform, for control and operation of the satellite in orbit and for operation of the data reception stations in Prince Albert, Saskatchewan and Gatineau, Quebec. The agreements are in the form of Memoranda of Understanding.

NASA will provide the launch services and will operate a data reception station in Alaska in exchange for radar data for its research programs. NOAA will facilitate the participation of the American private sector in the distribution of data.

All Canadian provinces have participated in planning the RADARSAT Program. Quebec, Ontario, British Columbia, and Saskatchewan share in the capital costs in proportion to technology development within their industries. An agreement has also been developed with the other provinces for their participation in the operational phase of the mission.

RADARSAT International Inc. (RSI), a private sector corporation, has been formed. RSI has the right to distribute the data in excess of the international partners' governmental requirements. In return, they will invest in developing the international market and provide royalty payments to the government from sales. RSI is seeking industrial partners in the U.S. to provide the U.S. private sector with an appropriate role in the global marketing of SAR data.

ENVIRONMENTAL MONITORING AND TECHNICAL ISSUES

RADARSAT design and approval has been based almost exclusively on identifiable domestic benefits for Canada (DTI Telecom-Econosult, 1987). Of all possible applications, however, coverage of vast and environmentally sensitive areas (such as high latitude ice cover; the Earth's forests, particularly in the tropics; large scale ocean features; and desert expansion) represents the most potentially significant use of radar satellite data on a global scale (see, for example, Werle, 1989). Whereas a C-Band SAR is not necessarily the ideal instrument for all such applications, it has the virtue that it can penetrate cloud cover, haze, smoke, and darkness, thus allowing reliable observations in all seasons, and under poor optical conditions. The resulting information would be useful in any geographic information system responsive to the needs of observing global change (Cihlar et al., 1989), and is an essential input to efforts aimed at gathering data of use for understanding global environmental phenomena (NASA 1988).

"Global environmental monitoring" has become a popular phrase in remote sensing and data base communities, yet it is far more easily said than done. The technical issues are demanding, the science issues daunting, and the implied policy and management issues may become the Sword of Damocles. Amongst these, selected technical issues are noted here. Policy issues are considered in the closing Section.

In looking forward to the use of RADARSAT data together with information from other sensors and sources for environmental monitoring, several technical issues may be identified. These arise both from the sheer quantity of data to be considered, and the variety and the nature of data sources. Archival strategies need to be developed, and funded, to accommodate the appetite of global monitoring activities. Access to the data base, and analysis of the data are also problematic when considered at the global level.

Of most concern to ground segment technology, however, are issues raised by the necessity to ingest radar remote sensing data into (regional) environmental information systems. For global applications, large area coverage spanning many countries is required, as illustrated in Figure 14.2. As a consequence, variations in scale (pixel size) on the order of 1000:1 are inevitable, stretching from the AVHRR resolutions for the global vegetation index (Choudhury and Tucker, 1987) to the finer resolutions available from SPOT or RADARSAT. Information is gained as resolution is improved, but of course the nominal size of the data base grows with the square of resolution ambitions (e.g. Townshend and Justice, 1988). Both image data and tabular files are required, and cross-referenced, in both pixel specific and polygonal classes. For SAR data in particular, area norms rather than single pixel classifiers need to be incorporated into the information system. SAR data, either logically analyzed (for spatial spectral signature, for example) or as image files, will need to be merged with information from other sensors, or with non-image records. Finally, for many if not all environmental issues, the variation of localized parameters over time is the most critical quantity to monitor. All of these issues are matters of current GIS research for example, although not necessarily vigorous at the present time (e,g. Nagy and Swain, 1987). These problems would seem to be tractable, however, and substantial progress may reasonably be expected over this decade.

POLICY IMPERATIVES

Upon reflection, data policy, rather than technical ability, would seem to be the dominant factor that precludes wide spread application of most satellite remote sensing information to the earth's pressing environmental problems. Current data policy is based on a market place philosophy, for which the watershed development in North America took place in the United States, with the Remote Sensing Act of Congress of 1984 (PL 98-365). This Act set the stage for transfer of operational (land) remote sensing out of NASA, with the objective to reach commercial viability for remote sensing within an aggressively short period of time, thus removing the burden of support or subsidy from the Federal Government. The arguments considered by the U. S. Congress at that time were almost exclusively ones of domestic market assessment (e.g., Office of Technology Assessment, 1984) analogous to those used in Canada for RADARSAT. The trend is now firmly established, although the present and future success of the approach continues to be the subject of discussion. Virtually all remote sensing data products are now available at a price rationalized by internationally agreed expressions of marketability.

The market place philosophy applies when a customer expects to realize value received for money spent. Thus, there are many applications of remotely sensed information for which this model is appropriate. Unfortunately, not all uses of remote sensing data satisfy this model (Aronoff, 1985). It is important to note that several of these non-marketable applications have been increasing in public awareness in recent years (e.g., Analytic Sciences Corporation, 1988). As a consequence, the fundamental basis for support of both the private good and public good aspects of remote sensing deserves to be reexamined (e.g., Mrazek, 1990). Chief among the public good aspects of relevance to Canada's RADARSAT is environmental monitoring, a use appropriately classed as a "public good", and thus by definition worthy of public support. Since radar is capable of cloud penetration, tropical forest monitoring emerges as the most important application of RADARSAT data to environmental issues. The extent to which this will actually be realized would seem to be tempered primarily by policy considerations at the present time.

Exclusive reliance on the market place philosophy for remote sensing data products effectively precludes their use on wide-scale global environmental problems. Environmental monitoring should lead to greater knowledge and understanding of the issues, and could lead to better resource management strategies (Raney and Specter, 1989), but only in the very long run. There would be substantial economic impact from effective monitoring and management, yet the benefits would be distributed over many beneficiaries, including, ultimately, all of the human race (World Commission on Environment and Development, 1987). The fact remains, however, that long run distributed gains are not very marketable.

The problem is not trivial. Consider the matter of data costs. For example, assuming a per frame cost of $5000 for RADARSAT medium resolution data, it would cost about $10 million simply to obtain the image data set for one complete coverage of the earth's 2 billion hectares of tropical forest. Allowance for repeat coverage for land cover change analysis or for skip or scene overlap, for selected secondary coverage at higher resolution, for value added processing, and/or for merge with other data sets, leads to an estimate of about $30-40 million for one inventory cycle of this one environmental regime. It is unreasonable to expect that tropical countries, even with assistance from aid agencies, would find the funds or motivation, in the current climate, to make such an investment. This example can be generalized to other environmental regimes of global importance.

The problem is not simply one of data costs. Given that there is now a market philosophy for distribution of remote sensing data, new policies need to be designed that would enable large scale environmental data collection and application at acceptable costs, yet at the same time would respect the present commercial basis of the remote sensing private sector. Both cost and policy are involved. This is the challenge.

A good beginning would be for agencies to establish and maintain a global data archive. Even this step is not trivial. Unlike the Landsat series, for example, systems such as RADARSAT will be activated to collect data only upon receipt of a customer's data request through the Mission Management Office. Large scale data archives from RADARSAT are not now foreseen. In order to accumulate an archive useful for global issues, a plan needs to be designed, funded, and implemented that would efficiently use spare satellite capacity for the purpose, for example, of accumulating an annual inventory of key regions of the tropical forests. Only in this way can we use the potential of RADARSAT to provide an essential data base of importance in global forestry monitoring.

But an archive of radar data is of little use in and of itself. SAR data needs to be processed to reach the level of image files. SAR data processing is not a trivial procedure. Again, there needs to be a plan in place to use available processing capacity to regularly create image files from the accumulated environmental data archive. Thus, it would seem that two archives are required to be established, maintained, and catalogued.

Again, an idle file of environmental data is of little use. There should be an active program to develop and apply suitable value-added processing to the image file such that the resulting information products are of direct utility for major data base efforts of UNEP/GRID or FAO, for example, the agencies with the international mandate to monitor tropical forests. Indeed, although they have the mandate for monitoring, they do not have the funding to procure the necessary remote sensing data in the commercial marketplace.

In short, RADARSAT has the potential to support significant contributions to a global environmental data base, and subsequently to support better management of vital global resources. Substantial and new policy initiatives are required before this potential will be realized.

CONCLUSIONS

The public consensus in Canada and elsewhere is that environmental issues are the dominant concerns of the age. Through remote sensing in combination with the ground segment technical capabilities expected in the next decade, in theory we will have the tools to effectively implement environmental monitoring on critical problems at global scales. Will this capability be utilized?

There remains the fundamental stumbling block of remote sensing data policy. Given the current commercial climate for most remotely sensed data products, there would seem to be no way to perform significant global monitoring of environmentally important regions such as tropical forests. There is a fundamental incompatibility between remote sensing as a marketable commodity, and global environmental responsibility. Under current terms of access, what nation, what agency, what interest group would step forward and "buy" sufficient data to address the long term global issues? It would seem imperative that the developed nations (especially Canada) adopt a new and creative data policy that would underwrite the collection and application of remotely sensed data for issues of global environmental importance. Significant use of remote sensing data, such as that expected from RADARSAT on issues of global importance, can take place only if this is done.

CHAPTER 15

SENSORS FOR
EARTH OBSERVATION
AND
GLOBAL CHANGE MONITORING

A.R. Raab
S.M. Till

INTRODUCTION

Both the importance and characteristics of remotely sensed data in the understanding of the processes of global change are becoming recognized across a much wider spectrum of the science-technology-policy community, due in large part to the impact of sensor data in the media, especially nightly cloud cover images on television weather reports. The importance of data bases in assessing, for example, the extent and impact of clear-cutting in the Pacific coast lumber industry is probably sufficiently clear to even the casual observer of environmental change.

The characteristics of data bases, their priorities and costs, how they are assembled, and how they age are subjects of pressing importance in an era of global change and of limited financial resources at all levels of government and industry. The setting of priorities, an analysis of costs and the definition of programs to assemble adequate data bases start with an examination of the phenomenology of global change and its components, (examined in other chapters of this volume), and include an identification of the technology of the sensing and measuring devices together with trade-off studies of their utility, their current state of development, and data characteristics derived from them.

This chapter aims to provide a brief introduction to a field of enormous extent and variety, and of great importance to global change programs in all parts of the world. How Canada, with its huge geographic compass, can best use its resources to contribute to meaningful global change investigations is illustrated by this chapter and its brief descriptions of a few of the immense variety of space and airborne sensors.

In a time of rapid development of novel detectors and devices, each new improvement in sensitivity carries the risk of diminishing the value of a whole subset of an earlier data base assembled at great cost, technical innovation and scientific dedication. The continuous development of state-of-the-art sensors, a lengthy process over many years, and the subsequent creation of relevant data bases over long and productive sensor lifetimes, are therefore matters of critical importance in determining priorities for funding of global change sensor programs.

Sensors for observation of the earth are designed to gather data from different platforms: aircraft, balloons, ships, satellites, etc. Arguments for one platform over another are varied and often depend on an advocate's position rather than the scientific merits. Space hardware is always more expensive than equivalent airborne equipment, and potentially more challenging and risky to an advanced-technology manufacturer. It is always necessary to achieve a compromise between what is feasible from both technical and funding points of view and what is essential for the full scientific understanding of phenomena. Many characteristics of the earth can only be satisfactorily measured from a satellite's orbit.

The Canadian RADARSAT project is a case in point. Originally conceived for the purpose of determining Arctic ice conditions to ensure safe passage of oil and liquefied natural gas carriers in the far north, the Radarsat Synthetic Aperture Radar (SAR) sensor on its satellite platform provides a good compromise between conflicting financial and socio-economic constraints, continuous observation of ice conditions, and other technical limitations. SAR sensors can also be effectively flown on aircraft platforms and are able to provide considerably better resolution than previous of such phenomena as crop and forestry conditions. The penalty, of course, is related to revisit time and the expense incurred in assembling a useful data base. Measurements currently planned for the

RADARSAT SAR include such parameters as crop and forestry conditions, made feasible by parallel advances in backscatter signature analysis and experiments in the intervening years and now assuming much greater importance in a global change scenario.

Canadian sensor design and manufacturing capabilities can only improve by a continuing commitment to a program of sensor development. The Canadian experience in sensor design has evolved in the past decade along some particular lines. SAR and SLAR (Side-Looking Airborne Radar) systems on aircraft have contributed to the development of a significant internationally recognized Canadian industrial capability (both manufacturing and user) for airborne and satellite sensors. Other areas of Canadian expertise, for example, include ground-based atmospheric probes such as Lidars (Light Detection and Ranging), used in the exploration of atmospheric pollutant, while satellite optical/infra-red sensors such as WINDII (Wind Imaging Interferometer) will be used on foreign space platforms to image upper-atmospheric phenomena of importance in global change investigations of the atmosphere. A Canadian sensor program focused on global change will probably embody the general characteristics given in Table 15.1.

The trend in Canada is likely to be away from very large and expensive single instruments and platforms because of the distortions they produce

---

TABLE 15.1

PROBABLE CHARACTERISTICS OF
A CANADIAN SENSOR PROGRAM

Low-cost sensors, typically in the range $2M - $20M.

Short lifetime, typically under 36 months, and complementary to longer life programs.

Platform-friendly, balloon, aircraft or satellite.

Broad scientific and user support.

Coordination with international and other national programs.

in funding support for the wide variety of sensors required in a global change monitoring program. Whether or not large polar orbiting platforms, such as those proposed in NASA's Earth Observing System, can continue to return useful data over their projected development and mission lifetimes of ten to twenty years is critically dependent, for example, on the evolution of global change climatic models which will almost certainly identify new parameters worthy of examination.

CANADIAN GLOBAL CHANGE CONCERNS

Canada's northern position is shared by only one other nation with comparable resources. Together, the Soviet Union and Canada encompass virtually the entire Arctic. This region of the earth, like the Antarctic, exerts a major influence on global climate, and will be subject to considerable environmental influences as global change takes hold. It is therefore axiomatic that Canadian sensor programs should:

- concentrate on projects relevant to the interactions of the polar and near-polar regions on global climate, the global biosphere and global circulation;

- seek to incorporate the concerns and scientific and technological communities of other Arctic Rim nations, notably the Soviet Union, Scandinavia and the United States in Alaska; and

- ensure that projects are complementary to international global change programs.

The global change concerns which are relevant to a Canadian sensor program are numerous:

- arctic haze;
- atmospheric chemistry;
- boreal forest changes;
- cloud processes;
- deforestation;
- frost-free day variations;

- greenhouse gases;
- ice edge changes;
- ionospheric interactions;
- maritime nutrient changes;
- ocean mixing processes;
- ozone depletion;
- permafrost changes;
- precipitation changes;
- upper atmospheric mixing processes; and,
- urban processes.

The variety of sensors capable of characterizing change in these areas is huge and well beyond the scope of a single chapter. In concentrating on northern phenomena, it will be possible, with study and a well-balanced program of airborne and spaceborne sensor development, to identify and develop small scale models of the Arctic and Canadian environments which will relate properly to global scale models under investigation through international programs such as the NASA and ESA (European Space Agency) polar platform programs. The interdependence of these small and large scale models will dictate the appropriate spatial, spectral and temporal resolutions and the particular sensor technologies required.

Current remote sensing systems for earth observation make use of the interaction of electromagnetic radiation with the earth's surface and atmosphere to acquire information about the earth's resources and the earth's environment. The spectral regions used are in the ultraviolet, visible, infrared and microwave regions, with limitations imposed by the spectral transmission of the atmosphere. Sensors for remote sensing may output data in imagery (examples include the aerial camera, and the Thematic Mapper on Landsat), or may be "profiling" sensors, acquiring data at specific points along a line or a grid (including the microwave scatterometer and the lidar altimeter). "Passive" remote sensing systems rely on energy that is either reflected and/or emitted from the atmosphere or earth surface features, while "active" systems, such as the synthetic aperture radar and the radar altimeter, include energy sources/transmitters and receivers. A complete remote sensing system includes not just the data acquisition sensor and its interface to the aircraft or satellite platform, but also the associated data recording and processing systems. Finally, data analysis systems are required to handle the data and to reduce it to the products of interest, such as resource maps or measurements of geophysical variables.

Major advances in the performance of remote sensing systems and in the information that they provide have resulted from advances in electronics technology, and specifically from advances in detectors and in digital processing. Global change monitoring requires systematic continuous earth observation. Satellite systems, with their ability to cover large regions in a uniform manner and repeatedly at set periods, have a very important role to play. Airborne systems, with their higher resolution capability but reduced coverage, offer precision data and smaller scale coverage for calibration, modelling and simulation purposes, while their response and flexibility of scheduling and targeting are valuable for emergency localized environmental monitoring.

DEVELOPMENT OF REMOTE SENSING SYSTEMS

The first major system used for remote sensing was the aerial camera. The use of aerial photography for civilian purposes increased rapidly after World War II, with specialized films such as colour infrared for vegetation monitoring, and improved photo-interpretation methods. Canada's aerial survey industry has been amongst the world leaders for several decades, both on the acquisition side and in the mapping service. The development in the 1950s and onwards of sensitive detectors with fast response time allowed the implementation of modern airborne and satellite multi-spectral imagers and radiometers. Instead of using film, such sensors use light-sensitive detectors to generate electrical signals that are digitized and stored on computer-compatible systems such as magnetic tape or computer disks.

Using silicon detectors, electro-optical remote sensors can be designed to provide enhanced multi-spectral information and to differentiate small changes in land surface/scene reflectance, allowing improved spectral discrimination of the scene and improved information content. The digital format of the output allows versatile processing and compatibility with computer based geographic information systems and data bases. As the responsivity and low noise characteristics of the detectors improve, there are corresponding improvements possible in the spatial and spectral resolution of the imagery (although higher resolution of course increases the amount of data to be processed, and requires efficient data handling and processing for effective use). The development of multi-element array detectors, both linear and two-dimensional, has resulted in the development of "pushbroom" imagers and imaging spectrometers, with further improvements in sensitivity and advantages in spectral band flexibility and selection.

Current satellite systems for earth observation, carried on the NOAA and Landsat series and on the SPOT and MOS series, include a number of passive electro-optical imagers, from the relatively low resolution systems, such as the Advanced Very High Resolution Radiometer (AVHRR) on NOAA, to the higher resolution pushbroom imager on SPOT. While airborne imaging spectrometers are already in operation, design studies for satellite-borne systems are under way for both the planned NASA and ESA polar platforms.

Advances in the use of space-based active electro-optical remote sensors for earth observation have been somewhat slower, and largely limited by the development of space-qualified lasers and by the increased mass and power requirements. However, airborne laser systems are in use; an airborne scanning lidar, LARSEN, has been in operation in Canada since 1985 for coastal charting, and the airborne laser fluorosensor, for marine pollution, productivity and water quality monitoring, has been in use since the 1970s. Both systems have potential roles in long-term environmental monitoring and emergency response. Plans for satellite-borne laser systems for earth observation programs are at the design stage, and include atmospheric sounders and altimeters to measure surface topography or atmospheric parameters.

In the area of microwave remote sensing, active microwave systems were first developed in the 1930s and 1940s for wartime applications, with the British airborne imaging radar "H2S", or Height-to-Surface, and the multicavity magnetron making possible high-power microwave radars. Side-looking airborne radar (SLAR) and synthetic aperture radar (SAR) were introduced as technology developed, and airborne radar systems began to be used for remote sensing by the 1960s. One of the advantages of radar, unlike electro-optical systems, is its ability to observe through cloud. Systems available include airborne (active) SARs and SLARs, profiling scatterometers, and (passive) microwave radiometers.

A major step was the launch by the United States in 1978 of Seasat-A which carried primarily microwave sensors, including a scatterometer to measure global wind speeds, a multi-channel microwave radiometer and an L-Band SAR. The SAR provided the first synoptic high resolution radar images of the earth's surface, and although Seasat-A was in operation for less than four months, this marked the start of an active development period for microwave remote sensing. Other radar satellites include the European resources satellite, ERS-1, carrying a C-Band SAR, which was launched in 1991, the Soviet Almaz 1, also launched in 1991, the Japanese JERS-1 launched in 1992, and Radarsat to be launched in 1994.

REMOTE SENSORS FOR GLOBAL CHANGE MONITORING

Orbital observations by the U.S. began in 1960 with the launch of TIROS-I, a meteorological satellite that carried a low resolution imaging system, and was the first in a long series of TIROS (and NOAA) satellites. Data acquired by the NOAA AVHRR (1 km resolution for six spectral channels from visible to near infrared), are used for monitoring sea surface temperature, snow cover, vegetation cover, etc.

The first satellite designed specifically to obtain information about the earth's surface and resources was the Earth Resources Technology Satellite, launched in 1972 and later renamed Landsat-1. This carried a four channel multispectral imager, which operated in the visible and near infrared, and was an opto-mechanical device, using a rotating mirror to sweep the field-of-view of the detector across the scene. By Landsat-3, in 1978, the multispectral scanner (MSS) included a thermal infrared band. Landsat-5 (launched in 1984 and still operating in 1993) included the MSS with four spectral bands and resolution about 80 m, plus the Thematic Mapper, an advanced scanner with six bands in the visible and near infrared with resolution about 30 m, and one in the thermal infrared with resolution of 120 m.

There have been steadily improving sensor capabilities; earth observation data are now available from the U.S. NOAA-10, 11 and Landsat-5, the French SPOT-1 (and SPOT-2, launched in February 1990), and the Japanese MOS-1 (and MOS-1B, launched in February 1990). The sensors carried on these platforms can be used for monitoring global change.In addition to the satellite sensors, airborne sensors currently available for earth observation in Canada include the microwave STAR/IRIS imaging radars and the research Convair-580 facility synthetic which carries aperture radar (SAR) and scatterometer systems. Airborne electro-optical systems available for commercial use include the linear array imager, MEIS, multi-spectral scanners, the Fluorescence Line Imager and the CASI imaging spectrometers, the active laser systems, LARSEN, and the laser fluorosensor.

Advances in Remote Sensors - Canadian Example

Canada has been active in some specific areas of sensor development and has gained world recognition and experience in certain hardware developments and related data processing and analysis systems and methodologies. Some examples will be discussed in detail, to illustrate the capabilities and potential role of Canadian developed sensors for management of renewable and non-renewable resources, and for monitoring global change. The list of sensors is by no means exhaustive, and does not include Canadian systems used for monitoring atmospheric constituents nor those developed primarily for ground-based use.

Linear Array Imagers

The development of linear array detectors led to a marked improvement in performance of the multispectral imager. The major advantage of the multi-element array imager compared to the opto-mechanical scanner is its increased sensitivity, the increase in detector number allowing much longer integration times with the associated higher signal-to-noise ratios.

The linear array is oriented perpendicular to the direction of sensor motion (i.e. perpendicular to the aircraft motion or to the satellite orbit), so that each element of the array images one pixel per swath on the ground. Image data in one dimension is obtained by simultaneous sampling of the response of each detector along the array. Successive lines forming two-dimensional coverage are obtained by repeated sampling of the array as the sensor moves over the earth. Each detector element is able to integrate the signal over one pixel for the complete sample/scan period, rather than for a fraction of the period. In the case of the multispectral scanner, with a rotating mirror to sweep the field-of-view of a few detectors across the scene, the signal from one pixel is integrated for a fraction of the scan period so the responsivity is lower.

One of the first prototype linear array imagers was the airborne MEIS I (1978) which used a 512-element reticon array. This system was developed for the Canada Centre for Remote Sensing (CCRS) by MacDonald-Dettwiler Ltd. (MDA) of Richmond, B.C. The MEIS II (1982) utilized a 1728-element charge coupled device silicon array (Fairchild 122) and was the first airborne "pushbroom imager" to be used operationally. It provides fore-aft stereo acquisition and spectral response from 450 nm to 1100 nm, and combines high radiometric sensitivity with geometric fidelity (Neville et al 1983; Till et al., 1986; Till et al., 1987). This has led to new capabilities in, for example, forest inventory mapping, forest damage assessment and water quality (Ahern and Leckie, 1987; Gibson et al., 1987; Strome, et al., 1990). It is now operated commercially by Innotech Aviation of Montreal (Till, 1987). The first pushbroom imager to be tested in space was the German MOMS (Modular Optoelectronic Multispectral Scanner) during a 1983 Space Shuttle Mission. This was followed in 1986 by the launch of the French SPOT-1 satellite, which carries two identical high resolution visible imagers, each unit operating as either a three-band spectral imager with 20 m resolution or as a single panchromatic imager with 10 m resolution (CNES, 1988).

Linear array silicon charge coupled devices are now widely available, and offer a range of detector element sizes and lengths. While the majority have been of U.S. manufacture, advances in ultra-violet and blue responses and in dynamic range have been made, for example, in Canada (Dalsa, 1989). However, the lack of availability of suitable detector arrays with response in the infrared regions has limited these imagers to visible and near infrared regions, although this is likely to change in the near future. With the advent of much longer silicon arrays with suitable characteristics for remote sensing (e.g. Fairchild 191 with 6000 elements), the linear array imager is also moving into the commercial airborne arena as an effective replacement for film-based aerial survey mapping technology. A prototype system WHiRL (Wide angle High Resolution Line Imager) has already been flown in Canada by CCRS, and a joint Canadian industry-government initiative is underway to develop a commercial fully digital airborne information system based on MEIS technology to provide digital mapping and forestry products (Neville and Till, 1989). Compared to the satellite linear array imagers, the airborne version can offer higher spatial resolution and mapping precision plus improved spectral sensitivity which allows better target discrimination. This is of value for specific global change applications such as forest change detection. In addition, airborne systems can offer a speedy and flexible response for emergency environmental monitoring. Canada enjoys a leadership role in the aerial survey industry, in the new digital imager technology, and in the associated data processing and image interpretation.

Imaging Spectrometers

The linear array imager offers geometric fidelity and radiometric sensitivity, plus digital output compatible with the resource digital data bases that are increasingly being used. However, the spectral information essential for thematic interpretation is limited to that in a few pre-selected spectral bands. By using a two-dimensional array detector in place of the linear array, and by combining it with a dispersive optical system such as a diffraction grating, both spatial and contiguous spectral information can be obtained; the across-track spatial information falls along one dimension of the array and the spectral information along the second dimension. This then allows output of the complete spectrum or the ready selection of pre-determined spectral bands. While imaging spectrometers, such as HIRIS (NASA) and MERIS (ESA) are planned for future polar platforms, current systems are designed for airborne use. Canada again has expertise in this area, through the development of the airborne Fluorescence Line Imager, FLI, (Borstad et al, 1985) and the Compact Airborne Spectrographic Imager, CASI (Babey and Anger, 1989). The FLI was developed for ocean applications by the Department of Fisheries and Oceans, with prime contractor Moniteq Ltd. of Ontario. It uses five silicon diode arrays, each with 385 elements by 288 elements. This provides a field-of-view of about 70^0 with 1925 detector elements across track, and a spectral response in the visible. It generally operates in one of two modes, either as a pushbroom imager with eight spectral bands, or as a lower spatial resolution imager with 288 spectral channels output. As the large number of detectors leads to a large increase in data and data rate, so data processing and interpretation methods have been developed to make effective use of the system.

The CASI was developed by ITRES Research Ltd. in Alberta, with support from the National Research Council of Canada, and is a compact airborne system, with a field-of-view of 15^0 (selectable) and spectral response from about 400 to 800 nm. It uses a single two dimensional array of 578 elements by 288 elements.

Active Laser Sensors

In 1985, Canadian hydrographers became the first to use airborne laser scanning techniques for chart making purposes, when the LARSEN system (developed under contract by Optech Inc.) was used to locate and survey shipping channels through parts of the Northwest Passage in the Canadian Arctic (Casey and Vosburgh, 1986). Other surveys have since been carried out by Terra Surveys Ltd. using LARSEN off the East and west coasts of Canada and along the St. Lawrence. It uses an optical radar (lidar) technique to measure water depths of up to 40 m in clear coastal water with an accuracy of about 0.3 m. The system generates a uniform sounding grid pattern, and covers a swath of 270 m width, with soundings spaced about 30 m apart and positioning accuracy about 15 m. While the system is primarily designed for coastal mapping, it could provide information about water quality and pollution.The airborne laser fluorosensor is a similar pulsed laser system, but by inducing fluorescence it is designed to detect and monitor marine pollution such as oilspills. It was one of the remote sensing systems tested in the Arctic Marine Oilspill Program of the Department of Environment in 1978 (O'Neil et al., 1983) and has been operated commercially by Barringer Research Ltd. of Toronto, Ontario. Further development optimized for operational monitoring of the Canadian offshore and Arctic is currently being supported by the Departments of Environment, and Fisheries and Oceans.

Microwave Remote Sensing

Within Canada, the potential advantages of microwave remote sensing for resource management and environmental monitoring of the country were well recognized, and led to policy decisions in the 1970s to develop expertise in this area. These decisions included the development of the CCRS airborne SAR system as a research facility and the proposal to develop a radar satellite. The CCRS airborne SAR evolved from the upgrade and development of a SAR system purchased from the United States to a new generation, fully digital SAR developed for CCRS by Canadian industry. Related airborne systems are now commercially available in Canada and operated by Canadian companies.

The research program at the Canada Centre for Remote Sensing has been evaluating the use of spaceborne and airborne synthetic aperture radars to fulfill Canadian remote sensing requirements and has been developing data processing, analysis and interpretation methodologies for microwave applications. Sensor development in close cooperation with industry and user agencies has helped develop expertise in radar design, radar data processing and in the understanding of radar signatures of terrestrial targets. In the development of spaceborne SAR, Canada is amongst the leaders, with RADARSAT scheduled for launch in 1994.

Radar Satellites

A major impetus for the development of microwave remote sensing was the launch by the U.S. of Seasat-A in 1978. During its 98 days of operation, the Seasat-SAR acquired images at L-Band covering approximately 100 million square miles, and revealed information about oceans, ice and atmospheric phenomena. At a nominal look angle of 20.5⁰ from nadir, the swath width was 100 km with a resolution of about 25 m by 25 m at 4 looks. Canada operated one of the five stations able to receive SAR data, and developed SAR processors and image processing capabilities.

Through its membership status in the European Space Agency, Canada has participated in the development of the ERS-1 satellite launched in 1991 (Duchossois, 1986). Participation has included some contract work by Canadian industry plus membership of the technical review teams. The payload includes the Active Microwave Instrument (AMI) capable of operating as a SAR or a wind scatterometer. Other sensors include a radar altimeter, an along-track scanning radiometer and microwave sounder, and precise range and range rate equipment. The AMI has three basic operating modes, imaging, wind and wave. In the imaging mode, the C-Band SAR (VV polarization) will obtain imagery with a swath width of about 100 km, resolution of 30 m (3 to 4 looks), and a 23⁰ incidence angle at mid-swath. In the wave mode, the SAR will image regularly spaced sample areas within the swath to be transformed into directional spectra. The wind mode uses a scatterometer to obtain information about the wind at the ocean surface, with a spatial resolution of about 50 km and a swath width of 500 km. Canada will be receiving ERS-1 data through the Gatineau station in Quebec.

Airborne SAR

Of the airborne radar systems available, the Canadian STAR imaging radar, has been flown commercially in over 20 countries by Intera Technologies of Calgary, Alberta, for applications such as ice monitoring (Mercer and Kirby, 1987).

The airborne STAR-1 system is an X-Band (HH polarization) SAR. Its ground swath width can be either 25 km with about 6 m resolution or 50 km with 12 m range resolution and 6 m azimuth resolution. It features real-time digital processing and is a compact system designed to allow mounting in a small aircraft. A version incorporating the Integrated

Radar Imaging System (IRIS) developed by MDA is now in operation in the Intera Canadair Challenger aircraft, providing ice monitoring on a routine basis.

The CCRS airborne C/X-Band SAR is the primary sensor in the Convair-580 radar research facility, and was developed under contract by MDA. It is a fully digital dual-polarized SAR, with digital motion compensation, real-time processed image data and signal data. It operates in one of three modes, nadir, narrow or wide, with swath widths of 16 km, 23 km or 60 km, and resolution of 6 m. Outputs include quick look hard copy, digital image data, and digital signal data (Livingston et al, 1987). Continuing developments include implementation of polarimetric and interferometric modes. The research and development has helped foster expertise in Canadian industry through contracts in the areas of, for example, SAR design (MDA), antenna design (COMDEV Ltd.), scatterometer development (MPB Ltd.), digital SAR processing (MDA), and image analysis, etc. The Convair-580 has proven to be a unique facility and is now the major vehicle for the Canadian Radar Data Development Program in preparation, through application and product development, for radar satellites such as ERS-1 and RADARSAT.

While the emphasis in recent years has been on active radar systems, passive microwave radiometric measurements are used for ice mapping (using imaging devices) or atmospheric sounding (using profiling systems).

CURRENT SPACE SENSOR TECHNOLOGY

Recent Canadian experience in space-borne sensors is illustrated by two major programs which demonstrate both the political-scientific-technology interaction as well as the benefits of international cooperation in global change science. They illustrate, too, several other important facts of life for the Canadian remote sensing community: it takes a long time to get from concept to program to launch, and costs a lot of money along the way. The need to remain within politically acceptable budgets over a long gestation period is probably the key driver in the ultimate success of a project. It is also a key driver in the ultimate success of new programs which evolve out of earlier ones.

The RADARSAT program has its roots going back to 1975 when the first concepts evolved with the important series of airborne instruments developed by the Canada Centre for Remote Sensing, discussed briefly in the preceding section. These early experiments and developments will, after 19 years, bear fruit in the launch of the RADARSAT SAR payload in 1994 at a cost of close to $500 million.

An example of a complex space science instrument, the WINDII instrument built by Canadian Astronautics Ltd. was delivered in December 1989 for integration onto NASA's Upper Atmosphere Research Satellite (UARS). UARS was launched in September 1991, and the WINDII instrument has been returning good data. WINDII will be used to study upper atmospheric winds and temperatures.

The RADARSAT SAR Payload

The RADARSAT program, planned to commence operations in 1994 with the launch of Canada's first earth observation satellite, is one of the most significant developments in sensor technology. The satellite is currently being developed by a Canadian team led by Spar Aerospace Ltd., under contract to the Canadian Space Agency. The Synthetic Aperture Radar payload is one of a number of SAR systems (by NASA, the European Space Agency and Japan) due for launch in the 1990s. Originally conceived as an instrument for assisting vessels to navigate ice-choked northern waters, parallel developments over the past decade have increased the utility of the instrument's data in measuring a wide range of parameters of particular interest to Canadian researchers in the fields of glaciology, hydrology, vegetation science, oceanography, and geology.

Glaciological phenomena are, of course, of more than passing interest to Canadians. In the context of global change, the interactions between the ice caps and the world's ocean and atmospheric circulations are crucial in understanding how climate is changing. SAR's capability of mapping in fine detail under all weather conditions such important glaciological parameters as ice edge, ice thickness, floe sizes and ice motion makes it the instrument of choice in glaciological studies. Providing imagery to resolutions as fine as 10 metres, the RADARSAT satellite will provide a unique international service in polar monitoring. With its 10 metre resolution, SAR can provide fine-scale data related to soil moisture, vegetation moisture and surface water areas, important inputs to the hydrologic cycle and its interactions with atmospheric circulation and global climate. The vegetation backscatter of SAR signals, because of the influence of moisture on reflectivity, can provide useful information on vegetation canopies and their water content, another important input parameter to the hydrologic cycle.

The RADARSAT SAR can also measure detailed ocean surface conditions, leading to better understanding of oceanic circulation, one of the major concerns in global change.

Finally, SAR plays an important role in the understanding of global surface features and the role played by plate tectonics. RADARSAT is a joint program of the Canadian Federal and Provincial governments together with the private sector and two United States agencies (NASA and NOAA) (Ahmed et al, 1989). The direct involvement of Provincial governments is a new initiative in Canadian space programs and reflects Canadian political and economic realities. Due for launch in 1995, with an expected lifetime of 5 years, the satellite will be injected into a 99° inclination circular, sun-synchronous orbit with an altitude of 798 km. This dawn-dusk equator crossing orbit will give a 24-day repeat cycle with 3-day and 7-day subcycles. Three North American ground stations, two in Canada, at Gatineau, Quebec, and Prince Albert, Saskatchewan, and one at Fairbanks, Alaska in the United States, are planned for initial operation. It is anticipated that other countries will seek readout licenses and install an eventual global network of ground stations to receive the data.

As RADARSAT travels along its orbital track , its deployed 15 m x 1.5 m slotted waveguide antenna will be able to operate in one of a number of modes. It will be possible to reconfigure the antenna by means of a complex electronically-switched beam-forming network to change both the antenna beam shape and pointing across-track. Using horizontally (along-track) polarized 5.3 GHz signals, the SAR antenna beams are designed to be selectable within a 500 km wide swath, between 20⁰ and 50⁰ away from nadir. In addition, experimental coverage is possible between 50⁰ and 60⁰. Each of the five modes (plus one experimental), has an associated resolution. The salient parameters of the spacecraft are as given in Chapter Thirteen.

The payload with its electronics portion located in the central structure and in the large deployed 15 m x 1.5 m slotted waveguide antenna, consists of the SAR, its associated payload computer and a high data rate subsystem comprising 85 Mbps tape recorders and a two-channel (105 Mbps for real-time data) X-Band downlink. The system is designed for autonomous operation when out of sight of ground stations. This and the reconfigurability of the antenna provide substantial operational versatility with an ability to select from the modes shown in Table 13.2 (Chapter 13) with a wide variety of resolutions, swath widths, and incidence angles. It is this versatility which distinguishes RADARSAT from the other SAR spacecraft in various stages of development in the Soviet Union, Europe, Japan or the United States.

WINDII - Wind Imaging Interferometer

WINDII, or Wind Imaging Interferometer, is the largest and most complex single space science instrument built in Canada. WINDII observes the Doppler shifts and temperature-widening of selected optical emissions generated by natural phenomena such as airglow and the aurora. The instrument was developed for the Canadian Space Agency (CSA) by Canadian Astronautics Ltd. as principal subcontractor. The instrument is the result of international cooperation between the U.S. (NASA), France (CNES) and the CSA in response to an Announcement of Opportunity from NASA for instruments to fly on the Upper Atmosphere Research Satellite (UARS). The scientific planning has been carried out by a team of scientists from Canada, France and the U.S. (Shepherd et al., 1985). Key technical features are listed in Table 15.1. The instrument is depicted in Figure 15.1.

WINDII is a complex spaceborne instrument using advanced techniques and typifies what can be achieved in Canadian sensor programs. Its utility to a global change sensor program lies in its inclusion on the

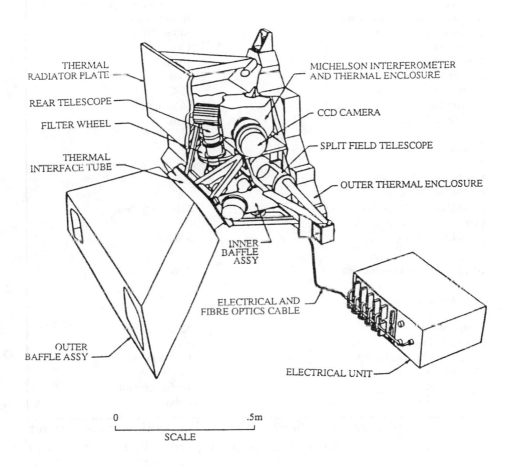

THERMAL RADIATOR PLATE

MICHELSON INTERFEROMETER AND THERMAL ENCLOSURE

REAR TELESCOPE

FILTER WHEEL

CCD CAMERA

THERMAL INTERFACE TUBE

SPLIT FIELD TELESCOPE

OUTER THERMAL ENCLOSURE

INNER BAFFLE ASSY

ELECTRICAL AND FIBRE OPTICS CABLE

OUTER BAFFLE ASSY

ELECTRICAL UNIT

0   .5m
SCALE

Figure 15.1: The WINDII Instrument

TABLE 15.1

KEY TECHNICAL FEATURES OF WINDII

Instrument Features

Fields of view	4 x 6° (2 orthogonal directions)
Altitude Range of Measurement	70 to 315 km
Spectral Range	540 to 770 nm
Spatial Resolution	1 km
Velocity Resolution	10 m/s
Detection Threshold	1 kR
Temperature Resolution	25K
Design Life	36 months
Radiation Hardening	>10k rad

Optical Features

Michelson Field of View	10°
Michelson Transmission	0.47
Michelson Resolving Power	7x104 at 630nm
Scan Mirror Resolution	0.2 nm
Scan Mirror Range	800 nm
Stray Light Attenuation	10^{-5}
Imaging Optics Transmission	0.36

Operating Features

Image Memory	32 kbytes
Exposure Time	0.128 to 512 sec
CCD Binning (Horiz. & Vert.)	1 to 32 pixels
Windowing	2/field of view
Dynamic Range	4096 counts full
Telemetry Rate	2 kbits/sec

UARS polar platform, a satellite launched in late 1991 to investigate the composition of the upper layers of the atmosphere. The measurement of ozone depletion will be one of the principal roles of UARS. To achieve the scientific objectives, as well as to satisfy NASA's mass, volume, and power requirements, an innovative, compact, low-power optical instrument operating in the visible to near-IR wavelength range has been developed. WINDII was designed to view two orthogonal 4 x 6° fields-of-view of the atmospheric limb; at 45° and at 135° with respect to the UARS velocity vector. Referring to Figure 15.1, collimated atmospheric light from the two look angles of the instrument is combined and relayed by a front end, dual port refractive telescope onto a filter wheel. The desired optical emission line is isolated by an interference filter after which the filtered light is relayed by another refractive telescope to a scanning Michelson Interferometer. The resulting interferogram is imaged onto a CCD camera and the optical path difference is varied over one fringe by the scanning motion of the interferometer. The sampled data is subsequently downlinked to the ground for further processing. Frequent calibration of the instrument is carried out during flight through the use of an on-board calibration system.

Although WINDII was designed for a specific scientific application, the instrument design concepts can be readily used for other scientific applications. WINDII is a novel, compact and complicated instrument. The engineering expertise gained in optical testing and opto-mechanical engineering during the course of this project augmented an already strong Canadian expertise in electro-optics and optical system design. This expertise gives Canada a strong pool of experience from which to draw upon in the development of other space and non-space optical instruments.

FUTURE EARTH OBSERVATION MISSIONS

An encouraging sign for the success of global change monitoring is the number of approved and planned earth observation programs. These include, for example, Japanese satellite missions (e.g. JERS-1, ADEOS), the SPOT-series, NASA earth science missions such as UARS and the Indian IRS series, to name a few. A major international program to monitor and understand the entire Earth as a system and on a global scale is the Earth Observing System (Eos) program, with polar platforms planned from U.S.A., ESA and Japan. The sensors proposed include microwave and optical imaging sensors, meteorological sensors, atmospheric sounders, etc. The instruments to be flown fall into two categories, core instruments and those resulting from announcements of opportunity. Canada's role in this program could include a small share in specific areas of sensor development (as has happened, for example, in the Earth Observation Preparatory Program of ESA where Canadian industry has received contracts related to SAR, imaging spectrometry, and imaging microwave radiometry). As well, Canadian scientists could be principal investigators on specific payload sensors such as, for example, MOPITT, a gas correlation spectrometer for monitoring pollution in the troposphere.

The use of "litesats" as platforms for short duration missions carrying low-cost sensors is another area receiving attention. Low cost monitors such as millimeter wave chlorine monoxide radiometers or space-qualified variants of the pushbroom MEIS instruments could provide useful data for specific highly focussed research projects. Other possible instruments include high resolution spectrometers. Another is the proposed international SeaWifs (Sea-viewing, Wide Field-of-View Sensor) project which could provide ocean-colour data, useful to the Canadian fishing industry, and hence potentially profitable. The number and variety of earth observation sensors has been severely limited in the past few years by budgetary constraints. The option of selecting individual parts of foreign instruments which match Canadian dollar contributions is being followed in a number of cases, but this policy may turn out to be short-sighted since the loss of system expertise in hardware design will eventually lead to a loss of scientific expertise. The loss of both industrial and scientific expertise will inevitably lead to a marginal role for Canadian investigators in global change. The urgent need for increased funding into future sensor programs is of great importance to the future of remote sensing and the understanding of global change in Canada.

RECOMMENDATIONS

While Canada has sensor expertise and credibility in specific areas, such as multispectral array imagers, synthetic aperture radar, and passive microwave sensors, a sensor development program should be encouraged to build on this expertise and to put Canadian industry in a position to respond to proposals and opportunities for spaceborne sensors. The objectives of such an earth observation instrument development program should tie in closely with the global change program, and would be directed to make Canadian contributions to the monitoring of global change developments in polar and near-polar regions The program should also encourage instrument innovation and development in Canada, and continue the promotion and development of the sensors to which Canada has already paid specific attention. Near-term possibilities could include an advanced SAR (to follow the RADARSAT), optical imagers, both pushbroom and spectrometers, and imaging passive microwave radiometers. For Canada to compete on an international level, and/or to develop powerful innovative sensors specific to Canadian needs, close cooperation between government, industry and university is required. The objectives in general would be designed to open up opportunities for Canadians to develop new instruments and related technology and use them scientifically, operationally and commercially.

It is important to recognize the advantages of Canadian sensor programs in the closing decade of the twentieth century. At moderate cost, the implementation of a sensor development program provides the opportunity for widely spread regional inputs into the building of these instruments. With direct links into the university sector, working in new and unfolding fields of earth and atmospheric science, these instruments provide a focus for the training of new graduates. Because the instrument costs are relatively modest (in terms of "big" science), and can be handled by smaller science-based companies, the linkage from the universities and their science to knowledge-based industries and their technology is efficient and rapid. The establishment of new companies to handle local sensor needs (e.g. oceans in the Maritimes, forestry on the west coast and in Alberta) could provide for regional distribution of the benefits. The development of user companies to acquire and market data is also an encouraging development, since the risk seed money from government in starting sensor programs is necessarily limited.

With the evidence of global warming now increasing, the need for a focussed program of sensor development is becoming increasingly urgent. To meet these objectives requires an ongoing funded program, comprising a large number of broadly based phase A studies open to all, providing conceptual design and data requirements; a number of phase B projects that would be good candidates for flight opportunities, and could include airborne prototypes; and a few phase C/D projects with specific mission objectives. Each phase A study could be at the $200 K level, phase B projects could be about $2 M in scope, with the phase C/D projects at the $15 - 20 M level or more. Such a program would allow Canada to build on its current expertise in state-of-the-art sensors and would ensure it a role in future missions critical to the understanding of global change. Canadian expenditures on scientific space programs currently run at about $17 M per year. These programs, which at present rely on cooperative international ventures, provide opportunities for Canadian investigators in widely separated fields, from spaceborne astronomy to global change tropospheric measurements from space, for example. With the creation of the Canadian Space Agency, the time is now ripe for a coordinated and expanded program of sensor development addressing global change concerns.

The principal recommendation of this chapter is for at least a doubling of current expenditures on space science, and a commensurate increase in remote sensing expenditures.In the longer term, the continuing development of the science and technology of sensors and their data will expose a need for more ambitious programs. The economies of low-cost satellites using low-cost launch systems may well revolutionize remote sensing and allow a greater variety of national and international programs.

CHAPTER 16

INFORMATION MANAGEMENT FOR THE CANADIAN GLOBAL CHANGE PROGRAM

M. Strome and D. Goodenough

INTRODUCTION

Crucial to the success of the Canadian Global Change Program is an Information Management System which will be able to store and retrieve information acquired by remote sensing and *in situ* measurements, and to use the information effectively to gain a better understanding of the forces which play a role in changing our environment. The system must help scientists to integrate reliable, large-scale data sets of geophysical and biological measurements made from remotely sensed data, such as that from RADARSAT (Strome, et al., 1984; Shaw, et al., 1984; Strome, et al., 1985), ERS-1, JERS-1 and the Earth Observing System (Eos). It will be crucial to interact, on a multidisciplinary basis, with other investigators in earth system science. Current progress in the use of remote sensing for science is hampered by the need for scientists to understand, in detail, the instruments, the electromagnetic properties of the surface, and a wide variety of data tape formats coupled with the inadequacy of some to the techniques for estimating geophysical and biological variables from remotely sensed data. These shortcomings must be overcome if remote sensing data are to be used effectively by a substantial number of scientists studying environmental change at global and national scales.

The Canadian Global Change Program is focusing on areas of particular Canadian concern and/or on topics where Canada can best contribute to the understanding of specific components of the global program. Thus, because of our geographical location and the specific capabilities of our scientific community, five priority areas have been identified: boreal forest; prairie ecosystem; Montane areas; ocean processes; and the arctic and sub-arctic.

The Canadian Global Change Program is closely related to larger, global programs such as the International Geosphere-Biosphere Programme (IGBP) and the International Space Year (ISY) whose theme is "Mission to Planet Earth" (NASA, 1986). Canadian scientists are also acting as Principal Investigators in the NASA Eos Program.

In its Canadian Global Change Program Report No. 3, "Contributions of Satellite Observations to the Canadian Global Change Program, the Royal Society of Canada (1989) presented five key recommendations:

- ensure access to space observations needed for the Canadian Global Change Program through reception, archiving, and affordable cost policy;

- incorporate global change as a mission objective for the Canadian RADARSAT Program;

- develop data handling technologies including global change network (GCNet), advanced workstation (GCNode), on-line catalogues and on-line data delivery;

- develop inversion algorithms for the extraction of quantitative information from satellite observations; and,

- coordinate Canadian plans with the plans of other countries and international agencies to facilitate studying the Earth as one system.

Canada has extensive, high quality experience in the areas of acquiring, processing and analyzing the data from remote sensing instruments from both space and aircraft. Canada has acquired, processed and analyzed data from most polar orbiting satellites since the beginning of the U.S. programs (Strome and Shaw, 1972; Strome, 1972a,b; Strome, 1973; Strome, 1983). Canada was the first country outside the U.S. to receive, process and distribute LANDSAT data. Canada has built and maintained facilities to receive and process data from most of the major remote sensing satellites, such as LANDSAT, SPOT, SEASAT and MOS-1. Some of the major innovations in processing of satellite image data have originated in Canada including: quick-look output products; World Reference System for cataloging satellite imagery; geocoded satellite image products; and digital processing of SAR satellite data. Plans are well advanced for facilities to receive, process and analyze data from ERS-1 and RADARSAT. Thus, it is safe to assume that, for data acquired in Canada, adequate facilities will be available for reception, processing and distribution. **Unfortunately, current NASA plans to not include direct read-out capability for the Eos system.**

The major focus of this paper will be the requirements for information handling downstream from the reception and initial processing of the data.

INVOLVEMENT OF CANADIAN SCIENTISTS

The integration of data sets from various sources and their use to provide reliable geophysical and biological information on large regional and global scales will pose a difficult challenge for the scientific community in Canada and throughout the world. The need for better integration of data sets has been recognized for at least 15 years (Strome et al., 1979; Strome and Grush, 1985; Strome and Billingsley, 1986). A CGCP Information Management System can only be successful if scientists working on the problems have a strong role in its development and gain a sense of ownership in the success. It is especially important that competent scientists are not "excluded" from access to the data and information.

Canada has a good "track-record" for enabling scientists to participate to the maximum extent possible in major remote sensing programs. Generally, we are able to have a few key scientists designated as "Principal Investigators" (PIs) on major international programs. Our practice has been to allow any interested scientists to then participate to the extent they wish (although they must find their own funding, as a rule). This approach helps to maximize the Canadian participation and the sense of "owning" a part of the results.

To make data, information and models available to the Canadian scientific community, it will be important to define format and documentation standards that are easy to understand and to use. Small volumes of data (e.g., software, models and reports) should be available through electronic communication networks, hard copy and magnetic and optical media. High volume data (such as images) are most cost-effectively distributed via magnetic and optical media. As stated in the Royal Society of Canada recommendations, the data should be "affordable".

CGCP SCIENCE OBJECTIVES

Goals to be achieved by 1996 (the scheduled launch of the first NASA Eos) include:

- complete the development of procedures, models, and data handling systems which are required to use satellite data for: a) detecting global changes over Canadian territory with emphasis on the boreal forest, grasslands, agricultural regions, the coastal zone, and the atmosphere; b) assessing the magnitude of the changes; and c) determining the current and future impact of the changes;

- develop next-generation satellite data processing and modeling technology with emphasis on the integration of image analysis, geographic information systems, and digital telecommunication networks; and,

- contribute to the definition, development, and implementation of international satellite observation programs for global change studies.

The science questions being addressed the CGCP are not significantly different than those being examined by Eos (NASA, 1986; NASA,

1989), which include: How does the earth function as an integrated system? At what rate is it changing? How are the changes being forced? What is the variability? Can the effects of human activities on the Earth system be unambiguously detected? Can the cumulative effects of human activity be predicted decades or centuries in advance? Can local manifestations that accompany global change be detected and predicted? The objective of the U.S. Global Change Research Program is: to monitor, understand and ultimately predict global change, both natural phenomena and the effects of human activity. Eos activities include monitoring and quantitative modeling. The tools include conceptual models, process models and comprehensive system models.

We can apply many of the concepts of the Eos Data and Information System (EosDIS) (NASA, 1989; NASA, 1990) as well as those of the International Geosphere-Biosphere Programme (IGBP) Working Group (ICSU, 1990) to help develop the requirements for the CGCP Information System.

EOS DATA AND INFORMATION SYSTEM

The key functional objectives of EosDIS are to provide the following (NASA, 1990):

- command and control of NASA polar platforms;

- Eos instrument command and control;

- processing and reprocessing of Eos data;

- networking capabilities;

- transfer of data to permanent archives; and,

- exchange of data, commands, algorithms, etc. with NOAA, ESA, Japan, Canada and possibly others.

The overall design of the EosDIS is being studied by two industrial teams with the active involvement of the EosDIS Science Advisory Panel. The key principles guiding the development are:

- EosDIS must serve a broadly distributed Earth Science Community;

- the system must be designed to evolve continuously in capacity;

- the processing, distribution and archival functions of EosDIS must be openly accessible to the research community; and,

- the command and control of Eos Space Measurement System (EosSMS) must be secure and highly reliable.

Data Processing Level - Definitions

For a better understanding of the type of data processing and information handling required, several processing "levels" have been defined for the Eos program. These are:

Level 0 - reconstructed unprocessed instrument data at full resolution; this is the form in which the data are transmitted from the satellite;

Level 1A -rReconstructed unprocessed instrument data at full resolution, time referenced and annotated with ancillary information, including radiometric and geometric calibration coefficients and georeferencing parameters such as platform ephemeris computed and appended but not applied to Level 0 data;

Level 1B - Level 1A data processed to sensor units, such as radar backscatter cross section, brightness temperature, etc.;

Level 2 - derived environmental variables such as ocean wave height, soil moisture, etc. at the same resolution and location as Level 1 data;

Level 3 -variables mapped on uniform space-time grid scales, usually with some completeness and consistency properties, such as interpolation for missing points, and complete mosaics for regions from multiple orbits; and,

Level 4 - model output or results from analyses of lower level data, i.e. variables not measured by the instruments but derived from them.

EosDIS Architecture

The EosDIS consists of several types of elements, many of which are redundant. Those related to the operation and control of the satellites and sensors include: Eos Mission Operations Center (EMOC); Customer Data and Operations System (CDOS); Tracking and Data Relay Satellite System (TDRSS); Instrument Control Center (ICC); and Instrument Support Terminals (ISTs). These elements will not be required in Canada, although some of the functionality of these will be incorporated into the RADARSAT command, control and data processing and distribution facilities.

Processing of Eos data, product generation, archiving and distribution are handled by several different elements in the EosDIS. These are described briefly below.

Institutional Data Product Generation Facilities (IDPGFs) perform the data processing functions to routinely produce standard and quick-look products, metadata and browse data sets.

Data Archive and Distribution System (DADS) archives and distributes Eos data and information via networks or high density storage media (such as optical disk) to Eos scientists, other Eos facilities and other research users. This includes data and products, metadata, command histories, algorithms, documentation, procedures for requesting special observations, simulation tools and system management data.

Active Archive Center (AAC) (also called Remote AAC or RAAC) processes, archives and distributes Eos data and products and contains functional elements which include both an IDPGF and a DADS. These may typically be managed and funded jointly by NASA and other non-NASA agencies for the duration of the Eos mission.

Permanent Archives will receive data and information from the AACs for permanent archiving to provide long term access beyond the scope of the Eos Mission. Such permanent archives are being planned for the United States Geological Survey (USGS) Earth Resources Observation System (EROS) Data Center (EDC) and the National Oceanic and Atmospheric Administration (NOAA) National Environmental Satellite, Data and Information Service (NESDIS) data centers.

Scientific Computing Facilities (SCFs) are computing facilities supplied to scientists at Team Member, Principal Investigator (PI) and Instrument Investigator Computing Facilities for development and maintenance of algorithms and software for generation of standard products, quality control of products, data set validation, in-flight calibration, scientific analysis, modelling research, generation of specialized data products, instrument operations planning and interface to scientists' institutional facilities.

Networks are the electronic means for distributing Eos data and information to all the nodes within the system and to the scientific research community at large, including international partners. Standard network protocols and widely used scientific networks will be used to the maximum extent possible. Audio-visual links may be incorporated into the network.

Field Support Terminals (FSTs) will provide mobile communication to field campaigns to coordinate platform data acquisition with field experiments and will have display facilities as required to support field experiment needs.

Eos Investigator Data System Responsibilities

The Eos Investigator is responsible for: the development of algorithms; development of specifications for standard products; development of requirements for scientific computing facilities; delivery of specialized products and algorithms for archiving; providing ongoing scientific quality control for standard products; providing up-to-date instrument calibration data on an ongoing basis; managing the collection and processing of correlative data required to calibrate or validate the data products; and, participating in the mission planning and scheduling and instrument operations.

System Management

An EosDIS standards office will work with EOS investigators and the EosDIS Scientific Advisory Panel to identify and develop standards for data structures, data formats, software code and documentation. Such standards will be essential so that interdisciplinary investigators can assimilate data from several instruments in the course of their investigations, and to permit the operation of algorithms on different computer elements within the EosDIS environment.

It is recognized that the EosDIS will have to evolve through a series of prototypes which will provide early functional elements to be used and evaluated by scientists using pre-Eos data. Overall system management will be the responsibility of NASA.

Eos Data Policy

The EosDIS data policy is designed to further the Eos objectives of acquiring a comprehensive, global, 15-year data set; maximize the utility for scientific purposes; and simplify long-term access to, and analysis of, Eos data. The key elements of the policy are:

- Eos data and products will be available to all users;

- there will be a nominal charge for data requested for research purposes which is consistent with actual marginal costs of filling the request;

- EosDIS will provide the capability for archiving and making available all science data products, models, algorithms and documentation at the cost of reproduction and distribution;

- all products derived from information so provided must be made available to the research community (refereed articles, models, algorithms and associated documentation); and,

- EosDIS will provide information about the data such as quality assessments, supporting literature references and catalogue and directory entries.

There are three categories of users who may access EOS data: Research Users; Operational Agency Users; and Other Users.

Research Users are those who agree to pay the nominal incremental cost to the Eos project of reproducing and delivering data requested, and who sign a "research agreement" stating that they will publish the results of their research in the open literature. They will make their detailed research results available, including data, algorithms and models, at the time their research is accepted for publication. The data are for the researcher's use for bona fide research purposes only, and the data may be copied and shared among other researchers provided that they are covered by a research agreement or the researcher who obtained the data from EosDIS is willing to take the responsibility for their compliance with the agreement.

Since Canada is an Eos-participating country, its research users will have the same access as those from the United States, including those whose investigations are funded by the NASA Eos Program.

Operational Agency Users are such organizations as NOAA and EUMETSAT. They may provide their own direct read-out, processing and archiving facilities.

Other Users (primarily commercial) will be able to access the data through a procedure consistent with the Land Remote Sensing Commercialization Act (or other suitable statutes) for commercial distribution on a non-discriminatory basis to other users. This procedure has not been developed.

Data Handling Requirements

The data rate for an Eos platform will be up to 300 Mbps. The average data rate is expected to be 70 Mbps, with a total volume of about 10^{12} bytes or one terabyte per day. The highest data volume system now in operation is LANDSAT. Each receiving and processing system is required to handle at most 10^{10} bytes or 10 gigabytes per day, a full two orders of magnitude less. Current plans are to have all data processed to Level 1 by a single facility in the United States, although Canada and NOAA have both proposed that direct X-band readout be made available.

Experience with LANDSAT, SPOT and SEASAT has demonstrated the difficulty of processing high volumes of data quickly. Much of the data will be required in near real-time for many of the field experiments. Quick-look data sets must be processed within the period of one orbit, and should be compressed to a form which can be transmitted efficiently at 9,600 bps over standard communication links. Image and graphic information should be capable of being displayed on readily available display terminals (such as a PC with a colour VGA display).

Little information is available on the actual system designs being proposed by the industrial teams studying the problem.

CANADIAN REQUIREMENTS

To meet the CGCP objectives, it will be necessary to access a variety of satellite data, some of which will be received and archived in Canada while some will be available from other countries.

RADARSAT is of special concern to Canada, which has the prime responsibility for this system. Because of the importance of its data for global change monitoring, and because of the high data volume, it is especially important that the archiving, cataloguing and access to the data be efficient and effective.

It is highly desirable to have direct read-out, processing and archiving capabilities for the Eos and other satellites in Canada. Where this is not possible, as a minimum, Canada should have a direct link to the centre receiving the data so that all Level 1 data for instruments of interest for Canadian coverage will be further processed, distributed and archived here.

Like all other countries, Canada has experienced some difficulties in processing high volume data and distributing it in a timely fashion. Nevertheless, the Canadian track record is better than most, if not all, of the other facilities throughout the world. Canada was the first country to provide quick-look products from LANDSAT and the first to provide geocoded satellite image products. The quality of Canadian digital satellite data has been as good as or better than that of any other system. Canada should have as much independent processing, archiving and distribution capability as possible.

System Concepts

The functional requirements of the CGCP are very similar to those of the EosDIS. The data reception, processing and archiving will almost certainly be performed at the two Canadian satellite receiving stations in Saskatchewan and Quebec. Meteorological data will be received and processed at facilities operated by the Atmospheric Environment Service (AES). Assuming that no direct readout is available from Eos, data should be obtained from the NASA facilities via communication satellites immediately following their acquisition.

Archiving of high volume data should be performed using optical tape recording systems (Strome, 1986). This is the most practical and cost-effective method of handling data which will likely amount to about 100-200 gigabytes per day for Canadian coverage.

Quick-look data should be available for all imaging sensors on the same day they are acquired via standard communication lines. A prototype system has been developed which uses laser video disk for image storage and which can transmit images in digital form for display on a PC equipped with a standard colour VGA compatible display.

Information on all data available in Canada should be catalogued as they are acquired, and the information should be available through an on-line system. This system should be coupled to the quick-look image transmission facility and an ordering system. From a remote terminal, the user should be able to determine what data are available for any particular area over a given time period, receive information on the quality, and obtain the quick-look images and low rate data. The user should also be able to place an order for high data volume products, such as images, from the remote terminal.

The Royal Society of Canada (1989) has proposed a Global Change Network (GCNet) which would take advantage of existing computer network capabilities and which could be used to provide user access to the above information. In addition, the Society has proposed that the following features be available: a) a capability to combine data from various data bases and forms (point, line/polygon, raster) into a unifying framework; b) a capability to manipulate elements of the integrated data set and to input the digital data into two, three or four dimensional models; and c) a capability to run the models as a part of the development, verification, validation or application activities and to exchange the results with other researchers.

The Royal Society has also identified some features which are required for a Geographic Information System (GIS) which are not normally available in today's commercial system. These include: systematic application of techniques and approaches developed in a variety of subfields of computer science; integration of approaches and procedures developed in computer vision, image understanding, digital cartography and remote sensing; application of procedures to minimize search effort involved in answering queries; and provision of features that enable a GIS to be easily tailored to specific applications and users. An additional feature, not identified by the Society, but also important, is a capability to handle volumetric (three dimensional) data and time series of such data (i.e. four dimensional).

Individual research users will require the equivalent of the Eos Scientific Computing Facility (SCF). Given the traditional methods of funding research in Canada, these will not likely be supplied to investigators as is the case in the United States. Thus, these facilities will vary greatly. Existing computing facilities will be used to a large extent. New equipment may be purchased by some investigators if they can obtain funding through the normal channels (such as NSERC). The diversity of equipment will dictate a stronger need for standardization of data formats, software design and coding and documentation.

Advanced Technology

Modelling. All the documents prepared to date which discuss plans for global change monitoring programs have identified the need for more work to be done in the development of better models to relate the instrument observations (from space, aircraft and *in situ*) to the variables and processes of concern. Such development will require the effort and cooperation of the majority of the scientists concentrating on global change issues throughout the world.

Information Extraction. New algorithms and techniques will have to be developed for the extraction of information from the new sensors. The greatest challenge will be presented by the high spectral and spatial resolution sensors. Some work has been done both in Canada and abroad with airborne imaging spectrometers (e.g. Strome et al., 1990), but the data are not widely available, and only a relatively few scientists have had the opportunity to work with it. We are at a stage that is very similar to that with multispectral image data prior to the launch of LANDSAT-1. SAR will present similar challenges. While there is more experience with SAR data, especially in Canada, it is well recognized that a great deal more research is required to fully and more effectively utilize the data.

Some of the tools which should be examined closely include signal processing techniques which are applied in other fields (e.g. acoustics, seismic) and the application of neural networks.

Data Archive. The most cost effective method to store the vast amounts of data to be acquired at this time is the optical tape recording system (Strome, 1986) developed by CREO Electronics with partial financial support from the Canadian government. This system permits the recording of 10^{12} bytes, or one terabyte of data on a single reel of optical tape. The media cost is less than one cent per megabyte. Maximum access time to any data on a tape is one minute. Lifetime is at least fifteen years, much longer than the normal lifetime of magnetic tape. The only limitation with the system is the data recording rate which is only three megabytes per second which is not adequate for real-time recording of satellite image data. Considerable work will be required to develop the information handling capabilities which will be required to take full advantage of this technology.

Expert Systems. The Eos, CGCP and related programs all require the integration of data from many sources, and in a highly complex fashion. The fundamental tools of analysis, the models and the data integration tools, do not exist in the form which will be required. The research to be carried out will, hopefully, result in a better understanding of how to use the available data in an optimum manner to extract the information required. For eventual practical, operational use, it is likely that expert systems will have to be developed so that the complexities can be effectively hidden from the operational user.

CONCLUSIONS AND RECOMMENDATIONS

Canada is recognized as a leader in the processing and analysis of remotely sensed data. It is essential that a wide range of the available expertise be utilized in the planning and implementation of the CGCP Information Management System. Consideration should be given to the establishment of a Data Handling Advisory Panel similar to NASA's Science Advisory Panel for Eos Data and Information to assist in the planning.

Adequate funding should be provided to ensure that high quality data needed by Canadian scientists will be readily available in a timely and affordable fashion.

High priority should be given by funding agencies to support the work required in modelling, information extraction, image analysis and artificial intelligence in support of the CGCP.

CHAPTER 17

THE ROLE OF SURFACE OBSERVATIONS IN SUPPORT OF REMOTE SENSING

P.M. Teillet

INTRODUCTION

With the advent of remote sensing technology, particularly weather satellites, to begin with, and photographs of the globe taken from Earth orbit and beyond, our thinking about the planet we live on has taken on a global perspective that was rather rare in the past. In the middle to latter portion of this century, we have begun to study plate techtonics, general/global circulation models, global change, global habitability, earth system science, etc., as well as environmental concerns such as global warming, ozone depletion, deforestation, desertification, wide-spread pollution of land, sea, and air, etc. Perhaps these investigations and concerns are early signs of Teilhard de Chardin's "noosphere" (Teilhard de Chardin, 1956), a form of global consciousness, but they are undoubtedly a tardy re-awakening to what native peoples who have lived off the land have known instinctively for thousands of years concerning nature as a system.

"Space technology provides unprecedented global synoptic coverage with a uniform instrument system" (Bretherton, 1985). Ironically, the extent to which data acquired by such systems can provide reliable and quantitative information depends critically on supportive measurements and investigations carried out at the surface of the Earth. Surface measurements make it possible to supplement and validate satellite observations and there will always be parameters that are inaccessible from space. The purpose of this chapter is to review ground-based methodologies that support remote sensing activities and recommend some of the key research areas requiring preferential treatment in the next few years.

In the overall framework of remote sensing, the ground segment (as opposed to the space or airborne segments) encompasses many activities, from data reception at relatively few locations, through to information extraction and data integration by end users at countless locations. However, aspects concerning the data and information management systems are not addressed here, although the discussion does include preprocessing and data correction methodologies. The main focus of the chapter is on preprocessing correction methods, field measurement activities and the characterization of test sites in support of remote sensing. Consideration of the thermal infrared and active laser systems, among others, is beyond the scope of this article. Emphasis is generally placed on the visible, near infrared, and short-wave infrared portions of the electromagnetic spectrum.

THE OBSERVATORIES CONCEPT

The International Geosphere-Biosphere Programme (IGBP) has developed the concept of Global Change Observatories, more recently renamed Regional Research Centres (Björklund, 1989). The goal is to establish a long-term coordinated network of land- and marine-based measurements of geospheric and biospheric processes. The network would facilitate observations and documentation of global change, studies of interactions among earth system components, acquisition of surface reference data for remote sensing measurements and models, and validations of regional and global simulation models. A hierarchical structure is envisaged, world-wide, with on the order of 10 international research and training centres, roughly 100 national observatory facilities, approximately 1000 stations in affiliated networks, and a great many transient research and monitoring test sites (IGBP, 1988).

The major multinational centres would focus on regional research issues of significance to global change, utilizing a variety of approaches including monitoring activities, experimental work, data integration, and modeling. The main activities would encompass the promotion of cooperative research, the provision of data management and exchange capabilities, the development of integration and modeling algorithms, and the establishment of training and exchange programs (Björklund, 1989).

Possibilities for a Canadian geosphere-biosphere network of research centres and observatories have been outlined in a discussion paper by Nisbet (1989). While describing a rather ambitious program, he advises that more focused, strategically chosen scientific efforts in essential areas are better than attempting to cover too much and doing poorly as a result. He also suggests that there is an urgent need for government to identify and preserve all long-term monitoring programs related to global change.

It is critical that measurement stations acquire a full complement of meteorological data. In global change studies, physical parameters at the surface have to be related to climatic processes (radiation balance, air-water and air-biome interactions, cloud effects on radiative transfer, etc.). In this respect, relevant ground stations should be integrated into the World Climate Research Programme.

As far as remote sensing is concerned, the Remote Sensing Technical Group of the Canadian Global Change Programme issued a report on the contribution of satellite observations to the program (Cihlar et al., 1989). In a section on ground observatories, the document briefly outlines observational requirements for the remote sensing proposals described in the rest of the report. It is likely that many of the requirements can be met at the various geosphere-biosphere sites in Canada, but there will undoubtedly be specific needs that will require separate test sites in Canada and elsewhere, as well as the usual transient field measurement sorties. An example of a non-Canadian test area that plays an important role in remote sensing internationally is the calibration site at White Sands, New Mexico. Collectively, the Canadian observatories should represent the major dynamic regimes, including vegetation biomes, urban areas, water environments, cordillera, and ice regimes. The report lists measurement requirements in the categories of atmospheric and surface data, radiation data, vegetation data, snow and ice data, topographic data, permafrost data, and ocean measurements. Some variables need to be measured concurrently with image data acquisition, whereas others require continuous monitoring.

SURFACE PROPERTIES

Although the measurement of surface properties is application-dependent, there are certain surface characteristics and related variables that are common to many remote sensing investigations. Dozier and Strahler (1983) have summarized a number of these common measurements, categorizing them as follows: calibration, topography, illumination and sensor geometries, solar and longwave radiation, reflectance, temperature and emittance, and other micrometeorological measurements. They then discuss specific surface measurement requirements for remote sensing studies in the contexts of geology, agriculture, forestry, and snow applications.

Calibration issues are addressed later in this article. Illumination and sensor geometries tie into all aspects of ground investigations in support of remote sensing but they are relatively straightforward to deal with. An evaluation of sun angle computation algorithms has been carried out by Teillet et al. (1986).

Digital Elevation Models

The provision of digital topographic data for all of Canada at high spatial resolution is a less straightforward matter. Global data sets are even less forthcoming. Accuracy requirements can be identified. Coarse-resolution digital elevation models (DEMs) are sufficient to correct satellite imagery to a common datum across the country and for Rayleigh scattering by the atmosphere. Such zero-order corrections can be achieved using DEMs with one grid point per 1000 square kilometers, for example. To correct image pixels for relief displacement, approximately half-pixel resolutions are needed from the DEMs. The highest resolutions required are on the order of one-tenth of a pixel for the purposes of applying good slope-aspect corrections to satellite data.

DEMs for the aforementioned zero-order corrections are readily available on a global basis. Canada is in a position to apply relief displacement corrections anywhere in the country for NOAA AVHRR data (1.1 km nadir resolution) and future EOS MODIS (Moderate-Resolution Imaging Spectrometer) data (214 m nadir resolution in some bands). It has been suggested to NASA by the MODIS Science Team that the Eos Data Information System (EosDIS) ought to have global DEM coverage at about 100 m horizontal resolution and 10 m height accuracy to satisfy the needs of many investigators. J.-P. Muller of University College London, England, suggests that global SPOT HRV data be used to solve this problem, whereas others advocate the use of interferometric radar imagery that can be used regardless of cloud cover.

Field Spectroscopy

"Field spectroscopy involves the study of the interrelationships between the spectral characteristics of objects and their biophysical attributes in the field environment. It is a technique of fundamental importance in remote sensing, yet its full potential is rarely exploited" (Milton, 1987). Being a difficult and expensive component of remote sensing, field spectroscopy often lacks financial and personnel resources, despite its fundamental role. Nevertheless, these limitations will have to be overcome for quantitative remote sensing to contribute to global change studies. Sound information and sound decisions have to be based on firm foundations.

A proper discussion of spectral reflectance measurements is beyond the scope of this article, or any single article for that matter. Some of the key issues involved are discussed by Milton (1987), Slater (1985), Duggin and Philipson (1982), Smith (1982), and Holmes (1970), for example. In addition, recent developments in both field reflectance measurements and modeling efforts in remote sensing are well represented in the proceedings of the international colloquia held by the Spectral Signatures working group of Commission VII of the International Society for Photogrammetry and Remote Sensing (Guyot and Verbrugghe, 1981, 1983; Guyenne, 1985; Guyenne and Hunt, 1988).

The Canada Centre for Remote Sensing (CCRS) has operated, with considerable success a mobile spectral measurement facility capable of collecting data in the spectral range from 0.35 to 14 micrometres. It consisted of a Spectrascan SP2000 scanning spectrometer, a 5000 kg truck with a hydraulic ladder, and various equipment for making ancillary measurements (Brown and Ahern, 1980). CCRS research activities supported by these facilities from 1978 to 1990 included:

- determination of optimum phenological stages for remote sensing of crops (Saskatchewan) (Brown et al., 1980; Ahern et al., 1981b);

- measurement of cloth photogrammetric targets and calibration panels in support of airborne sensor investigations (New Brunswick; Saskatchewan; British Columbia) (Fung and Lasserre, 1987);

- untangling of complex spectral characteristics of rangeland (Alberta) (Ahern et al., 1981a; Brown et al., 1983);

- ground-based segment of multi-stage sampling studies in agriculture (New Brunswick; Saskatchewan; Ontario) (Ahern et al., 1981b; Horler et al., 1983);

- simulation and assessment of future sensor band performance (British Columbia; Saskatchewan; Alberta; Ontario; Maritimes) (Brown et al., 1980; Ahern et al., 1981b; Horler et al., 1983; Leckie et al., 1988a,b);

- spectral band optimization for studying tree defoliation (Maritimes) (Teillet et al., 1985; Leckie et al., 1988a,b,c);

- investigation of new approaches to postlaunch sensor calibration (United States; Ontario) (Teillet et al., 1987, 1988, 1990);

- measurement of spectral properties of rock outcrops in support of thermal inertia modeling (Ontario) (Wood et al., 1987, 1990); and,

- ground-based measurements of surface reflectance and atmospheric conditions for validation of atmospheric correction algorithms (Québec; Ontario) (Gauthier et al., 1989; Ahern et al., 1990).

Microwave Scatterometry

The use of passive and active microwave systems in remote sensing studies has been increasing steadily, as have the related ground-based measurements in support of these investigations. The interaction of microwave radiation with natural surfaces differs considerably from that of optical radiation and provides complementary information. There is a considerable literature on ground-based microwave measurement systems in this context. Therefore, this section primarily serves to make the point that the instrumentation differs considerably from systems operating in the visible, near-infrared, and short-wave infrared, and that ground reference data requirements can differ as well. Site characterization and data recording procedures developed for the optical regime (for example, NASA, 1980; King and Mack, 1984) have been modified to handle the different requirements in the microwave regime (for example, Teillet et al., 1984; Cihlar, 1986; Cihlar et al., 1987).

In 1985, CCRS acquired a three-band, ground-based microwave scatterometer system, operating in the L, C, and Ku frequency bands (Brisco et al., 1988; Sofko et al., 1989). The three scatterometers are mounted on a hinged-arm hydraulic boom installed on a five-ton flat-bed truck. The facility has been operated under contract by the University of Saskatchewan. Observations have been made over several growing seasons over wheat, barley, canola, and fallow fields in various stages of tillage and moisture. The three radars are currently being converted to full polarimeters.

Supporting Remote Sensing Investigations

Apart from the more specific spectroscopic types of measurements outlined in the previous sections, there are many other types of observations that provide supporting data for remote sensing studies. Some of these include the following.

- Ground reference data have long been used to assist in the selection of representative training and testing data for the automated classification of digital imagery. Stated in a more general sense, ground reference data facilitate the verification and accuracy assessment of information derived from remotely sensed data. (See, for example, Fitzpatrick, 1977). Although many classification studies have been carried out with image sensor data over the years, it has only been recently that investigators have concerned themselves with statistical assessments of confidence in their results (Congalton et al., 1983; Guindon and Neeman, 1986).

- Investigations have recently begun on the use of low-cost GPS (Global Positioning Systems) receivers in both the acquisition of control for image-to-map coordinate transformation and for positioning of field sites (Wilkie, 1990; Lasserre and Pouliot, 1991).

- A significant part of the development of methodological tools in remote sensing concerns the development of models, algorithms and procedures, all of which require validation.

- Surface characteristics also enter into play in the development of sensor systems as the designated targets of interest and through simulations and optimizations.

Sample Sizes

In a series of articles, P.J. Curran and colleagues have discussed the issue of sample sizes for ground and remotely sensed data (Curran and Williamson, 1985a,b, 1986; Curran and Hay, 1986). It is common in remote sensing investigations to have to limit sample sizes in ground data collection for time and logistics reasons. (It is hoped that the importance of global change issues will help to outweigh these problems.) Curran and Williamson (1985a,b, 1986) conclude that there is a need for an increased awareness of the magnitude of sampling error and suggest that investigators should try to use the known spatial autocorrelation in the data to reduce error for a given sample size. Curran and Hay (1986) argue that there are problems with the use of linear regression and the correlation coefficient to relate remotely sensed data to ground variables. Several alternative methods are suggested, the favoured one being the "least squares" approach, if estimates of measurement variances are available.

Portable radiometers and, increasingly, spectroradiometers are widely used for acquiring reflectance data for vegetation, environment, geologic and other investigations. Such measurements require the careful and proper use of the instrumentation, with reliable measurement procedures capable of producing calibrated and reproducible target reflectance data (Daughtry et al., 1981; Jackson and Slater, 1986). Established statistical tests can and should be brought to bear on remote sensing field studies to establish the number of replications needed for a desired level of accuracy (Cochran and Cox, 1957; John and Quenouille, 1977; Cochran, 1977).

It is important to mention the issues of scaling and the compatibility of different data sets. Data fusion and, particularly, the aggregation of data from very localized measurements to the cell sizes used in Global Climate Models (GCMs), for example, will be a central aspects of data processing in the global change context. Remotely sensed data acquired from airborne platforms will play a key role in the scaling process and can be considered to provide "surface measurements" extended over large areas in many situations.

Site Characterization

The characterization of a site has traditionally been very much a function of the scientific discipline under study. With the advent of modern remote sensing and its multidisciplinary impact, the size and scope of field measurement campaigns have increased significantly. There are numerous examples today of concerted field sorties that characterize a test area in many different ways (for example, the First ISLSCP (International Satellite Land Surface Climatology Project) Field Experiment (FIFE); the Atmospheric Boundary Layer Experiment (ABLE); the Maricopa Agricultural Center (MAC) experiments; etc.). In these studies, specialized and sophisticated instruments are deployed at the test site to acquire many types of discipline-specific data.

It would seem that there is a need for the rapid and precise measurement of certain site characteristics that would be of benefit to all of the participating experiments. Particularly in the situation of a forest canopy, but applicable to other contexts, it should be possible to use automated, three-dimensional photogrammetric and spectral measurement techniques to assist in the full characterization of the architecture and optical properties of the canopy and rapidly derive related parameters such as gap-probability distributions, visible sky geometry, species distribution, radiation field, etc. (Lasserre, 1989).

CALIBRATION AND CORRECTION

Accurate and quantitative interpretation of remotely sensed data requires that digital images be calibrated and corrected radiometrically and geometrically during systems processing and in preparation for information extraction analysis. Experimental and ongoing surface measurements play a key role in the development and use of the preprocessing methodologies involved.

In terms of major categories of radiometric effects viewed from the perspective of image analysis, one can distinguish between considerations which are sensor-related (such as calibration and de-striping), and those which are scene-related (such as atmospheric effects, surface reflectance characteristics, and georadiometric factors). All of these effects can place limitations on the proper classification of targets of interest in satellite and aircraft imagery.

In order to optimize information extraction from remotely sensed data, radiometric corrections will often be necessary to compensate for the effects of illumination conditions, observation geometry, atmospheric phenomena, and topographic variations, on the spectral signatures of objects. Each of these four types of correction usually will have the same three prerequisites: radiometric calibration, an atmospheric model, and a target reflectance model. These prerequisites are applicable to those analyses which involve multi-temporal or multi-sensor image data, as well as those which require a conversion of digital signal level to physical parameters at the surface (such as surface reflectance, chlorophyll concentration, etc.). Discussions of image correction for radiometric effects in remote sensing can be found in Slater (1980), Slater (1985), Duggin (1985), and Teillet (1986).

Absolute Radiometric Calibration of Optical Sensors

The key issues pertaining to the absolute radiometric calibration of optical sensors have been discussed extensively in the literature by Professor Philip N. Slater of the Optical Sciences Center at the University of Arizona and colleagues at various other institutions (Begni et al., 1986; Teillet et al., 1987; Slater et al., 1987; Slater, 1988). In essence, absolute radiometric calibration provides the relationship between the digital signal level recorded by a sensor and the spectral radiance at its entrance aperture. With correction for atmospheric effects, absolute calibration allows surface radiances, weighted by the sensor's bandpass, to be determined. A knowledge of surface radiance is needed to determine, for example, energy balance relationships, retrieve ground reflectance, and map ocean chlorophyll concentrations. An accurate knowledge of the absolute calibration of sensors over their lifetimes allows data collected by different sensors at different times to be compared. An historical record of changes in sensor response is crucial to the success of long-term global science studies.

A broad classification of radiometric calibration procedures has been presented by Kastner and Slater (1982), and Slater (1983) has reviewed some of the main problems and methods involved. The principal distinction is between relative calibration, dealing with compensation for detector-to-detector, band-to-band, and time-to-time variations, and absolute calibration of radiometric responses. In the domain of absolute calibration, Slater defines three categories of procedures: (1) pre-flight absolute calibration with only focal plane calibration in flight; (2) sun or on-board standard source, usually not illuminating the full aperture; and, (3) in-flight reference to a ground area of known reflectance. The last approach depends on an accurate determination of atmospheric aerosol extinction during the sensor over-flight. Nevertheless, it has the important advantage that it best replicates actual conditions of image data acquisition, with a full irradiation of the entrance aperture by the scene. The large uniform area of gypsum sand in the alkali flats at White Sands, New Mexico, is an ideal site and it has been used by Slater and others to provide in-flight calibrations for the Landsat TM, SPOT HRV, and NOAA AVHRR sensors.

The possibility of developing and maintaining artificially-created reference targets has begun to receive some attention (Forster, 1985; Guenther, 1989), but remains somewhat impractical for satellite sensor calibration. Developers of global change Regional Research Centres might give some consideration to the construction of such targets. Reference targets for ground-based and airborne sensor calibration pose less of a problem. A promising material for surface-based measurements is Spectralon, which is halon-based, stable, light-weight, and washable (Labsphere, 1990). It is interesting to note the construction of a plastic, 380,000 square-meter symbol of the Earth in the Crau region of France. Created by artist Pierre Comte, the symbol is very clearly visible in a SPOT HRV image acquired on 6 October 1989 (SPOT Newsletter, 1989).

No single absolute calibration method can be guaranteed to be free of systematic error and so there is a need for redundant calibration methods. The identification of a difference between two or more independent methods may also help diagnose a change in the condition of a sensor. In addition, an analysis of the differences between two precise methods may expose an inadequacy or error in one of the approaches which then may be corrected to improve the accuracy of future calibrations and measurements (Slater, 1988).

Atmospheric Extinction Measurements at High Spectral Resolution

Numerous investigators have studied the effects of the atmosphere on remotely sensed data and emphasized the importance of correcting for these effects. As discussed earlier, an atmospheric model is a key prerequisite for proper radiometric scene correction since it is needed to remove unwanted atmospheric effects and also to take atmospheric phenomena into account while correcting for other factors such as topography, illumination and view angle. Atmospheric conditions can vary significantly, both spatially and temporally, as a result of molecular absorption due to gases such as water vapour, carbon dioxide and ozone, and especially scattering due to haze or dust particles. Thus it may be necessary to remove scene-to-scene variations and to correct for within-scene variations due to large changes in ground elevation, due to sun angle effects and due to transmission variability across the scene.

Corrections for atmospheric, illumination and view-angle effects are essential or desirable for many of the remote sensing applications that Canadians have been developing for sensor systems over the years, and Canadian research and development in these areas are well advanced (Gauthier et al., 1989; Robertson et al., 1989; Teillet, 1989, 1990; Teillet et al., 1990; Ahern et al., 1990). As an example, extensive observational monitoring of atmospheric optical conditions were carried out by Ahern et al. (1990) near Ottawa, Ontario, during the months of July through October 1987 and May through September 1988. In particular, a modified implementation of the Langley method was used to measure the atmospheric optical depth spectrum at 5 nm intervals from 0.36 to 1.10 micrometres. 644 spectra were obtained during the two field seasons using a Li-Cor 1800 spectroradiometer. An exo-atmospheric calibration of the instrument was established using a combination of the extrapolation of the Langley plot to zero air mass and a laboratory standard lamp calibration. The Rayleigh component of the optical depth was subtracted, taking atmospheric pressure and temperature into account.

Wavelengths judged to be free of significant molecular absorption were identified from the optical depth spectra and published data on molecular absorption to determine aerosol extinction. Using a power-law model to describe the relationship between wavelength and aerosol extinction, the aerosol optical depth at 550 nm and the Junge exponent (describing the aerosol size distribution) were determined for each observation. These observations showed that there was a distinct separation of atmospheric conditions into clear and hazy conditions (Ahern et al., 1990).

Bidirectional Surface Reflectance Effects

Image data acquired by satellite and aircraft sensors are usually view-angle dependent as a result of a combination of atmospheric effects and the bidirectional surface reflectance of non-lambertian targets (Staenz et al., 1981; Holben and Fraser, 1984). Wide-angle imagery is acquired by sensors such as the Advanced Very High Resolution Radiometer (AVHRR) on-board the NOAA series of satellites (Begue et al., 1988) and Airborne Multi-Spectral Scanners (AMSS) (Barnsley, 1984), with off-nadir angles reaching +/-55° and +/-45°, respectively. Without information on the directional reflectance properties of natural surfaces, and in order to avoid making time-consuming atmospheric corrections, it is common to correct such wide-angle images in an approximate way by means of an empirical profiling technique, also known as the additive adjustment technique (Brown et al., 1982; Irons and Labovitz, 1982; Guindon et al., 1984; Royer et al., 1985).

Oblique angle or pointable imagery is acquired by sensors such as the SPOT High Resolution Visible (HRV) instrument (Moran et al., 1988) and the Advanced Solid-State Array Spectroradiometer (ASAS) (Irons and Irish, 1988). Pointing capability is also planned for several Earth Observing System (Eos) instruments, including the MODIS-T (Moderate-Resolution Imaging Spectrometer-Tilt) (Salomonson et al., 1989), the HIRIS (High-Resolution Imaging Spectrometer) (Goetz and Herring, 1989), and MISR (Multiangle Imaging SpectroRadiometer) (Diner et al., 1989). In the case of oblique-angle image data, the scan angle range is so small that the empirical profiling technique used to correct wide-angle imagery is not applicable.

To exploit the advantages of oblique image data in multitemporal analyses, view angle effects due to atmospheric and surface bidirectional reflectance characteristics must be accounted for. Once the atmospheric correction capability is available, the remaining view-angle effect due to the non-lambertian character of natural surfaces can be removed if the bidirectional reflectance distribution function (BRDF) of each target-type is known and a suitable correction algorithm is implemented. There is an increasing interest in coordinated efforts towards the derivation of BRDFs for various ground cover types (Gauthier et al., 1989). The complete BRDF for even a single surface type and condition is not easily obtained because all possible illumination and viewing geometries have to be encompassed. Because of the difficulty in specifying the complete BRDF, it is usually approximated by measuring bidirectional reflectance factors (BRFs) for a limited set of illumination and viewing geometries.

One approach to ground-based BRF measurements is to acquire data for the same target at a number of view angles using an apparatus that positions a radiometer such that it can move along an arc of a circle having a radius equal to the distance from the radiometer to the target (Jackson et al., 1990). Jackson et al. (1990) report on BRF measurements over four surfaces having vastly different characteristics: wheat, bare soil at several degrees of roughness, a dry lake bed (playa), and gypsum sand. The apparatus was aligned in a plane perpendicular to the along-track direction of a satellite's orbit or an aircraft's flight line to produce BRFs at a view angle nearly the same as that of the satellite or aircraft sensor. View angle correction factors obtained in this way will necessarily only be reliable for the particular surface measured and perhaps other targets with similar roughness patterns.

Another approach to ground-based measurements in support of remote sensing experiments is to acquire data using two radiometers mounted side-by-side on a backpack apparatus and suitably configured with bandpass filters and viewing orientations matching those of the relevant satellite sensor (Pinter et al., 1990). In particular, one radiometer is pointed toward nadir and the second rotated fore or aft to match the view angle of the satellite sensor that overpasses that day.

If the surface of interest is relatively uniform, another approach is to use a unique instrument called PARABOLA (Portable Apparatus for Rapid Acquisition of Bidirectional Observations of Land and Atmosphere), developed by Dr. Donald W. Deering at the NASA Goddard Space Flight Center (Deering and Leone, 1986; Deering and Eck, 1987; Deering, 1988; Deeringet al., 1989). The device is highly portable and features a two-axis, scanning head, motor-driven radiometer that acquires radiance data for almost the complete 4 steradians of sky and ground. It samples in 15 instantaneous field-of-view sectors in three spectral channels (red, near-infrared, short-wave infrared). Examples of data sets that have been acquired by PARABOLA include: plowed fields and crops, rangeland, vegetation types, forest stands, prairie grasslands, desert playa, and alkali flats.

RECOMMENDATIONS

Regional Research Centres or Equivalents

It is suggested that Canada move cautiously on this concept and, if anything, build on existing ground-based measurement/monitoring programs/facilities. Objectives related to global change should be carefully focused and strategically chosen. Remotely sensed data should be used whenever possible to extend results from localized measurements to larger areas. Selected portions of both ground and remotely sensed data from the Regional Research Centres should be packaged and made available to anyone, from elementary and secondary schools to practising scientists and managers, on a convenient medium such as CD-ROM and at very little cost. Aerial photography libraries could be expanded to include the image data for easy access. More specific points are as follows.

- The report of Cihlar et al. (1989) could be used as the framework for a more complete document outlining specific courses of action regarding surface measurements in support of remote sensing for the Canadian Global Change Program. Someone should match identified measurement requirements with current data acquisition programs and develop proposals for filling the gaps. Even though Regional Research Centres may not be instigated as such, it should be possible to identify long-term, standard test sites encompassing the major biomes, regimes, and environments in Canada. Spatial, temporal, and spectral aspects of biogeophysical phenomena should be emphasized when taking the remote sensing perspective.

- Instrumentation for the rapid, three-dimensional, optical and architectural characterization of localized test sites should be developed to facilitate multidisciplinary science investigations.

- The issue of having maintained and unmaintained reference and calibration targets in Canada warrants further study before any specific recommendations can be made. Meanwhile, the monitoring and dissemination of sensor calibration coefficients and other performance indicators is a function that is ideally suited to government research and development.

- Apart from the ongoing importance of proper radiometric calibration and the development of advanced atmospheric correction methodologies, the next major problem to be seriously addressed in the area of optical radiometric correction research is bidirectional surface reflectance effects.

- Since the CCRS mobile spectroscopy laboratory is no longer in operation, there is no major mobile visible and infrared spectroscopy facility available in Canada. Given the extensive research results achieved by the old CCRS system and related instruments, and the increasing interest in high spectral resolution sensors, some kind of facility is warranted. Several models are possible, but one might be for the government microwave facility to be operated by a university.

- The uniformity and continuity of measurements and standards in time and space are needed throughout the 15-year time span of the Eos program. Conformity with current and past measurement systems must be assured.

Digital Elevation Models for all of Canada

A great many scientific studies and practical applications would benefit significantly from the availability of good-quality topographic information in general and digital elevation models (DEMs) in particular, for the entire country. It has been suggested that there is a need for global DEM coverage at about 100 m horizontal resolution and 10 m height accuracy and that it should be part of EOSDIS. This would provide sub-pixel accuracy for use with MODIS, but not for higher resolution sensors such as Landsat TM and SPOT HRV. Thus, it would be beneficial to have, at least on a regional basis, national DEM coverage at about 10 m horizontal resolution.

There should be a Canadian repository of reflectance spectra of natural surfaces, with, for example, user access through published catalogues on paper and a data base on CD-ROM. CCRS is currently working on tasks that, if amplified, could very well generate the prototype of such a repository system.

CONCLUSIONS

This review has necessarily been rather limited, given the broad range of subjects that are included. If there is a common thread, it would perhaps be that surface observations in support of remote sensing require high quality work under often difficult logistic conditions and that adequate resources, as well as care and attention to detail, are required for success. Inter-agency cooperation is vital given the difficulty of any one person or group being able to collect, analyze, and derive information from all the different kinds of data. As remote sensing analyses increasingly move beyond statistical image classification methods to more biogeophysical approaches, greater resources will have to be devoted to surface observation requirements in order to supplement, support and validate satellite observations.

CHAPTER 18

INTERNATIONAL COLLABORATION WITH RESPECT TO GLOBAL MONITORING: THE IMPACT OF CANADIAN POLICY

W.R. Trenholm, M.D. Thompson, I.K. Crain

It might be said that the impact is significant but the policy minimal.

Global monitoring is an activity involving and requiring a myriad of technologies, information and data sets, multidisciplinary technical and academic capabilities, long-term commitment, plus trust, collaboration and understanding among nations. Most importantly, it is an activity which requires focused collaboration at all levels of involvement. In order to provide effective global monitoring, regardless of purpose, it must be guided by informed national and international policies which enunciate clearly and concisely the objectives to be achieved and the results to be provided. It must be treated as a ongoing process which is managed and monitored meticulously and scrupulously.

In the authors' view, Canada as a nation, although evidencing concern for world environmental issues, does not have an apparent nor comprehensive policy in the matters pertaining to global monitoring, nor are there any indications that one is forthcoming. Meanwhile, Canadians in both the public and private sectors are involved in countless ad hoc activities which are contributing elements to the process of global monitoring.

Internationally there are many organizations which have and are making efforts to create a conducive environment for international collaboration concerning global monitoring. As yet, these efforts have not resulted in a concerted, focused and sustained process which could achieve the essential coordination of effort, energy and resources necessary to effect the implementation of the process of global monitoring.

THE MONITORING CHALLENGE

"The ability of a living system to sense change in its environment is one of the requisites for the survival of the system. People have many and varied ways of sensing their environments and either modifying them or changing location. A group will generally sense its environment through the observations of its members who pool information. Groups generally have the same options as individuals when the environment begins to turn sour: modify it or move. At the level of the organization, the problem becomes more difficult. This is particularly true if the organization is large and has responsibility for considerable territory. Moving is out of the question; further, a number of difficulties arise in the system's determination of what its environment is, when changes occur to it, and what the effects of the changes are.

Perhaps only recently has it been necessary, due to the modifications of the environment by human endeavor, for states to develop more than a rudimentary sensing(monitoring) system. In any event, most states do not, today, have adequate mechanisms for comprehending their environments, either for making intelligent decisions about how they might be changed constructively or for dealing with changes that occur as a result of natural or human activity over time" (Counc. State Gov.,1974).

Today, the world has undergone and is still undergoing traumatic changes caused by human activity within the natural environment. These changes coupled with natural events have created a situation where no individual, group, organization, state or geographic region can contain, control or mediate these problems. We have reached a point in time where the speed at which humans can and do change a state's environment is threatening the well being(or even survival) of both the humans and the state itself. Indications of this are well stated in the Brundtland Report, The World Commission on Environment and

Development (1987), entitled *Our Common Future*. These problems are exemplified in such phenomena as acid rain, international transport of airborne and waterborne pollutants, desertification, famine, drought, tropical rainforest depletion, fisheries stocks declines, etc.. The symptoms are being addressed but the root cause(s) of the problem(s) have not been individually nor collectively addressed. Data bases at an appropriate degree of resolution on the world resources have been attempted but are not in any way adequate nor complete for effective, executive, proactive management decision making pertinent to the problem(s) at hand. Understanding the problem(s) and the extent to which this problem(s) may have a systemic or topical impact on immediate and/or adjacent territories is critical to finding sustainable solutions to the problem(s). **Treating the symptoms without proper knowledge of the implications of both the problem and the symptomatic treatment is tantamount to palliative care**.

Monitoring is only one component of a whole management process, and will not, if implemented in a vacuum, provide anything more than an ever increasing volume of data which has not, and most probably will not, be further reduced into useable information. This will simply provide fuel to the argument that monitoring tools, techniques, and expertise are expensive and trivial pursuits. The concepts, tools and capabilities of monitoring must be concisely understood and the contributions of their products to a holistic management process demonstrated.

Management, decision making and monitoring are inseparable entities in the process of sustainable global development. Timely, appropriate and accurate information provided in a spatial and relatable format is the lifeblood of the management process, provided that all of the information supply and management systems are harmoniously orchestrated. Ironically, this process and the perceived problems facing the world today are treated as independent entities through uncoordinated legislation and policy efforts, by a variety of independent and competing individuals, groups, states and organizations.

The problems associated with proactively managing these processes,the international dialogue and the systems within which they are active are extremely complex and equally difficult to enunciate. Also, it has been found that one of the major reasons for governments' inability to mitigate many of the pervasive environmental and resource problems of the world today is, "the lack of ability to collate and comprehensively understand the great amount of environmental(so-called) data already in existence" (Larsen et al., 1978). It has been twelve years since this statement was put into print and it may be even more appropriate today.

The word "finite" is in popular usage in today's world when reference is made to land and oceans and the biological substance, energy and mineral resources contained on, within and under these ecological and geographic areas. One might ask, how finite is finite, how fast is the resource being dissipated, where are these resources located, what is the cost of developing or extracting these resources, are these resources being used for economic gain or for the necessities of life, or both, is there an alternative or substitute, what is the impact of the resource development on other adjacent resources, what area is or will be impacted either directly or indirectly, etc.? Decisions regarding the allocation and use of these resources are becoming more complex and often multi-jurisdictional in nature, giving rise to the "need to know philosophy" which is indicative of today's better informed society and its concern for a future world which can sustain life as we know it today.

The ecological realities as to how these resources are viewed(understood), related(linked to other resources), and used(consumed or transformed), and the identification of the effects or by-products of using them are paramount to the management and survival process. Issues related to such concepts as ecological regions, natural constraints, ecological irreversibility, materials flow, assimilation capacities, and fragile environments must be identified, assessed, managed and monitored.

The management process must also take into account the economic realities of the market process, costs of production, ease of access, both to the resource being developed and to the market place, the competitive aspects of resource development, the demand, and the pricing structure that the market will bear. The information to support the necessary economic decisions is also a major monitoring activity. In many cases the information necessary for the economic aspects of the management and decision making process is derived from the same basic data as that for the environmental and natural resources management processes. The critical factor is how the data are transformed to meet the needs of the end user.

Monitoring is a data collection and data management process, either at the beginning of where it is usually referred to as an **inventory activity**, throughout the life of a process where it is referred to as a **quality control measure** or a post-process activity where it is referred to as **updating or change detection**. Each of these activities requires an expertise unique to that activity and a full understanding of what will be required of the data collected, the types of information processing systems within which the data will be used, and the timeliness and accuracy of data required. Jurisdictional responsibilities, managerial requirements, political desires, implications, competitiveness, and implementation initiatives all have differing requirements regarding detail, timeliness, level of security and confidentiality (i.e. sovereignty) and form of monitoring data products, in order to satisfy individuals, groups, organizations, states or regions. In addition, the level of technical competence and familiarity with the data, its derivation and the uses to which it might be put are all considerations which must become part of the monitoring-management matrix.

Monitoring of the resource base on a global basis , including ecosystems and their constituent parts, is only one element of the holistic management process which must be in place to effectively and economically benefit from the technological resources which are available today. Additionally, each sovereign state must establish, internally, its policy position relative to the issues confronting it and the world around it. Secondly, it must establish procedures and have a willingness to effectively collaborate globally to create an environment conducive to global monitoring or management.

THE COLLABORATION CHALLENGE

Webster's Encyclopedic Unabridged Dictionary defines "to collaborate" as "to work, one with another willingly". It further indicates that this word infers working with the enemies of one's nation or it could be interpreted to refer to one's competitors. This being the case and interpreting the concept of collaboration within the process of monitoring and, in particular, global monitoring, it should be apparent from the previous section of this discussion paper that collaboration is an essential and fundamental component of the monitoring process. However, before collaboration becomes an effective reality people must have a reason and a focus upon which to work together. There must be a disciplinary point of common interest and a feeling of equity between the collaborating partners, each of whom anticipates that the process will result in some mutual benefit and that the time and effort spent collaborating will be worth the energy and effort expended on his or her part. This could range from purely a monetary-gain motive to the most esoteric of reasons, and will vary from situation to situation. In the case of global monitoring, collaboration will be predicated on information and the communication of that information or knowledge. The communication of information must also be seen as a collaborative process in order that all parties gain fully from the information. In 1932, Bertold Brecht was quoted as having said, "Broadcasting has to be changed from a means of distribution to a means of communication. What a wonderful apparatus broadcasting could be if it would only receive instead of just transmit, make the recipient speak instead of just listen, relate him to others instead of isolating him from them." In many parts of the world the information which is essential is simply not getting to the proper level for appropriate action. This is primarily due to the power and profit motives of the elite.

Collaboration can be as simple as two persons working together, two or more groups working together, organizations working together, nations or states working together or any combination of the above. However, no matter what the situation, without a common goal or purpose(at least a perceived goal or purpose) and the necessary economic resources, social organization or political leverage in support of the participants, collaboration will fail. It is a commonly held feeling that information about the world's resources is the missing link relative to global sustainable development, however, monitored data is only one very small component in the present state of affairs. Data or information may be very useful and powerful resources once the means to properly incorporate and use them in collaborative and managerial processes is established, and the data is reduced to the point where all levels of technical and managerial personnel who require this information have gained the necessary level of confidence in the technical systems and information being provided to them.

In the domain of global monitoring there are many elements of potential collaboration where Canadians can be extremely effective. Some of these are: research, technical activity, planning, strategic goal development, tools development, standards development, tools supply, processing techniques, analysis techniques, interpretive techniques, modelling techniques, training and education, use of systems as they relate to remote sensing, geographic information management systems, communications, management of resources techniques, and many, many more. These could be applied to almost any sector within the Canadian fabric. Examples could be in the fields of forestry, agriculture, exploration, mining, fisheries, environment, planning, urban development, watershed development, water management, erosion controls, weather observation and prediction, sovereignty control over borders and territories, coastal and marine management and development, aircraft systems, radar and other remote sensing systems, computer systems, mapping systems, aerial photographic systems, and consulting services in a broad range of capacities which all bear directly on global monitoring.

However, as previously stated, it is essential to any collaborative process that there be political leverage, or appropriate policy, as a component to ensure the success of this activity.

CANADIAN POLICY ON
INTERNATIONAL COLLABORATION
WITH RESPECT TO GLOBAL MONITORING

To the best of the authors' knowledge there is no specific policy in place which addresses directly the above topic. However, based on the activities and the involvement of Canadians in both the public and private sectors in a broad range of fields directly related to the topic one must assume that there exists some form of defacto policy or a variety of policies which are interpreted to relate to this broad field. It is clear that there is no coordinated policy thrust which focuses on collaboration specific to global monitoring.

Canada has been and is active in a variety of international forums where collaboration on some components and aspects of global monitoring are included. Some of these forums, but not a complete list, are: The World Economic Summits, the United Nations, NATO, The Commonwealth of Nations, the IBRD, the OECD, etc..

Public sector organizations within Canada which are contributing to this activity, albeit not in a coordinated way, are: the Canadian International Development Agency, the Department of Energy, Mines and Resources, the Department of Environment, the Department of Fisheries, the Department of Agriculture, the Department of External Affairs, Statistics Canada, the Department of National Defence, and the Canadian Space Agency.

Private and academic sector involvement in this field has been active but again not coordinated or focused from a Canadian perspective.

Some activities which will illustrate the involvement of Canadians in this field are:

- the ozone conference and the Montreal Accord;
- support to the UN programs-GRID and GEMS;
- support to the FAO programs;
- the SARSAT Program;
- support to the UN committees on the Peaceful Uses of Outer Space;
- acid rain monitoring programs;
- Canadian aid programs to many countries;
- support to an international conference on remote sensing for development;
- soils survey program support and technical assistance in many countries;

- hydrographic support and training to many countries;
- surveys and mapping support and training to many countries;
- training of thousands of foreign nationals in the appropriate technologies;
- sales and services of Canadian technology in many countries;
- geological surveys and training to many countries;
- technology transfer to many countries in disciplines and technologies directly related to global monitoring;
- industry and individual linkages to many countries in appropriate technologies;;
- contributions to the development of the Law of the Seas Convention
- forest inventory programs support in many countries;
- agricultural inventory programs support in many countries; and,
- water resources development and river management programs support in many countries.

This is by no means an exhaustive listing of Canada's or Canadians involvement in the collaborative process of world development and resources management, but will serve to illustrate the cross section of disciplinary and technical linkages already in place.

All of the above indicate the degree to which Canada and Canadians are implicated in elements of the necessary components of global monitoring, in spite of the absence of a comprehensive policy for collaboration on this topic.

One can only speculate on the potential implications and impact of Canada in this arena if in fact an official policy were in place and implemented with vigour.

CANADIAN POTENTIAL IN GLOBAL MONITORING

Another perspective relative to this issue should be to show the ability of Canada and Canadians to become involved in the collaboration and activities necessary to address the problems associated with global monitoring and world natural resources development issues.

Canada is very well endowed with the tools, techniques and expertise to be extremely effective in the process of implementing a global monitoring program. Also, Canada has the research, education and training facilities to support any funded initiatives in these fields if focus and policy were forthcoming to support such endeavors.

A PRIVATE SECTOR PERSPECTIVE ON CANADIAN POLICY RELATED TO GLOBAL CHANGE INITIATIVES

The Canadian remote sensing private sector views their past, present and potential contribution to global change initiatives as significant, both within Canada and in the international scene. In response to a perceived requirement worldwide, it has developed and implemented unique technologies for addressing global change, and has done so with Canadian government support in some areas, and on its own initiative and internal funding in others. The following outlines the development of Canada's strong private sector, and provides a perspective on how Canadian government policy has influenced our contribution to global change initiatives related to remote sensing technology.

The private sector in Canada, involved in remote sensing activities, has grown rapidly since the early 1970s. At that time, the Canadian government recognized the value of remote sensing for the management of Canadian resources and formed the Canada Centre for Remote Sensing (CCRS) as the centralized government coordinating agency for remote sensing research, development and training activities, for both airborne and spaceborne sensors and data handling. There were only a few small, private sector companies involved in the remote sensing field, and these were carrying-out training for use of new ERTS-1 (now Landsat) satellite data, or data acquisition for CCRS. Through the 1970s, government policy moved from one of focus on internal research and development to an expanded program of contracting to industry, with the intent of fostering development of a strong, broadly-based remote sensing private sector within Canada, and careful concern was addressed to the issue of non-competition between government and industry. In response, the private sector grew from a few small companies to over 100 firms by the mid-1980s. The development of remote sensing within Canada is now within a third phase - that of strong private sector expansion into international markets.

The Canadian remote sensing private sector is relatively unique in the international marketplace, and has reached this position through a combination of government support (internal and external) and its own initiative. For example, one large Canadian remote sensing systems company almost completely dominates the world market in satellite ground station development and implementation. The development of this technology began with a small CCRS contract, grew further with a large contract from Canada's then "Unsolicited Proposal" (UP) fund, and was then introduced worldwide with support from the Canadian International Development Agency (CIDA). These systems are now operating in many locations around the world, as part of the remote sensing data acquisition and handling technology which permits global change to be addressed.

A second example is that of another Canadian company which has captured nearly the whole world market for synthetic aperture radar (SAR) data acquisition and production, based on an efficient digital SAR system mounted in a cost-effective aircraft. The development of this system began with a CCRS contract for remote sensing market evaluation and technology transfer in the 1970s, a UP proposal supported by CCRS to bring a SAR system to Canada, and finally, a private sector undertaking to design, build and operate a new SAR system. This system provides the best current technology in the cloud-covered regions of the world for acquiring information related to global deforestation, soil degradation and topography. Large SAR data acquisition programs have been carried out in developing countries in tropical regions over the past five years; however, these have been supported by funding agencies such as the World Bank, or by individual governments such as the U.S. Defence Mapping Agency, and not, to date, by Canada's international aid agency, CIDA.

There are several Canadian government policy issues which are directly related to Canada's potential international contribution to global change initiatives. These include internal funding for the development of science and technology in Canada, Canada's "Open Skies" policy, and the interest and coordination of Canadian government aid for activities related to global change in developing countries.

Research and development in science and technology in any field is key to national advancement in this field, and this applies directly to remote sensing and global change. Over the past decade, Canadian government funding for scientific research has decreased drastically; at the present time, there are few sources of funds for universities and the rest of the research community to continue their important research efforts in the environmental/global change disciplines. A recent report by the Science Council of Canada (1988) notes the "pervasive uncertainty inherent in current scientific knowledge of environmental effects and causes", and Canada's uncoordinated approach to environmental research. Of significance to such uncertainty and lack of coordination is the lack of a "sustained research commitment", in which it is necessary to "pay science to investigate the state of the environment so as to provide the sorts of answers needed for informed public and private sector actions". Satellite and airborne remote sensing technology is of paramount importance to obtaining a "global view", and programs such as the Canadian Global Change Program (CGCP) Boreal Forest Experiment, NBIOME, CRYSYS and International Satellite Land Surface Climatology (ISLSCP), and Canada's participation in research programs such as the World Ocean Circulation Experiment (WOCE) and the Tropical Oceans-Global Atmosphere (TOGA) must be ensured as important contributions not only to international global change, but also to an improved understanding of Canada's own environment and resources.

Canada's "Open Skies" policy also has important influences on our participation in national and international activities related to remote sensing and global change. At the present time, the policy restricts the operation of foreign aircraft in Canada such that there is little competition for Canadian aerial survey and other remote sensing data acquisition companies. One result of this policy directly relates to the remote sensing of global change; it is historically very difficult to bring airborne remote sensing systems into Canada to participate in global change programs. Also, the unfortunate complement to this policy is that other countries (eg., the United States) then restrict operation of Canadian airborne remote sensing services. The Canadian survey industry, through its industry association, the Geomatics Industry Association of Canada (GIAC), supports abolishment of this restrictive policy, and believes such a change would be beneficial for all concerned.

In order for Canadian efforts related to the use of remote sensing technology for identifying and monitoring global change in the international scene to be effective, they need to be well-planned, coordinated, and committed, with long-term consideration. This requires not only planning and coordination regarding the direction and placement of overall effort, but also planning and coordination amongst the sectors of government, industry and universities. Several examples of such programs are currently operational. One is the Earth Environment Space Initiative (EESI), a new program which is jointly funded by Canadian federal and provincial governments and the private sector. Its objective is to develop spaceborne sensor and data handling technologies related to earth environment monitoring, with the specific proviso that the results be directly applicable to an operational contribution to both Canadian and global environmental programs. The initiative and direct funding participation of the remote sensing industry in this program is a demonstration of the strength and global perspective of this part of the private sector in Canada. A second example is that of a CIDA-sponsored program which is directed toward institution-building in developing countries, and is particularly related to developing their strengths related to environmental monitoring and global change. The Environmental Management Development Initiative (EMDI) in Indonesia, sponsored by CIDA and being implemented by Dalhousie University, is focusing on the use of mapping technologies to build an institution in Indonesia for evaluating and monitoring their environment. To some extent, this program has promoted the Canadian private sector (eg. use of Canadian geographic information systems), and has indicated a growing interest in involving the remote sensing private sector as well. This is viewed as a positive development and an important Canadian contribution. However, expanded coordination between this and other programs, current or planned, within a country would optimize Canadian contributions in global change. CIDA should consider this part of its responsibility.

Thus, Canada has the capability, the demonstrated interest and the technology to make significant progress in international collaboration on global change programs, and has done so through the efforts of government, the private sector and the universities. However, positive changes in Canadian government policy related to basic scientific research, Open Skies and coordination of international programs would serve to optimize Canada's significant potential contribution in this field.

A SUMMARY OF
CANADIAN INTERNATIONAL COLLABORATION
THROUGH THE UNITED NATIONS SYSTEMS

General Background

Canada has been an active supporter of the United Nations (U.N.) since its inception. Although clearly a western-aligned nation and a signatory to NATO, Canada has earned an excellent reputation for moderation, mediation and "peace keeping" initiatives. Our former ambassador to the U.N., Stephen Lewis, clearly demonstrated Canada's strong support for the concept of the U.N. and its system of agencies, as well as a willingness to present a view which is independent of the United States, for instance by resisting the use of funds-withholding as a weapon to reform the more politicized units of the U.N..

In the arena of global monitoring, Canada was an active participant in the Stockholm Conference on the Human Environment in 1972 which was instrumental in the birth of the U.N. Environment Program (UNEP) in 1974 and its Global Environmental Monitoring System (GEMS) (GWYNNE, 1982). UNEP has a system-wide mandate as a coordinator and catalyst of environmental programs. GEMS works through the other U.N. agencies by enlisting their support in five key areas defined by the Stockholm Conference: climate, long-range transport of air-pollutants, renewable resources, the oceans, and human health. Programs are operationally carried out by agencies such as UNESCO, FAO and WHO. Inter-governmental groups such as IUCN also work to provide data and specialized expertise. As a result UNEP is the keystone agency for exercising Canada's global change policy.

Canada is formally a member of UNEP and makes direct monetary contributions. In terms of formal links, External Affairs is the official interface and our High Commissioner to Kenya is also the permanent representative to the UNEP Governing Council held every two years at UNEP Headquarters in Nairobi. Environment Canada is the designated technical department. Canada is a voting member at the Governing Council and is normally represented by a delegation led by the Permanent Representative and including officials from External Affairs and Environment Canada.

In its coordination role, UNEP is expected to leave on-ground implementation to the so-called specialized agencies. The most significant of these for global change are FAO, WHO, WMO and UNDP. Canada's relationship with these agencies varies, and in general also has formal and informal components. (Informal components include joint projects, seconded personnel, participation in advisory meetings, working groups, etc.). Canada's formal relationship to FAO was soured recently through geo-political in-fighting surrounding the election of the Executive Director, but informal collaboration continues strongly.

At any time, there are a few dozen Canadians occupying senior official posts within the U.N., mainly on leave of absence from federal and provincial government departments. Although such officials are primarily to provide specialized expertise, and are specifically prohibited from projecting national policy, their views are usually well respected.

Their presence serves two useful functions: to expose Canadian expertise in environmental management technology, geographic information systems and remote sensing; and, to unofficially exemplify Canada's concern for the global environment.

It can be seen, therefore, that the relationship to the U.N. agencies is multi-faceted and complex. In its catalytic role, UNEP also interacts with non-U.N. intergovernmental agencies which often have Canadian participation, such as IUCN, WWF, the Ramsar Convention, OECD, ICSU, ISO, etc., as well as supporting and encouraging various commissions and meetings, such as the Brundtland Commission and the ozone meeting, both hosted by Canada.

Interaction with UN Agencies

UNEP - GRID

In 1986, a senior official of Environment Canada was seconded at the initiation of UNEP to establish the Nairobi facilities of the Global Resources Information Database (GRID) project. As a companion to the GEMS program, the initial objectives of GRID were (UNEP, 1986):

- to develop geographic information system (GIS) methodologies and procedures for constructing and manipulating global environmental data sets for the purpose of conducting environmental assessments (the continent of Africa has been selected as the case study for this objective);

- to demonstrate that GIS technology, as applied within GRID, is an effective tool which can combine continental and national data sets for resource management and planning applications at the national level (some candidate countries for these demonstrations are China, Indonesia, Kenya, Panama, Peru, Sudan, Tunisia, Thailand and Uganda);

- to establish the framework for cooperation and data exchange within international and intergovernmental organizations which deal with environment-related matters; and,

- to provide training opportunities in GIS and resource data management technologies employed by GRID to the scientists and resource managers from participating developing countries.

The invitation for Canadian participation largely stemmed from our international reputation for expertise in the fields of remote sensing and GIS. Since 1986, the project has expanded and proved very successful (Mooneyhan, 1988) with continuing (very modest) Canadian participation by way of advice.

Policy Note

This type of activity clearly helps showcase Canadian technology and would seem to further national goals as they are understood in the field of climate change. On the other hand this participation was sharply questioned within Environment Canada and only supported very modestly. Line departments such as this do not have a clear mandate to support multilateral or bilateral programs. A number of scientific departments in federal agencies such as Environment Canada, Agriculture Canada, Energy Mines and Resources, and the Department of Fisheries do indeed engage in significant international collaboration, but may have difficulty justifying the resource expenditures when their mandates are interpreted strictly in the Canadian context, for instance against objectives of improving the <u>Canadian</u> environment.

UNEP Governing Council

The 1988 "Special Session" of the UNEP Governing Council was one at which Canada may have played a significant role, although in a low-profile manner. The principal issue of concern to Canada was identified as an apparent shift of emphasis of UNEP toward more operational interactive programs aimed at Africa. This change would represent a reduction in the coordination/catalyst role and a potential duplication of work of these UN agencies. With some consultation with line government departments, the Canadian "position" was developed in a highly informal manner and included in a formal speech to be presented by the Permanent Representative. Canada's plea was for UNEP to maintain a global and long-term perspective and avoid becoming yet another operational aid agency. Canada favored the development of international agreements on such global issues as CFC's, greenhouse gasses, desertification, wetland protection, oceanic pollution, etc.

This position allied Canada with the Scandinavian countries which were very keen to have the Brundtland recommendations incorporated in UNEP policy (the concept of sustainable development or integrated resource management). This alignment was somewhat opposed by traditional allies including the United States and United Kingdom which, at that time, were concerned with the economic effects of agreements to control industrial emissions. Other nations clearly had very specific positions; for instance, Brazil opposed any efforts to regulate deforestation on the basis that this interfered with sovereignty.

Canada played a low-key moderator role and was successful in obtaining small but important adjustments on wording of the various resolutions, and the alliance with Scandinavian countries led directly to the successful Montreal ozone meeting.
Policy Note:

> The Canadian position was developed within the delegation at the last minute with little or no official direction from the political or senior bureaucratic levels. Thus the position resulted from an overall understanding of the Canadian moderate view as embodied in the delegation's work as public servants. It is worthy of note that specific positions were provided with regard to sensitive political issues such as the PLO and certain governments, but no specific positions on environmental issues.

WHO - Water Quality Monitoring

Shortly after the inauguration of the GEMS/Water program in 1976, Canada took on the job of maintaining a data base of global water quality on behalf of WHO (the program is sponsored by UNEP but WHO is the operational agency along with UNESCO and WMO). This data base, now called GLOWDAT, is held at Environment Canada's water research facilities in Burlington, Ontario. Since it is only partially funded by UNEP/WHO, it in fact represents an in- kind contribution to global monitoring.

Policy Note:

> The provision of the free service to WHO has recently been internally audited and reviewed (implying negative concerns). The policy issue again is whether this is legitimately part of the mandate of Inland Waters, or, is it a good thing to do? who has the mandate to do it? are we getting sufficient credit for the service?

Collaboration with other International Agencies

A study in 1988 of the "International Water-Related Activities" within one branch of Environment Canada indicated some sort of participation in 36 separate international organizations. The total involvement of Canada is largely on an individual basis by government officials, academics and private sector scientists. Many of the organizations have close relationships to UN Agencies, and many deal with various aspects of global change, such as OECD, IUCN, ISO, ICSU (eg. their CODATA and SCOPE committees), IUG (eg. IGBP) and so on. Relationships between these are complex and membership is in no way targeted or coordinated.

Memberships, chairmanships, etc. are largely the result of personal expertise, personal contacts and personal commitments. From an organizational perspective, the members are not necessarily the most appropriate persons, hierarchically, but on the other hand this process of personal involvement seems to be both effective and welcome, seemingly an extension of the concept of academic freedom. For whatever reason, Canada has a high representation at senior levels in these organizations. This reflects well on the country and provides a valuable, albeit informal, mechanism for the promotion of Canadian policy.

Some Issues

All of the above examples are unscientific and anecdotal. If these are as typical as believed to be, they raise a number of issues such as the following.

- **Lack of a well documented national policy:** It appears that our official and unofficial delegates to international collaboration have no specific instructions or unified national policy to provide guidance. It is clear that some other countries do have very specific positions for their delegates. Is this good or bad? Fixed positions surely limit flexibility. Perhaps Canada gains from this lack of "policy" in the freedom available for compromise and mediation. Perhaps a clear policy would provide strength and even greater success.

- **Lack of national coordination of international collaboration:** The examples show a lack of coordination even within one particular agency, giving the impression of a hit-and-miss approach. In general it is not only unclear what the policy is but, as well, who is putting it forward. Conflicting views thus may be (and are) put forward by different Canadian representatives. Yet it seems to work well. It seems doubtful that such "ad-hocery" is optimal. The key would be to increase effectiveness through a level of coordination which does not infringe on traditional freedoms and practical flexibility.

- **Level of Recognition:** Except for a few ribbon-cutting events, such as the signing of conventions, there is little public knowledge or recognition of the on-going contributions and successes of Canadian "policy" and practices. There is similarly little official support for individual and group efforts which may bend conventional mandates to the national benefit. This extends to a lack of tangible recognition in the forms of program or resource funding (government and academic). Perhaps a well defined policy and objectives would also aid in providing a framework for recognition of success. Or is it the contrary? Are we successful and maintain credibility as a nation because we do not "gloat" over "victories" in the global environment?

REFERENCES

INTRODUCTION

Rasool, S.I., 1987, Potential of Remote Sensing for the Study of Global Change, Advances in Space Research 7(1), Pergamon Press.

IFIAS (International Federation of Institute for Advanced Study) 1988, The Human Dimensions of Global Change: An International Programme on Human Interactions with the Earth. Report of the Tokyo International Symposium on the Human Response to Global Change. Hosted by the United Nations University, 56 pp.

ICSU (International Council of Scientific Union), no date, A Study of Global Change, 9 pp.

Cihlar, J., E. LeDrew, H. Edel, W. Evans, D. McKay, L. McNutt, A. Roger, 1989. Contribution of Satellite Observations to the Canadian Global Change Program, Report No. 3. Canada Centre for Remote Sensing and the Royal Society of Canada, 48 pp.

Joint Communiques of the Economic Summit of Paris France, July, 1989.

CHAPTER ONE

Boer, G.J., N.A. McFarlane, R. Laprise, J.D. Henderson, and J.-P. Blanchet, 1984a: The Canadian Climate Centre spectral atmospheric general circulation model, Atmos.-Ocean, 22, 397-429.

Boer, G.J., N.A. McFarlane, and R. Laprise, 1984b: The climatology of the Canadian Climate Centre general circulation model as obtained from a five-year simulation, Amos.-Ocean, 22, 430-475.

Boer, G.J., N.A. McFarlane, and M. Lazare, 1991a: Greenhouse gas induced climate change simulated with the Canadian Climate Centre second generation general circulation model. Accepted for publication in J. Climate.

Boer, G.J., K. Arpe, M. Blackburn, M. Déqué, W.L. Gates, T.L. Hart, H. Le Treut, E. Roeckner, D.A. Sheinin, I. Simmonds, R.N.B. Smith, T. Tokioka, R.T. Wetherald and D. Williamson, 1991b: An intercomparison of the climates simulated by 14 atmospheric general circulation models. CAS/JSC Working Group on Numerical Experimentation Report No. 15, WMO/TD-No. 425, World Met. Organiz., Geneva, 37 pp.

Boer, G.J., 1992: Climate change and the regulation of the surface moisture and energy budgets, submitted to J. Climate.

Cess, R.D., G.L. Potter, J.P. Blanchet, G.J. Boer, A.D. Del Genio, M. Déqué, V. Dymnikov, V. Galin, W.L. Gates, S.J. Ghan, J.T. Kiehl, A.A. Lacis, H. Le Treut, Z.-X. Li, X.-Z. Liang, B.J. McAvaney, V.P. Meleshko, J.F.B. Mitchell, J.-J. Morcrette, D.A. Randall, L. Rikus, E. Roeckner, J.F. Royer, U. Schlese, D.A. Sheinin, A. Slingo, A.P. Sokolov, K.E. Taylor, W.M. Washington, R.T. Wetherald, I. Yagai and M.-H. Zang, 1990: Intercomparison and interpretation of climate feedback processes in nineteen atmospheric general circulation models, J. Geophys, Res., 95, 601-16, 615.

Hartmann, D.L., V. Ramanathan, A. Berror, and G.E. Hunt, 1986: Earth radiation budget data and climate research. Rev. Geophys., 24, 493-468.

McFarlane, N.A., G.J. Boer and M. Lazare, 1991: The Canadian Climate Centre second generation general circulation model and its equilibrium climate. Accepted for publication in J. Climate.

Parkinson, C.L., Comiso, J.C., Zwally, H.J., Cavalieri, D.M., Gloersen, P., and Campbell, W.J., 1987: Arctic Sea Ice, 1973-976: Satellite Passive-Microwave Observations. NASA SP-489. NASA Scientific and Technical Information Branch, Washington, D.C.

Zwally, H.J., J.C. Comiso, C.L. Parkinson, W.J. Campbell, F.D. Carsey and P. Gloersen, 1983: Antarctic sea ice, 1973-1976: satellite passive-microwave observations. SP-459, NASA, Washington, DC, 206 pp.

CHAPTER TWO

Evans W. F. J., Boville B. W., McConnell J. C. and Henderson G., The Simulation of Antarctic Ozone with Chemical and Dynamical Effects, Geophys. Res. Lett., 13, pp 1323-1327, (1986).

Evans W. F. J., A Hole In the Arctic Ozone Layer During March, 1986, Can. J. Phys., 67, pp 161-163 (1989).

Evans W. F. J., Henderson G. H. and McConnell J. C. , The Simulation of Antarctic Ozone Profiles During
the 1986 Spring Depletion Anomaly, J. Geophys. Res., 95, 1899-1908 (1990).

Evans W. F. J., Ozone Depletion In the Arctic Vortex at Alert During February 1989, Geophys. Res. Lett. 17, pp 167-170 (1990).

Henderson G. S., Evans W. F. J., McConnell J. C. and Templeton E. J., A Numerical Model for One Dimensional Simulation of Stratospheric Chemistry, Atmosphere-Ocean, 25, No.4, pp 427-457 (1987).

McConnell J.C. and Evans W. F. J., Model Simulation of Chemical Depletion of Ozone in the Arctic in Winter 1989, J. Geophys. Res., 96, pp xx-yy (1990).

CHAPTER THREE

Beamish, R.J. and Harvey, H.H. 1972. Acidification of the La Cloche Mountain lakes, Ontario and resulting fish mortalities. Journal of the Fisheries Research Board of Canada 29:1131-1143.

Brooks, D.J. 1975. Landsat measures of water clarity. Photogrammetric Engineering and Remote Sensing 40:1269-1272.

Conroy, N.I., Hawley, K., and Keller, W. 1978. Extensive Monitoring of Lakes in the Greater Sudbury Area, 1974-76 Technical Report, Sudbury: M.O.E.

Dillon, P.J., Yan, N.D., and Harvey, H.H. 1984. Acidic deposition: effects on aquatic ecosystems. Critical Reviews in Environmental Control 13:167-194.

Effler, S.W., Schafran, G.C., and Driscoll, C.T. 1985. Partitioning light attenuation in an acidic lake. Canadian Journal of Fisheries and Aquatic Sciences 42:1707-1711.

Fisher, L.T., Scarpace, F.L., and Thomsen, R.G. 1979. Multidate Landsat lake quality monitoring program. Photogrammetric Engineering and Remote Sensing 45:519-527.

Fung, T. and LeDrew, E. 1987. Application of principal components analysis to change detection. Photogrammetric Engineering and Remote Sensing 53:1649-1658.

Gallie, E.A. 1990. Chromaticity analysis of Landsat MSS and TM imagery of Chilko Lake, British Columbia, using a theoretical optical water quality model. Ph.D. Thesis. University of British Columbia. 262 pp.

Gordon, H.R., O.B. Brown and M.M. Jacobs. 1975. Computed relationships between the inherent and apparent optica properties of a flat homogeneous ocean. Applied Optics 14:417-427.

Gorham, E. and Gordon, A.G. 1960. The influence of smelter fumes upon the chemical composition of lake waters near Sudbury, Ontario, and upon the surrounding vegetation. Canadian Journal of Botany 38:477-487.

Hilton, J. 1984. Airborne remote sensing for freshwater and estuarine monitoring. Water Research 18:1195-1223.

Keller, W. and Pitblado, J.R. 1986. Water quality changes in Sudbury area lakes: A comparison of synoptic surveys in 1974-76 and 1981-83. Water, Air, and Soil Pollution 29:285-296.

Keller, W. and Pitblado, J.R. 1990. Long-term chemical responses of acidic lakes in the Sudbury, Ontario area to reduced smelter emissions. (In preparation)

Keller, W., Pitblado, J.R., and Conroy, N.I. 1986. Water quality improvements in the Sudbury, Ontario, Canada area related to reduced smelter emissions. Water, Air, and Soil Pollution 31:765-774.

Lathrop, Jr., R.G. and Lillesand, T.M. 1986. Use of Thematic Mapper data to assess water quality in Green Bay and Central Lake Michigan. Photogrammetric Engineering and Remote Sensing 52:671-680.

Lillesand, T.M., Johnson, W.L., Deuell, R.L., Lindstrom, O.M., and Meisner, D.E. 1983. Use of Landsat data to predict the trophic state of Minnesota lakes. Photogrammetric Engineering and Remote Sensing 49:219-229.

Lindell, L.T. 1986. Operational water quality surveillance in Sweden using Landsat MSS data. Proceedings, Tenth Canadian Symposium on Remote Sensing, pp. 385-394

Middleton, E.M. and Munday, Jr., J.C. 1980. Landsat - What is operational in water resources? Proceedings, Sixth Canadian Symposium on Remote Sensing, Halifax, pp. 43-52.

Pitblado, J.R. 1984. Monitoring the impacts of airborne pollutants with digital remote sensing: progress and prospects in the Sudbury area. Laurentian University Review 16:67-79.

Pitblado, J.R. 1987a. Lake Water Quality Monitoring Based on Remotely Sensed Data: Final Report. M.O.E./R.A.C Project No. 267RR. (Unpublished report).

Pitblado, J.R. 1987b. Remote sensing determinations of Northeastern Ontario lake characteristics. Proceedings, Part B. Water Quality Research, 3 pp., Technology Transfer Conference, Ontario Ministry of the Environment, Royal York Hotel, Toronto, November 30 - December 1.

Pitblado, J.R. 1988. Differences in Landsat MSS/TM senso responses for acidic and non-acidic lakes in the Sudbury area. Proceedings, 31st Conference, International Association for Great Lakes Research. McMaster University, Hamilton. May 17-20.

Pitblado, J.R. 1990a. Feasibility of monitoring the recovery of acidified lakes in the Sudbury area using remotely sensed data. Proceedings, International Conference on Acidic Deposition: Its Nature and Impacts. Glasgow, Scotland. September 16-21.

Pitblado, J.R. 1990b. Sudbury (Canada) lakes viewed from Landsat-5. (In preparation).

Pitblado, J.R. and Dempsey, D.A. 1989. What does an acidic lake "look" like? Operational Geographer 7:20-23.

Pitblado, J.R. and Keller, W. 1984. Monitoring of Northeastern Ontario Lakes, 1981-1983. Data Report. Sudbury: Ontario Ministry of the Environment. (348 pp.).

Pitblado, J.R., Tanis, F.J., and Woitowich, W.A. 1987. Remote sensing and the monitoring of lake acidification in Northeastern Ontario, Canada: Preliminary observations. pp. 364-371, IN R.

Perry, R.M. Harrison, J.N.B. Bell and J.N. Lester (eds.) Acid Rain: Scientific and Technical Advances. London (England): Publications Division, Selper Ltd. (Proceedings, International Acid Rain Conference, Sheraton Hotel, Lisbon, Portugal September 1-3).

Richards, J.A. 1986. Remote Sensing Digital Image Analysis. N.Y.: Springer-Verlag.

Scarpace, F.L., Holmquist, K.W., and Fisher, L.T. 1979. Landsat analysis of lake quality. Photogrammetric Engineering and Remote Sensing 45:623-633.

Verdin, J.P. 1985. Monitoring water quality conditions in a large western reservoir with Landsat imagery. Photogrammetric Engineering and Remote Sensing 51:343-353.

Witzig, A. and Whitehurst, C. 1981. Literature review of the current use and technology of MSS digital data for lake trophic classification. Proceedings of the 1981 Fall Meeting of the American Society of Photogrammetry, San Francisco, pp. 1-20.

Yan, N.D. 1983. Effects of changes in pH on transparency and thermal regimes of Lohi Lake, near Sudbury, Ontario. Canadian Journal of Fisheries and Aquatic Sciences 40:621-626.

CHAPTER FOUR

Aber, P.G., E. Vowinckel, 1972, Evaluation of North Water Spring Ice Cover From Satellite Photographs, Arctic, 25:263-271

Barber, D. G., J.M. Piwowar, E.F. LeDrew, 1990, The SIMS Project: The Study of Sea Ice as a Climate Change Indicator, Proceedings, ISPRS Symposium on Global and Environmental Monitoring, Victoria, B.C., September.

Barry, R.G., 1984, Possible CO2-Induced Warming Effects on the Cryosphere, pp 571-604 in, N.-A. Morner and W. Karlen (eds.), Climatic Changes on a Yearly Millennial Basis, D. Reidel Publishing Company.

Barry, R. G., A. Henderson - Sellers, K. P. Shine, 1984,Climate Sensitivity and the Marginal Cryosphere, pp.221-237, in J.E. Hansen, T. Takahashi (eds.), Climate Processes and Climate Sensitivity, Geophysical Monograph 29, Maurice Ewing Volume 5, American Geophysical Union, 368 pp.

Bliss, L. C., 1977, General Summary, Truelove Lowland Ecosystem, pp. 657-675, in., L. C. Bliss (ed.), Truelove Lowland, Devon Island, Canada: A High Arctic Ecosystem. The University of Alberta Press, 714 PP.

Bradley, R. S., J. England, 1978, Recent Climatic Fluctuations of the Canadian High Arctic and Their Significance for Glaciology, Arct. Alp. Res., 10(4), pp. 715-731.

Carleton, A.M., (1985), Synoptic Cryosphere-Atmosphere Interactions in the Northern Hemisphere from DMSP Image Analysis, Int. J. Rem. Sens., 6:239-261.

Cavalieri, D.J., C. L. Parkinson, 1987, On the Relationship Between Atmospheric Circulation and the Fluctuations in the Sea Ice Extents of the Bering and Okhostk Seas, J. Geophys, Res., 92, (C7):7141-7162

Cavalieri, D.J., H.J. Zwally, 1985, Satellite Observations of Sea Ice, Adv. Space Res., 5:247-255.

Central Intelligence Agency, 1978, Polar Regions Atlas, Nat. Foreign Assessment Cen. CIA, Washington, D.C., 66 pp.

Gloersen, P., W.J. Campbell, 1988, Variations in the Arctic, Antarctic, and Global Sea Ice Covers During 1978-1987 as Observed with the Nimbus 7 Scanning Multichannel Microwave Radiometer, J. Geophys. Res., 93 (C9):10666-10674

Hansen, J., A. Lacis, D. Rind, G. Russell, P. Stone, I. Fung, R. Ruedy, J. Lerner, 1984, Climate Sensitivity: An Analysis of Feedback Mechanisms, pp. 130-163, in, J.E. Hansen, T. Takahashi (eds.), Climate Processes and Climate Sensitivity, Geophysical Monograph 29, Maurice Ewing Volume 5, American Geophysical Union. 368 pp.

House of Commons, 1987, Canada's Space Program: A Voyage to the Future, Report of the Standing Committee on Research, Science and Technology, House of Commons, Issue No. 35, 51 pp. Ottawa, Ontario.

Jones, P.D., and P.M. Kelly, 1983, The Spatial and Temporal Characteristics of Northern Hemisphere Surface Air Temperature Variations, J. of Climatology, 3(3), pp. 243-252.

Jones, P.D., 1988, Hemispheric Surface Air Temperature Variations: Recent Trends and an Update to 1987, J. Climate, 1:654-660.

Kellogg, W.W., 1983, Feedback Mechanisms in the Climate System Affecting Future Levels of Carbon Dioxide, J. of Geophys. Res., 88, pp. 1263-1269.

LeDrew, E.F., 1988, Development Processes for Five Depression Systems Within the Polar Basin, J. Climatology, 8:125-153.

McLaren, A.S., M.C. Serreze, R.G. Barry, 1987, Seasonal Variations of Sea Ice Motion in the Canada Basin and Their Implications, Geophy. Res. Letters, 14(11):1123-1126.

Muller, F., A. Ohmura, R. Braithwaite, 1976, On the Climatic Influence of North Water, XXII Int. Geographical Congress, Symposium on the Geography of Polar Countries, Hydrometeorology Publications House, Leningrad, pp 55-58.

Naskamura, N., A.H. Oort,1988, Atmospheric Heat Budgets of the Polar Regions, J. Geophys. Res., 93,(D8):9510-9524.

NASA, (no date), SAR, Earth Observing System, Instrument Panel Report, Volume IIf, 233 pp.

NASA, (no date), HMMR, Earth Observing System, Instrument Panel Report, Volume IIe, 59 pp.

Parkinson, C.L., 1983, On the Development and Cause of the Weddell Polynya in a Sea Ice Simulation, J. Phys, Ocean., 13: 501-511.

Parkinson, C. L., W. W. Kellogg, 1979, Arctic Sea Ice Decay. Simulated for a CO2-induced Temperature Rise, Climatic Change, 2(2), pp. 149-162.

Sansom, J., 1989, Antarctic Surface Temperature Time Series, J. Climate, 2:1164-1172.

Sarmiento, J.L., J.R. Tottweiler, 1984, A New Model for the Role of the Ocean in Determining Atmospheric CO2, Nature, 308:621-623.

Schlesinger, M.E., 1984, Climate Model Simulation of CO2- Induced Climatic Change, pp 141-235 in, Advances in Geophysics, 26, B. Salzman, Ed., Academic Press, New York, ix,349 pp.+illust.

Steffen, K., 1989, Energy Flux Estimation over Sea Ice in Northern Baffin Bay Based on Satellite Passive Microwave Measurements, International Geographical Union Study Group on Marine Geography, MareCont '89, Wilhelmshaven FRG. 12pp.

Steffen, K., J.E. Lewis, 1988, Surface Temperatures and Sea Ice Typing for Northern Baffin Bay, Int. J. Remote Sensing, 9:409-422.

Steffen, K., J.A. Maslanik, 1988, Comparison of Nimbus 7 Scanning Multichannel Microwave Radiometer Radiance and Derived Sea Ice Concentrations with Landsat Imagery for the North Water Area of Baffin Bay, J. Geophys. Res., 93(C9):10769-10781.

UCAR, 1988, Arctic Interactions, Recommendations for an Arctic Component in the International Geosphere-Biosphere Programme, UCAR Office for Interdisciplinary Earth Studies, Report OIES-4, Boulder Colorado, 45 pp.

Zwally, H.J., C.L. Parkinson, J.C. Comiso, 1983, Variability of Antarctic Sea Ice and Changes in Carbon Dioxide, Science, 220:1005-1012

CHAPTER FIVE

Andersen, T. and H. Odegaard, 1980: Application of satellite data for snow mapping. Report no. 3, Norwegian National Committee for Hydrology, Oslo, Norway.

Bowley, C.J., J.C. Barnes, and A. Rango, 1981: Application systems verification and transfer project. Vol. VIII: Satellite snow mapping an runoff prediction handbook. NASA Technical Paper 1829, Washington, USA.

Bergstrom, Sten and Maja Brandt, 1985: Snow mapping and hydrological forecasting by airborne gamma ray spectrometry in northern Sweden. In, Hydrological Applications of Remote Sensing and Remote Data Transmission (Proc. Hamburg Symp., August, 1983) (ed.B.E. Goodison). IAHS Publ. no. 145, 421-428

Carroll, T.R. 1987: Operational airborne measurements of snow water equivalent and soil moisture using terrestrial gamma radiation in the United States. In, Large Scale Effects of Seasonal Snow Cover (Proc. Vancouver Symp., August, 1987) (ed. B.E. Goodison, R. Barry and J. Dozier). IAHS Publ. no. 166, 213-223.

Carroll, T.R., J. Glynn and B.E. Goodison, 1983: A comparison of U.S. and Canadian airborne gamma radiation snow water equivalent measurements. Proc. Western Snow Conference, 51st Annual Meeting, Vancouver, Washington, April 1983, 27-37.

Chang, A.T.C., J.L. Foster and D.K. Hall, 1987: NIMBUS-7 derived global snow covr parameters. Annals of Glaciology, 9, 39-44.

Chang, A.T.C., J.L. Foster, D.K. Hall, A. Rango and B.K. Hartline, 1982: Snow water equivalent estimation by microwave radiometry. Cold Regions Science and Technology, 5, 259-267.

Dewey, Kenneth F. and Richard Heim, Jr., 1982: A digital archive of Northern Hemisphere Snow Cover, November 1966 through December 1980. Bull.Am.Met.Soc., 63(10), 1132-1141.

Dhanju, M.S., 1985: Studies of Himalayan snow cover area from satellites. In, Hydrological Applications of Remote Sensing and Remote Data Transmission (Proc. Hamburg, Symp. August, 1983)(ed. B.E. Goodison). IAHS Publ. no. 145, 401-409.

Dozier, Jeff and Danny Marks, 1987: Snow mapping and classification from Landsat Thematic Mapper data. Annals of Glaciology, 9, 97-103.

Ferner, S., and I. Sutherland, 1987: The utility of computer processed NOAA imagery for snow cover mapping and streamflow simulation in Alberta. In, Large Scale Effects of Seasonal Snow Cover (Proc. Vancouver Symp., August, 1987) (ed. B.E. Goodison, R. Barry, J. Dozier). IAHS Publ. no. 166, 173-185.

Fortin, J.P., J. P. Villeneuve, A. Guilbot and B. Seguin, 1985. Development of a modular hydrological forcasting model based on remotely sensed data, for interactive utilization on a microcomputer. In, Hydrologic Applications of Space Technology (ed. A.I. Johnson). IAHS Publ. no. 160, 307-320.

Goodison, B.E., 1989: Determination of areal snow water equivalent on the Canadian prairies using passive microwave satellite data. In, Quantitative Remote Sensing: An Economic Tool for the Nineties. Proc. IGARSS'89, July 10-14, 1989, Vancouver, Canada. Vol. 3, 1243-1246.

Goodison, B.E. (ed.), 1985: Hydrological Applications of Remote Sensing and Remote Data Transmission. Proc. Hamburg Symp., August 1983. IAHS Publ. no. 145, 684 pp.

Goodison, B.E., I. Rubinstein, F.W. Thirkettle, 1986: Snow cover determination on the Canadian Prairies using microwave radiometry. In, Modelling Snowmelt Induced Processes (Proc. Budapest Symp., July, 1986) (ed. E. Morris). IAHS Publ. no. 155, 163-173.

Goodison, B.E., S. Waterman, and E. Langham, 1980: Application of synthetic aperture radar to snow cover monitoring. Proc., 6th Canadian Symp. on Remote Sensing, Halifax, N.S. May 21-23, 1980, 263-271.

Gray, D.M. and D.H. Male (ed.), 1981: Handbook of Snow: Principles, Processes, Management and Use. Pergamon Press, London, 776 pp.

Hall, Dororthy K. and Jaroslav Martinec, 1985: Remote Sensing of Ice and Snow. Chapman and Hall, New York, 189 pp.

Hall, D.K., A.T.C. Chang and J.L. Foster, 1986: Detection of the depth hoar layer in the snow-pack of the Arctic coastal plain of Alaska, USA, using satellite data. J. Glaciol., 32, 87-94.

Hallikainen, M.T., 1984: Retrieval of snow water equivalent from NIMBUS-7 SMMR data: effect of land cover categories and weather conditions. IEEE J. of Oceanic Eng., Vol. OE-9(5), 372-276.

Hallikainen, Martti, Petrie Jolma, Martti Tiuri and Risto Kuittinen, 1986: Mapping of snow cover parameters by a spaceborne microwave radiometer. In, Hydrologic Applications of Space Technology (Proc. Cocoa Beach Workshop) (ed., A.I. Johnson). IAHS Publ. no. 160, 1986.

Johnson, A.I. (ed.), 1986: Hydrologic Applications of Space Technology. Proc. Cocoa Beach Workshop, August, 1985. IAHS Publ. no. 160, 488 pp.

Johnstone, K. and S. Ishida, 1984: An Analogue/Digital Procedure for the Mapping of Snow Cover from Satellite Imagery. Canadian Climate Centre Report No. 84-9, Atmospheric Environment Service, Downsview, 28 pp.

Kuittinen, R., 1988: Application of Remote Sensing to Hydrology. Report to the 8th session of the WMO Commission for Hydrology, January 1988. World Meteorological Organization, Geneva, Switzerland.

Kuittinen, R., 1986: Determination of areal snow water equivalent values using satellite imagery and aircraft gamma-ray spectrometry. In, Hydrologic Applications of Space Technology (Proc. Cocoa Beach Workshop, August, 1985) (ed. A.I. Johnson). IAHS Publ. no. 160, 181-189.

Kukla, G. and D.A. Robinson, 1980: Annual cycle of surface albedo. Mon.Wea.Rev., 108, 56-68.

Kunzi, K.F., S. Patil and H. Rott, 1982: snow cover parameters: Retrieval from NIMBUS-7 Scanning Multichannel Microwave Radiometer (SMMR) data. IEEE Geosci. Rem. Sens., GE-20, 452-467.

Lucas, Richard M., Andrew R. Harrison and Eric C. Barrett, 1989: A multispectral snow area algorithm for operational 7-day snow cover monitoring. In, Remote Sensing and Large Scale Global Processes (Proc. Baltimore Symp., May 1989) (ed. A. Rango). IAHS Publ. no. 186, 161-166.

Matson, M., 1986: NOAA satellite-derived snow cover data base: past, present and future. In, Snow Watch'85, Glaciological Data Report GD-18, World Data Center for Glaciology, Boulder, 115-124.

Matson, M., C.F. Ropelewski and M.S. Varnadore, 1986: An Atlas of satellite-derived Northern Hemispheric Snow Cover Frequency. NOAA Atlas, NOAA/NESDIS/NWS, Washington, 74pp.

Matson, M. and D.R. Wiesnet, 1981: New data base for climate studies. Nature, 189, 451-456.

McGinnis, D.F., J.A. Pritchard and D.R. Wiesnet, 1975: Determination of snow depth and snow extent from NOAA-2 satellite very high resolution radiometer data. Wat.Resour.Res., 11(66), 897-902.

O'Neill, A.D.J., and D.M. Gray, 1973: Spatial and temporal variations of the albedo of prairie snowpack. The Role of Snow and Ice in Hydrology: Proc.Banff Symp., Sept. 1972, Unesco-WMO-IAHS, Paris, Vol. 1, 176-186.

Peteherych, S., B. Goodison, V. Swail, and A. Saulesleja, 1983: CLOUDS: A fundamental limitation to satellite remote sensing in the visible spectral region. Proc. 8th Canadian Symp. on Remote Sensing. Montreal, Que., May 3-6, 1983, 223-228.

Power, J.M., C.J. Merry, N.B.A. Trivett and S.E. Waterman, 1980: Snowpack estimation in the Saint John River Basin. Proc. 14th Int. Symp. on Rem.Sens. of Envir. San Jose, Costa Rica, April 23-30, 467-486.

Prokacheva, V.G., 1985: Snow Cover on the Stanovoe Upland determined by satellite imagery. In, Hydrological Applications of Remote Sensing and Remote Data Transmission (Proc. Hamburg Symp., August, 1983) ed. B.E. Goodison), IAHS Publ. no. 145, 395-399.

Ramamoorthi, A.S., 1987: Snow cover area (SCA) is the main factor in forecasting snowmelt runoff from major river basins. In, Large Scale Effects of Seasonal Snow Cover (Proc. Vancouver Symp., August, 1987) (ed. B.E. Goodison, R. Barry, J. Dozier). IAHS Publ. no. 166, 187-198.

Rango, A., 1988: Progress in developing an operational snowmelt-runoff forecast model with remote sensing input. Nordic Hydrology, 19, 65-76.

Rango, A.J. Martinec, J. Foster, D. Marks, 1985: Resolution in operational remote sensing of snow cover. In, Hydrological Applications of Remote Sensing and Remote Data Transmission (Proc. Hamburg Symp., August 1985) (ed. B.E. Goodison). IAHS Publ. no 145, 371-382.

Rango, A., 1985: A survey of progress in remote sensing of snow and ice. In Hydrological Applications of Remote Sensing and Remote Data Transmission (Proc. Hamburg Symp., August, 1983) (ed. B.E. Goodison). IAHS Publ. no. 145, 347-359.

Rango, A., A.T.C. Chang and J. Foster, 1979: The utilization of spaceborne radiometers for monitoring of snowpack properties. Nordic Hydrology, 10, 25-40.

Robinson, D.A., M. Wilson, G. Kukla and A. Henderson-Sellers, 1983: Observation of surface albedo and its variation for climate models. Proc. 17th Int. Symp. Remote Sensing of Environment, Ann Arbor, ERIM, 469-477.

Robinson, David A. and George Kukla, 1985: Maximum surface albedo of seasonally snow-covered lands in the Northern Hemisphere. J. Clim. and Appl. Met., 24, 402-411.

Robock, A., 1980: The seasonal cycle of snow cover, sea ice and surface albedo. Mon. Wea. Rev., 108, 2667-285.

Rott, H., G. Domik, C. Matzler, H. Miller, K.G. Lenhart, 1985: Study on Use and Characteristics of SAR for Land Snow and Ice Applications, Final Report. Institut fuer Meteorologie and Geophysik Universitaet Insbruck, Mitteilung Nr. 1, 162 pp.

United States National Weather Service, 1988: National Remote Sensing Hydrology Program, Airborne and Satellite Snow Cover Measurements, A User's Guide, Version 3.0. Internal Publication of the Office of Hydrology, November 1, 1988, 54 pp.

Schultz, G.A., 1986: Satellite data as input for long-term and short-term hydrological models. In, Hydrologic Applications of Space Technology (Proc. Cocoa Beach Workshop, August, 1985) (ed. A.I. Johnson). IAHS Publ. no. 160, 297-306.

Vershinina, L.K., 1985: The use of aerial gamma surveys of snowpack for spring runoff forecasts. In, Hydrological Applications of Remote Sensing and Remote Data Transmission (Proc. Hamburg Symp., August, 1983) (ed. B.E. Goodison). IAHS Publ. no. 145, 411-420.
Waterman, S.E., W.D. Hogg, A.J. Hanssen and V.L. Polavarapu, 1980: Computer analysis of TIROS-N/NOAA- 6 satellite data for operational snowcover mapping. Proc. 6th Symp. on Remote Sensing, Halifax, N.S., May 21-23, 1980, 435-442.

Wiesnet, D.R., C.F. Ropelewski, G.J. Kukla and D.A. Robinson, 1987: A discussion of the accuracy of NOAA satellite-derived global seasonal snowcover measurements. In, Large Scale Effects of Seasonal Snow Cover (Proc.k Vancouver Symp., August, 1987) (ed. B.E. Goodison, R.G. Barry and J. Dozier). IAHS Publ. no. 166, 291-304.

Zeng Qunzhu, Cao Meisheng, Feng Zuezhi, Liang Fengxian, Chen Xianzhang and Sheng Wenkun, 1985: A study of spectral reflection characteristics for snow, ice and water in north China. In, Hydrological Applications of Remote Sensing and Remote Data Transmission (Proc. Hamburg Symp., Aug. 1983) (ed. B.E. Goodison). IAHS Publ. no. 145, 451-462.

CHAPTER SIX

Arthur, M.A., W.E. Dean, S.O. Schlanger, 1985, "Variations in the global carbon cycle during the cretaceous related to climate, volcanism and changes in atmospheric CO_2," in "The carbon cycle and atmospheric CO_2: natural variations Archaean to present," AGU Geophysical Monograph No. 32, Sundquist and Broeker, Eds, 504-529.

Ayers, G.P., J.P. Ivey and R.W. Gillett, 1991, "Coherence between seasonal cycles of dimethyl sulphide, methane sulphonate and sulphate in marine air," Nature, 349, 404-406.

Bakun, A., 1990, "Global climate change and intensification of coastal ocean upwelling," Science, 247, 198-201.

Bardach, J.E., 1989, "Global warming and the coastal zone: some effects on sites and activities," Climatic Change, 15, 117-150.

Barnett, T., F. Kelley, and B. Holt, 1989, "Estimation of the two-dimensional ocean current shear field with a synthetic aperture radar," J. Geophys. Res., 94, 16087-16096.

Barnola, J.M., D. Raynaud, Y.S. Korotkevich and C. Lorius, 1987, "Vostok ice core provides 160,000 year record of atmospheric CO_2," Nature, 329, 408-414.

Bolin, B., B.R. Doos, J. Jaeger and R.A. Warwick, 1986, "The greenhouse effect, climatic change and ecosystems," SCOPE 29, Scientific Committee on Problems of the Environment, Wiley, UK.

Bernstein, R.L., 1982, "Sea surface temperature estimation using the NOAA-6 satellite Advanced Very High Resolution Radiometer," J. Geophys. Res., 87, 9455-9465.

Broecker, W.S., 1987, "Unpleasant surprises in the greenhouse?" Nature, 238, 123-126.

Budyko, M.I., 1974, "Climate and life," International Geophysics Series, Vol. 18, Academic Press.

Canadian Global Change Program, 1989, "Contributions of satellite observations to the Canadian Global Change Program," Canadian Global Change Program, Report No. 3, Royal Society of Canada.

Cane, M.A. and S.E. Zebiak, 1985, "A theory for El Nino and the Southern Oscillation," Science, 228, 1085-1087.

Charlson, R.J., J.E. Lovelock, M.O. Andreae and S.G. Warren, 1987, "Oceanic phytoplankton, atmospheric sulphur, cloud albedo and climate," Nature, 326, 655-661.

Cushing, D.H., 1982, "Climate and fisheries," Academic Press, London, UK.

Davidson, J. and D.E. Harrison, 1990, "Comparison of Seasat scatterometer winds with tropical Pacific observations," J. Geophys. Res., 95, 3403-3410.

Department of Fisheries and Oceans, 1989, "Global warming, the oceans, and Canada's fisheries" Submission to the House of Commons Standing Committee on Environment.

Douglas, B.C. and R.E. Cheney, 1990 "Geosat: beginning a new era in satellite oceanography," J. Geophys. Res., 95, 2833-2836.

Dugdale, R.C., A. Morel, A. Bricaud and F.P. Wilkerson, 1989, "Modelling new production in upwelling centers: a case study of modelling new production from remotely sensed temperature and chlorophyll," J. Geophys. Res., 94, 18119-18132.

Fily, M., and D.A. Rothrock, 1990, Opening and closing of sea ice leads: digital measurements from synthetic aperture radar," J. Geophys. Res., 95, 789-796.

Freeland, H.J., 1990, "Sea surface temperatures along the coast of British Columbia: regional evidence for a warming trend," Can. J. Fish. Aquat. Sci., 47, 346-350.

Gerlach, T.M., 1989, "Degassing of carbon dioxide from basaltic magma at spreading centers; II, Mid-oceanic ridge basalts," J. Volcanology and Geotherm. Res., 39, 221-232.

Glantz, M.H., 1990, "Does history have a future? Forecasting climate change effects on fisheries by analogy," Fisheries, 15, No 6 (Special issue: Effects of Global Climatic Change on Fisheries Resources), 39-44.

Glantz, M.H., and L.E. Feingold, 1990, "Climate variability, climate change and fisheries," Environmental and Societal Impacts Group, NCAR, Boulder, USA, ESIG/NMFS/EPA study.

Goodberlet, M.A., C.T. Swift and J.C. Wilkerson, 1989, "Remote sensing of ocean surface winds with the Special Sensor Microwave/Imager," J. Geophys. Res., 94, 14547-14555.

Gordon, H.R., D.K. Clark, D.W. Brown, O.B. Brown, R.H., Evans, and W.W. Broenkow, 1983, "Phytoplankton pigments in the Middle Atlantic bight: comparison of ship measurements and CZCS estimates," Applied Optics, 22, 20-36.

Halpern, D., 1989, "Seasat A scatterometer measurements of equatorial surface winds," J. Geophys. Res., 94, 4829-4833.

Hecky, R.E., 1987, "Predicting the effects of climate change on the inland and Arctic fisheries of Canada," Paper presented at the DFO Symposium on Climate, IOS, Sidney, BC, January.

Holland, W.R. and P. Malanotte-Rizzoli, 1989, "Assimilation of altimeter data into an ocean circulation model: space versus time resolution studies," J. Phys. Oceano., 19, 1507-1534.

Kawasaki, T., 1985, "Fisheries," Chapter 6 of "Climate impact assessment," Kates, Ausubel, Berberian Eds., SCOPE 27, Wiley, UK.

Liu, T, 1983, "Tropical Pacific sea surface temperature measurements by the Seasat microwave radiometer and by ships," J. Geophys. Res., 88, 1909-1914.

MacDonald, G.J., 1990, "Role of methane calthrates in past and future climates," Climate Change, 16, 247-281.

Marko, J.R., D.B. Fissel, P. Wadhams, P.M. Kelly and R. Brown, 1992, "Mechanisms governing variability in iceberg number off Canada's east coast," in preparation.

McKibben, W, 1989, "The end of nature," New Yorker, Sept 11, 47-105.

Mikolajewicz, U., B.D. Santer and E. Maier-Reimer, 1990, "Ocean response to greenhouse warming," Nature, 345, 589-593.

Munk, W.H. and A.M.G. Forbes, 1989, "Global ocean warming: an acoustic measure," J. Phys. Oceano., 19, 1765-1778.

Mysak, L.A., 1986, "El-Nino interannual variability and fisheries in the north-east Pacific Ocean," Can. J. Fish. Aquat. Sci., 43, 464-497.

Parkinson, C.L., and D.J. Cavalieri, 1989, "Arctic sea ice 1973-1987: Seasonal regional and inter-annual variability," J. Geophys. Res., 94, 14499-14523.

Platt, T. and S. Sathyendranath, 1988, "Ocean primary production estimation by remote sensing at local and regional scales," Science, 241, 1613-1620.

Ramanathan, V., 1988, "The greenhouse theory of climate change: a test by an inadvertent global experiment," Science 240, 293-299

Ramanathan V., B.R. Barkstrom and E.F Harrison, 1989, "Climate and the earth's radiation budget," Physics Today, 42, May, 22-32.

Regier, H.A., J.J. Magnuson and C.C. Coutant, 1990, "Introduction to proceedings: Symposium on effects of climate change on fish," Trans. Am. Fish. Soc., 119, No 2, 173-175.

Regier, H.A. and J.D. Meisner, 1990, "Anticipated effects of climate change on freshwater fishes and their habitat," Fisheries, 15, No 6 (Special issue: Effects of Global Climatic Change on Fisheries Resources), 10-15.

Roots, E.F., 1989, "Climate change: High latitude regions," Climatic Change, 15, 223-254.

SCOR Working Group 70, 1986, "Opportunities and problems in satellite measurements of the sea," UNESCO Technical Papers in Marine Science, No. 46.

Stephens, G.L., G.G. Campbell and T.H. von der Haar, 1981, "Earth radiation budgets," J. Geophys. Res., 86, 9739-9760.

Thurman, H.V., 1990, "Essentials of Oceanography," Merrill Publ. Co., Columbus, USA, 3rd Ed., p 332.

Zlotnicki, V., L.L. Fu, and W. Patzert, 1989, "Seasonal variability of global sea level observed with the Geosat altimeter," J. Geophys. Res., 94, 17959-17969.

CHAPTER SEVEN

Aase, J.K., J.P. Millard and B.S. Brown, 1986, "Spectral Radiance Estimates of Leaf Area and Leaf Phytomass of Small Grains and Native Vegetation", IEEE Transactions on Geoscience and Remote Sensing, Vol. GE-24, No. 5, pp. 685-692.

Allison, E.W., R.J. Brown, H.E. Press, J.G. Gairns, 1989, "Monitoring Drought Affected Vegetation With AVHRR", Proceeding of IGARSS'89, Vancouver, British Columbia, pp. 1965-1967.

Asrar, G., E.T. Kanemasu, and M. Yoshida, 1985, "Estimates of Leaf Area Index from Spectral Reflectance of Wheat Under Different Cultural Practices and Solar Angle", Remote Sensing of Environment, Vol 17. No. 1. pp. 1-10.

Beaudoin, A., Q.H.J. Gwyn, and T. Le Toan, 1990, "C-Band Backscatter Sensitivity to Multiscale Geometry and Soil Moisture Variability of Agricultural Surfaces", IEEE Transactions for Geoscience and Remote Sensing.

Begin, D., Q.H.J. Gwyn, and F. Bonn, 1987, "Radiometric Correction of SAR Images: A New Correction Algorithm", International Journal of Remote Sensing, Vol. 8, pp. 385-398.

Brakke, T.W., E.T. Kanemasu, J.L. Steiner, F.T. Ulaby, and E. Wilson, 1981, "Microwave Radar Response to Canopy Moisture, Leaf-Area Index, and Dry Weight of Wheat, Corn, and Sorghum", Remote Sensing of Environment, Vol. 11, pp. 207-220.

Boisvert, J. ,1990, Agriculture Canada, Private Communications.

Brisco, B., R.J. Brown, J. Cihlar, and R.W.S. Brancker, 1989, "A Field Instrument for Surface Roughness Measurement", Proceedings of IGARSS'89, Vancouver, British Columbia, pp. 1177-1180.

Brisco, B., R.J. Brown, B. Sneider, G.J. Sofko, J.A. Koehler, and A.G. Wacker, 1990a, "Tillage Effects on Radar Backscatter of Grain Stubble Fields", submitted to the International Journal of Remote Sensing.

Brisco, B., R.J. Brown, J.A. Koehler, G.J. Sofko, and M.J. McKibben, 1990b, "The Diurnal Pattern of Microwave Backscatter by Wheat", accepted for publication in the Remote Sensing of Environment.

Brisco, B., and R.J. Brown, 1990, "Drought Stress Evaluation in Agricultural Crops Using CHH SAR Data", Special Issue of the Canadian Journal of Remote Sensing on SAR Applications in Agriculture.

Brown, R.J., F.J. Ahern, R.A. Ryerson, K.P.B. Thomson, D.G. Goodenough, J.A. McCormick, P.M. Teillet, 1980, "Rapeseed: Guidelines for Operational Monitoring", Proceedings of the 6th Canadian Symposium on Remote Sensing, Halifax, Nova Scotia, pp. 321-330.

Brown, R.J., K.P.B. Thomson, F.J. Ahern, K. Staenz, J. Cihlar, S.G. Klump, and C.M. Pearce, 1981, "Landsat MSS Applied to Rangeland Management in Western Canada", Proceedings of the 15th International Symposium on Remote Sensing of Environment, Ann Arbor, Michigan, pp. 1435-1447.

Brown, R J , B. Guindon, P.M. Teillet, and D.G. Goodenough, 1984, "Crop Type Determination from Multitemporal SAR Imagery", Proceedings of 9th Canadian Symposium on Remote Sensing, St. John's, Newfoundland, pp 683-691.

Brown, R.J., 1986, "An Overview of Remote Sensing Agricultural Applications in North America: Past, Present, and Future", Proceedings of IGARSS'86, Zurich, Switzerland, pp. 733-737.

Brown, R.J., W.G. Best, G.K. Walker, 1990a, "Satellites Monitor Global Vegetation Conditions", GEOS, Vol. 19, No. 2, pp. 12-16.

Brown, R.J., B. Brisco, and C.A. Hutton, 1990b, "C-Band Polarization Differences in SAR Imagery in an Agricultural Environment: Diurnal and Free Water Effects", submitted to IEEE Geoscience and Remote Sensing.

Camillo, P, and T.J. Schmugge, 1983, "Estimating Soil Moisture Storage in the Root Zone from Surface Measurements", Soil Science, Vol. 135, No. 4, pp. 245-264.

Cihlar, J., 1987, A Methodology for Mapping and Monitoring Cropland Soil Erosion", Canadian Journal of Soil Science, Vol. 67, pp. 433-444.

Cihlar, J., R. Protz, and C. Prevost, 1987, "Soil Erosion Assessment Using Remotely Sensed Data", Proceeding of the 11th Canadian Symposium on Remote Sensing, Waterloo, Ontario, pp. 395-407.

Gillespie, T.J., R.J. Brown, B. Brisco, R. Protz, and S. Sweeney, 1990a, "Plant Surface Wetness Detection in an Agricultural Environment with SAR Data", Proceeding of the 13th Canadian Symposium on Remote Sensing, Fredericton, New Brunswick.

Gillespie, T.J., B. Brisco, R.J. Brown, and G.J. Sofko, 1990b, "Radar Detection of a Dew Event in Wheat" accepted for publication in Remote Sensing of Environment.

Hanuschak, G.A., R.D. Allen, and W.H. Wigton, 1982, "Integration of Landsat Data into the Crop Estimation Program of USDA's Statistical Reporting Service (1972-1982)", Proceedings of 8th International Symposium on Machine Processing of Remotely Sensed Data, West Lafayette, Indiana, pp. 45-56.

Hastings, D., M. Matson, and A.H. Horvitz, 1989, "Using AVHRR for Early Warning of Famine in Africa", Photogrammetric Engineering and Remote Sensing, Vol. LV, No. 2, pp. 168-169.

Henricksen, B.L., 1986, "Reflections on Drought: Ethiopia 1983-1984", International Journal of Remote Sensing, Vol. 7, No. 7, pp. 1447-1451.

Holben, B.N., 1986, "Characteristics of Maximum-Value Composite Images from Temporal AVHRR Data", International Journal of Remote Sensing, Vol. 7, No. 11, pp. 1417-1434.

Hutton, C.A., and R.J. Brown, 1986, "An Evaluation of Filter Types and Sizes", Proceedings of the Sixth Symposium of L'Association quebecoise de teledetection, Sherbrooke, Quebec, pp. 264-278.

Hutton, C.A., and R.J. Brown, 1987, "Radar Backscatter Dependence Upon Look Direction", Proceedings of the 11th Canadian Symposium on Remote Sensing, Waterloo, Ontario, pp. 541-557.

Le Toan, T., 1985, "Study of the Potential of SAR for Crop Identification and Monitoring", Proceedings of a Workshop on Thematic Applications of SAR Data, ESRIN, Frascati, Italy, pp. 73-85.

Le Toan, T., A. Lopes, and M Huet, 1986, "On the Relationships Between Radar Backscattering Coefficient and Vegetation Canopy Characteristics", Proceedings of IGARSS'86, Strasbourg, France, pp. 155-160.

Le Toan, T., H. Laur, E. Mougin, A. Lopes, 1989, "Multitemporal and Dual-Polarization Observations of Agricultural Vegetation Covers by X-Band SAR Images", IEEE Transactions on Geoscience and Remote Sensing, Vol. 27, No. 6, pp.709-718.

Major, D.G., G.B. Schaalje, G. Asrar, and E.T. Kanemasu, 1986, "Estimation of Whole-Plant Biomass and Grain Yield from Spectral Reflectance of Cereals", Canadian Journal of Remote Sensing, Vol. 12, No. 1, pp. 47-54.

Manore, M.J., E. Huffman, J. Dumanski, S-L.R. Konrad, R.S. Rempel, and R.P. Kollasch, 1990, "Radar and Optical Data for Monitoring Conservation Farming: Preliminary Results", Proceedings of the 13th Canadian Symposium on Remote Sensing, Fredericton, New Brunswick.

Martin, R.D.,Jr., G. Asrar, and E.T. Kanemasu, 1989, "C-Band Scatterometer Measurements of a Tallgrass Prairie", Remote Sensing of Environment, Vol. 29, pp. 281-292.

O'Neil, R., 1990, "RDDP Workshop Report", Canada Centre for Remote Sensing.

Paltridge, G.W., and J. Barber, 1988, "Monitoring Grassland Dryness and Fire Potential in Australia with NOAA/AVHRR /Data", Remote Sensing of Environment, Vol. 25, pp. 381-394.

Pokrant, H., and L. Magahay, 1986, "Operational Province Wide Crop Area Estimation for Manitoba", Proceedings of the 10th Canadian Symposium on Remote Sensing, Edmonton, Alberta, pp. 83-89.

Pultz, T.J., and R.J. Brown, 1987, "SAR Image Classification of Agricultural Targets Using First- and Second-Order Statistics", Canadian Journal of Remote Sensing, Vol. 13, No. 2, pp. 85-91.

Pultz, T.J., R. Leconte, R.J. Brown, B. Brisco, and T.I. Lukowski, 1989, "SAR Response to Spatial and Temporal Variations in Soil Moisture and Vegetation", Proceedings of IGARSS'89, Vancouver, British Columbia, pp. 2755-2757.

Rivard, L., A.M. Turner, R.A. Ryerson, and P. Vincent, 1990, "Land Use Mapping with Thematic Mapper Imagery: A Canadian Perspective", Geocarto International, Vol. 5, No. 1, pp. 33-50.

Ryerson, R.A., P. Mosher, and J. Harvie, 1980, "Potato Area Estimation Using Remote Sensing Methods", Report 80-2, Canada Centre for Remote Sensing, Ottawa, Canada, 46p.

Schaal, G.M., 1986, "Analysis of Thematic Mapper Classification of Tillage Practices in Seneca County, Ohio", Report for the Great Lakes National Program Office, U.S. Environmental Protection Agency, Region V, Chicago, Illinois, 65p.
Schmugge, T., P.E. O'Neill, and J.R. Wang, 1986, "Passive Microwave Soil Moisture Research", 1986, IEEE Transactions on Geoscience and Remote Sensing, Vol. GE-24, No. 1, pp. 12-22.

Stephens, P.R., and J. Cihlar, 1981, "The Potential of Remote Sensing to Monitor Soil Erosion on Cropland", Proceedings of the 15th International Symposium on Remote Sensing of Environment, Ann Arbor, Michigan, pp. 985-1005.

Theis, S.W., B.J. Blanchard, and A.J. Blanchard, 1986, "Utilization of Active Microwave Roughness Measurements to Improve Passive Microwave Soil Moisture Estimates Over Bare Soils", IEEE Transactions on Geoscience and Remote Sensing, Vol GE-24, No. 5, pp. 334-339.

Thomson, K.P.B., S. Poirier, G.B. Benie, C. Gosselin, G. Rochon, 1987, "Filter Selection and Processing Methodology for Synthetic Aperture Radar (SAR) Data in Agricultural Applications", Canadian Journal of Remote Sensing, Vol. 13, No. 1, pp. 6-10.

Tucker, C.J., B.N. Holden, J.H. Elgin, Jr.,and J.E. McMurtrey III, 1981' "Remote Sensing of Total Dry-Matter Accumulation in Winter Wheat", Remote Sensing of Environment, Vol. 11, No. 3, pp. 171-190.

Tucker, C.J., C.O. Justice, and S.D. Prince, 1986, "Monitoring the Grasslands of the Sahel 1984-1985", International Journal of Remote Sensing, Vol. 7, No. 11, pp. 1571-1581.

Ulaby, F.T., and P.P., Batlivala, 1976, "Optimum Radar Parameters for Mapping Soil Moisture", IEEE Transactions on Geoscience and Electronics, Vol. GE-14, No. 2, pp. 81-93.

Ulaby, F.T., P.P. Batlivala, and M.C. Dobson, 1978, "Microwave Backscatter Dependence on Surface Roughness, Soil Moisture, and Soil Texture: Part I-Bare Soil", IEEE Transactions on Geoscience Electronics, Vol. GE-16, No. 4, pp. 286-295.

Ulaby, F.T., G.A. Bradley, and M.C. Dobson, 1979, "Microwave Backscatter Dependence on Surface Roughness, Soil Moisture, and Soil Texture: Part II-Vegetation-Covered Soil", IEEE Transactions on Geoscience Electronics, Vol. GE-17, No. 2, pp. 33-40.

Ulaby, F.T., C.T. Allen, G. Eger, III, and E.T. Kanemasu, 1984, "Relating the Microwave Backscatter Coefficient to Leaf Area Index", Remote Sensing of Environment, Vol. 14, pp. 113-133.

Ulaby, F.T., R.K. Moore, and A.K. Fung, 1986, "Microwave Remote Sensing: Active and Passive: Volume II", Addison-Wesley Publishing Company, Reading, Massachusetts, Chapter 12.

Ulaby, F.T., K. Sarabandi, K. McDonald, M. Whitt, M.C. Dobson, 1988, "Michigan Microwave Canopy Scattering model (MIMICS)", The University of Michigan Radiation Laboratory Report 022486-T-1.

Wang, J.R., E.T. Engman, T. Mo, T.J. Schmugge, and J.C. Shiue, 1987, "The Effects of Soil Moisture, Surface Roughness, and Vegetation on L-Band Emission and Backscatter", IEEE Transactions on Geoscience and Remote Sensing, Vol. GE-25, No. 6, pp. 825-833.

CHAPTER EIGHT

Adeniyi, P.O. (1983) "An Aerial Photographic Method for Estimating Urban Population" Photogrammetric Engineering and Remote Sensing 49 (4): 545-560.

Binsell, R. (1967) Dwelling Unit Estimation from Aerial Photography Department of Geography, Northwestern University, Evanston, Illinois, U.S.A.

Brown, L.R. and J.E. Young (1990) "Feeding the World in the Nineties" State of the World, 1990 W.W. Norton and Company, New York and London: 59-78

Carignan,M., D. Morin, R. Brochu, and A. Royer (1987) "Evaluation du Potentiel de la Teledetection spatiale pour L'etude du Milieu Urbain: Le cas de Montreal" Canadian Journal of Civil Engineering 14: 111-117.

Cihlar, J., E. LeDrew, H. Edel, W. Evans, D. MacKay, L. McNutt, and A. Royer (1989) "Contribution of Satellite Observations to the Canadian Global Change Program" Report No. 3, Canadian Global Change Program Joint Publication of the Canada Centre for Remote sensing, EMR and the Royal Society of Canada, Ottawa, Canada. 49pp.

Clawson, M. (1965) Land Information Resources for the Future, Washington, D.C.

Clayton, C. and J.E. Estes (1980) "Image Analysis as a Check on Census Enumeration Accuracy" Photogrammetric Engineering and Remote Sensing 46 (6): 757-764.

Collins, W.G. and A.H.A. El-Beik (1971) "Population Census with the Aid of Aerial Photographs: An Experiment in the City of Leeds" The Photogrammetric Record 7: 16-26.

Digim 1988 Photo Carto, Phase II Cameroun, Programme d'aide multisectorielle, Canadian International Development Agency, Project No. 232/14034.

Gierman, D.M., R.A. Ryerson, G. Moran, and W. Switzer (1975) "Remote Sensing and the Canada Geographic Information System for Impact Studies" 3rd Canadian Symposium on Remote Sensing Canadian Remote Sensing Society, Ottawa, Canada: 235-241.

Han, K-H. (1985) The estimation of Major City Population in Korea using Landsat Imagery Doctoral Dissertation, University of Utah, Department of Geography, Salt Lake City, Utah, United States. 121 pages.

Henderson,F.M. (1979) "Housing and Population Analysis" in K. Ford (ed) Remote Sensing for Planners Centre for Urban Policy Research, Rutgers, The States University of New Jersey, New Brunswick, New Jersey, United States: 135-154.

Harris, R. (1985) "SIR-A Imagery of Tunisia and its POtential for Population Estimation" International Journal of Remote Sensing 6 (7): 975-978.

Howarth, P.J., L.R.G. Martin, G.H. Holder, D. D. Johnson and J.F. Wang (1988) "SPOT Imagery for Detecting Residential Change on the Rural-Urban Fringe of Toronto, Canada" SPOT-1 Image Utilization Assessment and Results, Paris, France: 491-98.

Hsu, S-Y (1971) "Population Estimation" Photogrammetric Engineering 37(5): 449-454.

Iisaka, J. and E. Hegedus (1982) "Population Estimation from Landsat Imagery" Remote Sensing of Environment 12: 259-272.

Jenson, J.R. (author/editor), M.L. Bryan, S.Z. Friedman, F.M. Henderson, R.K. Holz, D. Lindgren, D.L. Toll, R.A. Welch, J.R. Wray (1983) "Urban/Suburban Land Use Analysis" in R.N. Colwell (Editor in Chief) Manual Of Remote Sensing American Society for Photogrammetry and Remote Sensing, Falls Church, Va. USA 1571-1666.

Kraus, S.P., L.W. Senger and J.M. Ryerson (1974) "Estimating Population from Photographically Determined Residential Land Use Types" Remote Sensing of Environment 3: 35-42.

Lambin, E. and H. Lemay (1986) "The Agricultural Inventory and Agrarian Systems Survey by Remote Sensing: Some Empirical Observations from Burkina Faso" Proc. 20th International Symposium on Remote Sensing of Environment Nairobi, Kenya. December 1986, ERIM, Ann Arbor, Michigan. Vol. 2, 687-698.

Lindgren, D.T. (1971) "Dwelling Unity Estimation with Color-IR Photos" Photogrammetric Engineering 37: 373-378.

Lo, C-P. (1989) "A Raster Approach to Population Estimation Using High-Altitude Aerial and Space Photographs" Remote Sensing of Environment 27: 59-71.

Lo, C-P. (1986) "Accuracy of Population Estimation from Aerial Photographs" Photogrammetric Engineering and Remote Sensing 52: 1859-1869.

Lo, C-P. (1986) "Human Settlement Analysis Using Shuttle Imaging Radar-A Data: An Evaluation" Symposium on Remote Sensing for Resources Development and Environmental Management Enschede, The Netherlands: 841-845.

Lo, C-P. and H.F. Chan (1980) "Rural Population Estimation from Aerial Photographs" Photogrammetric Engineering and Remote Sensing 46: 337-345.

Lo, C-P. (1979) "Surveys of Squatter Settlements with Sequential Aerial Photography - A Case Study in Hong Kong" Photogrammetria 35: 45-63.

Lo, C-P. and R. Welch (1977) "Chinese Urban Population Estimates" Annals of the Association of American Geographers 67: 246-253

Lowry, R.T., P. Van Eck, and R.V. Dams (1986) "SAR Imagery for Forest Management" International Geoscience and Remote Sensing Symposium (IGARSS '86) ESA, Paris. vol 2. pp901-906.

Luscombe, A.P. (1987) The RADARSAT Synthetic Aperture Radar: A Flexible Imaging System Spar Aerospace, Ste-Anne-de-Bellevue, Quebec H9X 3R2

Mace, T. (1990) Mace, Environmental Protection Agency, Las Vegas, Nevada, Personal Communication.

Martin, L.R.G. (1989) "Accuracy Assessment of Landsat-Based Visual Change Detection Methods Applied to the Rural-Urban Fringe" Photogrammetric Engineering and Remote Sensing 55 (2) 209-215.

Morrow-Jones, H.A. and J.F. Watkins (1984) "Remote Sensing technology and the U.S.Census" Photogrammetric Engineering and Remote Sensing 50 (2): 229-232.

Nordbeck, S. (1965) "The Law of Allometric Growth" Discussion Paper 7, Michigan Inter-University Community of Mathematical Geographers, Ann Arbor, Michigan.

Ogrosky, C.E. (1975) "Population Estimates from Satellite Imagery" Photogrammetric Engineering and Remote Sensing 41: 707-712.

Olorunfemi, J.F. (1984) "Land Use and Population: A Linking Model" Photogrammetric Engineering and Remote Sensing 50 (2): 221-227.

Olorunfemi, J.F. (1985) "Application of Remote Sensing for Census Surveys and POpulation Estimation in Nigeria: Problems and Prospects" Advanced Technology for Monitoring and Processing Global Environmental Data Remote Sensing Society and CERMA, University of London, U.K.: 91-96.

Prout, N.A., J. Sutton, J. Wessels, M. Manore, and R.J. Brown (1986) "Technological Feasibility for Mobilization for Operations: The NOAA Crop Monitoring Case" Proc. 10th Canadian Symposium of Remote Sensing, Edmonton, Alberta. Canadian Remote Sensing Society, Ottawa. 787-796.

Rivard, L.A., A.M. Turner, R.A. Ryerson and P. Vincent (1990) "Land Use Mapping with Thematic Mapper Imagery: A Canadian Perspective" Geocarto International March 1990. 33-50.

Ryerson, R.A. (1989) "Image Interpretation Concerns for the 1990s and Lessons from the Past" Photogrammetric Engineering and Remote Sensing 55 (10) 1427-1430.

Ryerson, R.A., F.J. Ahern, E. Boasson, R.J. Brown, P.J. Howarth, N.A. Prout, C. Rubec, P. Stephens, K.P.B. Thomson, K.L.E. Wallace, and R. Yazdani (1982) "Landsat for Monitoring Agricultural Intensification and Urbanization in Canada" in M.D. Thompson (ed.) Landsat for Monitoring the Changing Geography of Canada, A Special Report for COSPAR, CCRS, Energy Mines and Resources, Ottawa, Canada: 41-64.

Ryerson, R.A. and D.M. Gierman (1975) "A Remote Sensing Compatible Land Use Activity Classification" Tech.Note 75-1 Canada Centre for Remote Sensing, Energy Mines and Resources, Canada. 18pp.

Seguin, J and R A Ryerson (1987) "Rural Change Monitoring and Remote Sensing: Towards an OPerational Project" 11th Canadian Symposium on Remote Sensing Canadian Remote Sensing Society, Ottawa: 125-136.

Statistics Canada "Postcensal Annual Estimates of Population by Marital Status, Age, Sex, and Components of Growth for Canada, Provinces and Territories" Cat. 91-210 Vol. VII.

Thie, J., R. Ryerson, and T. Alfoldi (1973) Mapping land Use in the Great Lakes Basin: An Evaluation of Conventional and Remote Sensing Techniques For Task Force "B", Pollution from Land Drainage Reference Group, International Joint Commission, CCRS, Energy Mines and Resources Canada, Ottawa. 17pp.

Thomas, B. (1988) "Monitoring Land Use Pressures on Wetlands with Landsat Thematic Mapper Imagery" in M.J. Bardecki and N. Patterson Wetlands: Inertia or Momentum Federation of Ontario Naturalists, Don Mills, Ontario. pp. 199-204.

Tomlins, G.F. 1986. Assessment Of Landsat-5 Thematic Mapper Data for Mapping and Monitoring Wetlands and Neighbouring Land-Cover/Landuse. contract report for Lands Directorate and Canadian Wildlife Service, Environment Canada. 250 pp.

Turner, A.M. (1990) Personal Communication

Tobler, W.R. (1969) "Satellite Confirmation of Settlement Size Co-efficients" Area 1: 30-34.

Vincent, P. (1990) Personal Communication, Photosur Geomat Inc., Montreal.

Warren, C.L., A. Kerr, and A.M. Turner (1989) Urbanization of Rural Land In Canada, 1981-86" State of the Environment Fact Sheet 89-1 Environment Canada, Ottawa, Canada.

Watkins, J.F. (1984) "The Effect of Residential Structure Variation on Dwelling Unit Enumeration from Aerial Photographs" Photogrammetric Engineering and Remote Sensing 50: 1599-1607.

Watkins, J.F. and H.A. Morrow-Jones (1985) "Small Area Population Estimates Using Aerial Photography" Photogrammetric Engineering and Remote Sensing 51: 1933-1935.

Wilson, D.A. M.L. McCourt, M. Poirier and J. Seel (1988) "An evaluation of the Applicability of SPOT Stereoscopic Imagery to the Canada Land Use Monitoring Program" SPOT-1 Image Utilization Assessment and Results, Paris, France: 551-557.

World Commission on Environment and Development (1987) Our Common Future (The Brundtland Report) Oxford University Press, Oxford and New York.

Yunus, H.S. (1978) "The Analysis of Urban POpulation Density Through Air Photos: Case Study of Yogyakarta City" Indonesian Journal of Geography 8 (36): 23-39.

CHAPTER NINE

Adams, G.D. 1978. Remote Sensing for Wildlife Habitat Analysis in Canada, An Overview. Proc. PECORA IV, Application of Remote Sensing to Wildlife Management. pp. 33-43.

Adams, G.D. 1987. Prairie Pothole Project - Redvers: Baseline Habitat Evaluation. Canadian Wildlife Service, Environment Canada, Saskatoon. 30 pp.

Allison, E.W., R.J. Brown, H.E. Press and J.G. Gairns 1989. Monitoring Drought Affected Vegetation Using AVHRR. Proc. IGARRS'89, Vancouver, pp. 1965-1967.

Bartlett, D.S. 1984 ed. Global Biology Research Program, Biogeochemical Processes in Wetlands. NASA Conference Publication 2316, 39 pp.

Bartlett, D.S., M.A. Hardisky, R.W. Johnson, M.F. Gross, V. Klemas and J.M. Hartman 1988. Continental Scale Variability in Vegetation Reflectance and its Relationship to Canopy Morphology. Int'l. J. Remote Sensing, Vol. 9, No.7, pp. 1223-1241.

Borstad, G.A. 1986. Colour and Temperature in the Beaufort Sea: Remote sensing in Support of Ecological Studies of the Bowhead Whale. 10th Canadian Symposium on Remote Sensing, Edmonton, Alta., pp. 405-412.

Borstad, G.A. and J.F.R. Gower 1984. Phytoplankton Chlorophyll Distribution in the Eastern Canadian Arctic. Arctic, Vol. 37, No. 3, pp. 224-233.

Bowles, L., R.Dixon, and B. Knudsen 1984. Moose Habitat Analysis in North Central Manitoba from Landsat Data. Manitoba Center for Remote Sensing.

Cihlar, J., E. LeDrew, H. Edel, W.Evans, D. Mackay, L. McNutt and A. Royer 1989. Contribution of Satellite Observations to the Canadian Global Change Program. CCRS and Royal Society, Canadian Global Change Program, Report #3. 47 pp.

CIRAC News 1989. Canadian Institute for Research in Atmospheric Chemistry, Project News, August. 10 pp.

Cooch, F.G. 1990. pers. comm. Canadian Wildlife Service, Ottawa, Ont., K1A OH3.

D'Iorio, M.A., J. Cihlar and L. St-Laurent 1989. Relationship Between AVHRR NDVI and Environmental Parameters. Proc. IGARRS'89, Vol. 3, Vancouver, pp. 1326-1334.

Dickson, H.L. and A.R. Smith 1989. Use of Thematic Mapper and Multi-spectral Scanner Imagery to identify Habitats and Shorebird Nesting Areas on the Outer Mackenzie River Delta, Northwest Territories. Proc. Mackenzie Delta Workshop, Saskatoon. 26 pp.

Eby, J.R. and L.R. Bright 1985. A Digital GIS Based on Landsat and Other Data for Elk Habitat Effectiveness Analysis. Proc. 19th Int'l. Symp. on Remote Sensing of Environment, Ann Arbor, 9 pp.

Environment Canada 1986. Wetlands in Canada: A Valuable Resource. Lands Directorate, Fact Sheet 86-4, 8 pp.

Environment Canada 1989. The Importance of Wildlife to Canadians in 1987: Highlights of a National Survey. Canadian Wildlife Service, 45 pp.

Falkowski, P.G. 1988. Ocean Productivity From Space. Nature, Vol. 335, 15 Sept., p. 205.

Freemark, K.E. and H.G. Merriam 1986. Importance of Area and Habitat Heterogeneity to Bird Assemblages in Temperate Forest Fragments. Biological Conservation, vol 36, pp. 115-141.

Gallo, K.P. and C.S.T. Daughtry 1987. Differences in Vegetation Indices for Simulated Landsat-5 MSS and TM, NOAA-9 AVHRR, and SPOT-1 Sensor Systems, Remote Sensing of Environment, Vol. 23, pp. 439-452.

Gallo, K.P. and T.R. Heddinghaus 1989. The Use of Satellite Derived Indices as Indicators of Climatic Variability. Sixth Conference on Applied Climatology, Charleston, SC, pp. 244-247

Goodison., B.E., J.E. Glynn, K.D. Harvey and J.E. Slater et al. 1987. Snow Surveying in Canada: A Perspective. Canadian Water Resources Journal, Vol. 12., No. 2, pp. 27-42.

Gower, J.F.R. 1987. Canadian Activities and Goals in Remote Sensing of Ocean Colour and Flourescence from Space. Proc. ESA Workshop (ESA SP-1083), Villefranche-sur-mer, pp. 41-48.

Haffer, J. 1982. General Aspects of the Refuge Theory. in G.T. Prance (ed.), Biological Diversification in the Tropics. Columbia Univ. Press, New York. pp. 6-24.

Hardisky, M.A., M.F.Gross and V. Klemas, 1986. Remote Sensing of Coastal Wetlands. Bioscience, vol. 36 No. 7. pp. 453-460.

Helie. R.G. and G.M. Wickware (in progress). Quantitative Assessment of Surface Water Resources at Risk Due to Acidification in Eastern Canada. Inland Waters Directorate, Ottawa.

Hewitt III, M.J., J.R. Eby, and L.W. Brewer 1986. The role of Landsat Multispectral Scanner Data in the Analysis of Northern Spotted Owl Habitat. 10th Canadian Symposium on Remote Sensing, Edmonton, Alta. pp. 937-942

Heyland, J.D. 1975. Monitoring Nesting Success of Greater Snow Geese by Means of Satellite Imagery. Proc. 3rd Canadian Symposium on Remote Sensing, Edmonton, pp. 243-256.

Houghton, A.M. 1987. Climate Impacts Detection in Southern Saskatchewan Using NOAA AVHRR Data. Proc. 11th Canadian Symposium on Remote Sensing, Waterloo. pp. 59-67.

Jacobson, J.E., R.A. Ritter and G.T. Koeln 1987. Accuracy of Thematic Mapper Derived Wetlands as Based on National Wetland Inventory Data. ASPRS Technical Papers, Reno Nevada, pp. 109-126.

Koeln, G.T., P. Caldwell and D.E. Wesley 1986. Inventory of Wetlands with Landsat's Thematic Mapper. Proc. 10th Canadian Symposium on Remote Sensing, Edmonton. pp. 153-162.

Konrad, S-L and R.S. Rempel 1989. Cost-Effectiveness of Landsat TM Classification by Operations Staff. Ducks Unlimited Canada,
3 pp.

Laymon, S.A., H. Salwasser and R.H. Barrett 1985. Habitat Suitability Index Models: Spotted Owl, Biological Report 82(10.113), Fish and Wildlife Service, USDI, Washington. 14 pp.

Leconte, R. 1990, pers. comm. Canada Centre for Remote Sensing, 1547 Merivale Rd. Ottawa, K2G 3J6.

Lohrenz, S.E., R.A. Arnone, D.A.Wiesenburg and I.P.DePalma 1988. Satellite Detection of Transient Enhanced Primary production in the Western Mediterranean Sea. Nature, Vol. 335, 15 September.

Maltby, W.W. 1986. Waterlogged Wealth: Why Waste the Worlds Wet Places? London, Earthscan, 200 pp.

McNicol, D.K., R.K. Ross, and P.J. Blancher 1989. Waterfowl as Indicators of Acidification in Ontario, Canada. XIX Congress of International Union of Game Biologists, Trondheim, Norway, 17 pp.

Morrison, R.I.G. 1990, personal communication. National Wildlife Research Centre, Canadian Wildlife Service, Ottawa K1A OH3.

Pain, S. 1988. No Escape From the Global Greenhouse. New Scientist, Vol. 120., No. 1638, pp. 38-43.

Perry, M.J. 1986. Assessing Primary Productivity from Space. Bioscience, Vol. 36, No.7, pp. 461-467.

Peters, R.L. 1988. Effects of Global Warming on Biological Diversity: An Overview. Workshop on Impact of Global Warming on Biological Diversity. Washington, D.C., pp. 169-185.

Pierce, R.N. 1989. Analysis of Landsat TM Imagery: An Approach for the Collection of Forest Cover Data for Mapping Forest Bird Habitat in Northern Ontario. Proc. IGARRS'89, Vancouver, Vol. 3. pp. 1577-1579.

Pilon, P. and A.M. Kerr 1984. Land use Change on Wetlands in the Southwestern Fraser Lowland, British Columbia. Lands Directorate, Environment Canada, Working Paper No. 34.

Reeves, H.M., F.G. Cooch, and R.E. Munro 1976. Monitoring Arctic Habitat and Goose Populations by Satellite Imagery. Journal of Wildlife Management, Vol. 40, No. 3, pp. 532-541.

Rizzo, B., and E. Wiken 1989. Assessing the Sensitivity of Canada's Ecosystems to Climate Change. in E.A. Koster and M.M. Boer (ed), Landscape Ecological Impact of Climate Change on Boreal/(Sub) Arctic Regions, pp 94-111.

Running, S.W. 1986. Global Primary Production from Terrestrial Vegetation: Estimates Integrating Satellite Remote Sensing and Computer Simulation Technology. The Science of the Total Environment No. 56, University of Montana, School of Forestry, Missoula, MT. pp. 233-242.

Smith, J.B. and D.A. Tirpak 1988, ed. The Potential Effects on Global Climate Change on the United States. Draft Report to Congress. Volume 2: National Studies. United States Environmental Protection Agency.

Snell, E.A. 1987. Wetland Distribution and Conversion in Southern Ontario. Inland Waters and Lands Directorate, Environment Canada, Working Paper No. 48.

Sullivan, C.W., C.R. McClain, J.C. Comiso, and W.O. Smith Jr 1988. Phytoplankton Standing Crops Within an Antarctic Ice Edge Assessed by Satellite Remote Sensing. Journal of Geophysical Research, Vol. 93, No. C10, pp. 12487-12498.

Thomas, B. and A.M. Turner 1990. Revising Land Use/Land Cover Maps Using Landsat Thematic Mapper Imagery, Proc. ISPRS Comm. VII, Victoria.

Tomlins, G.F. 1986. Assessment Of Landsat-5 Thematic Mapper Data for Mapping and Monitoring Wetlands and Neighbouring Land-Cover/Landuse. contract report for Lands Directorate and Canadian Wildlife Service, Environment Canada. 250 pp.

Topping Jr., J.C. and J.P. Bond 1988. The Potential Impact of Climate Change on Fisheries and Wildlife in North America. report of the Climate Institute to the U.S. Environmental Protection Agency.

Tucker, C.J., J.R.G. Townshend, and T.E. Goff 1985. African Land-cover Classification using Satellite Data. Science, 227(4685), pp. 369-375.

Wagner, C.L., R.N. Pierce, and S.W. Hounsell 1989. The Integration of Remote Sensing Data with a Geographic Information System to Develop Forest Parameters for Wildlife Impact Assessment in Southern Ontario. Proc. IGARSS'89, Vancouver, pp. 2027-2029.

Wickware, G.M. and P.J. Howarth 1981. Change Detection in the Peace-Athabasca Delta Using Digital Landsat Data. Remote Sensing of Environment, Vol. 11, pp. 9-25.

CHAPTER TEN

Bukata, R.P, J.E. Bruton, and J.H. Jerome. 1985. Application of Direct Measurements of Optical Parameters to the Estimation of Lake Water Quality Indicators. Environment Canada Scientific Series No. 140, 35 pp.

Bukata, R.P., J.E. Bruton, and J.H. Jarome. 1989. Optical Properties of Inland Waters: An Essential Requirement for Monitoring Natural and Anthropogenic Climate Changes from Space National Water Research Institute Contribution #RRB 89-168, 33 pp.

Goodison, B.E., J.M. Whiting, K. Wiebe, and J. Cihlar. 1983. Operational Requirements for Water Resources Remote Sensing in Canada, IUGG, IAHS, pulication IAHS/WMO #HSI.

NASA. 1984. Earth Observing System: Science and Mission Requirements Working Group Report: Vol. 1, Technical Memorandum 86129, 51 pp.

NASA. 1986. Earth System Science - Overview: A Program for Global Change, Earth System Science Committee, NASA Advisory Council, Washington, 48 pp.

NASA Advisory Council. 1988. Earth System Science: A Closer View, Report of the Earth System Sciences Committee, 208 pp.

Whiting J. 1989. Northern Hemisphere Weekly World Crop Assessment Index. Saskatchewan Research Council Remote Sensing image pamphlet.

CHAPTER ELEVEN

Antarctic Ozone Hole Special Issue ,1987. Geophysical Res. Letters, 13(12), 11911362

Hansen, J., D. Johnson, A. Lacis, S. Lebedeff, P. Lee, D. Rind, and G. Russell, 1981. Climate impact of increasing atmospheric carbon dioxide, Science, 213, 957966.

Harrington, J.B., 1987. Climatic change: a review of causes, Canadian Journal of Forest Research, 17, (11), 13131339.

McElroy M.B. and S.C. Wofsey, 1986. Tropical Forests: Interactions with the atmosphere. In: G.T. Prance (Ed.): Tropical Rain Forests and the World Atmosphere, p 3360, Westview Press, Boulder, Colorado, USA.

Mitchell, J.F.B., 1983: The seasonal response of a general circulation to changes in CO2 and sea temperature, Quatern. J. Roy. Met. Soc., 109, 113-152.

Mooney H.A., P.M. Vitousek, P.A. Matson, 1987. Exchange of materials between terrestrial ecosystems and the atmosphere; Science, 238; 926932.

National Research Council, 1984. Global Tropospheric Chemistry. A plan for action, National Academy Press, Washington D.C., USA.

National Research Council, 1988. Report on Global Change, National Academy Press, Washington, D.C., USA.

Ramanathan, V., 1988. The greenhouse theory of climate change: a test by inadvertent global experiment. Science, 240, 293299.

Rotty, R.M., 1983. Distribution of and changes in industrial carbon dioxide production, J. Geophys. Res., 88, 13011308.

Sato, N., P.J. Sellers, D.A. Randall, E.K. Schneider, J. Shukla, J.L. Kinter III, YT Hou and E. Ablertazzi, 1989. "Effects of implementing the Simple Biosphere Model ((SiB) in a general circulation model"; J. Atmos Sci., 46, 2757-2782.

Schlesinger, M.E. and J.F.B. Mitchell, 1987. Climate model calculations of the equilibrium climatic response to increased carbon dioxide. Reviews of Geophysics, 25, (4), 760798.

Sellers, P.J., F.G. Hall, G. Asrar, D.E. Strebel and R.E. Murphy, 1988. The first ISLSCP field experiment (FIFE), Bull. Amer. Met. Soc., 69, (1), 2227.

Shuttleworth, W.J., J.H.C. Gash, C.R. Lloyd, C.J. Moore, J. Roberts, A.O. Marques Filho, G. Fisch, V.P. Silva Filho, M.N.G. Ribeiro, L.C.B. Molion, L.A. De Sa, J.C.A. Nobre, O.M.R. Cabral, S.R. Patel and J.C. De Moraes, 1984. Eddy correlation measurements of energy partition for Amazonian forest, Quart. J. Roy. Met. Soc., 110, 11431163.

Tans P.P., I.Y. Fung and T. Takahashi, 1990. Observational Constraints on the global atmospheric CO2 budget, Science, 247, 14311438.

Trabalka, J.R. (Ed.), 1985. Atmospheric Carbon Dioxide and the Global Carbon Cycle, U.S. Department of Energy, Washington, D.C., (Available at NTIS DOE/E/R0239 from Natl. Tech. Inf. Serv., Springfield, VA).

CHAPTER TWELVE

Avery, T. E. 1975, Natural Resources Measurements, McGraw-Hill Book Co., New York.

Anon. 1988, Report of a Workshop: GIS: Geographic information systems, ESCAP/UNDP, Bangkok, Thailand.

Anon. 1989, Proceedings: Challenges for the 1990s GIS, Ottawa, Canada.

Beaudoin, M. 1988, The Landsat Thailand project resource information management system in Thailand: Overview and trends in GIS systems, In Report of a Workshop on GIS: Geographic Information Systems, ESCAP/UNDP, Bangkok, Thailand.

Bell, J. F. and T. Atterbury, ed. 1983, Proceedings: Renewable resource inventories for monitoring changes and trends, Oregon State Univ. Corvallis.

Bickford, C. A. 1952, The sampling design used in the forest survey of the Northeast: Journal of Forestry, Vol. 50, pp. 290-293.

Brann, T. B., House, L. O., and H.G. Lund, ed. 1981, Proceedings: In-place resource inventories: principles and practices, Univ. Maine, Orono.

Bruce, D. and F. X. Schumacher, 1942, Forest Mensuration, McGraw-Hill Book Co., New York.

Cochran, W. G. 1953, Sampling Techniques, John Wiley & Sons, New York.

Cunia, T. 1974, ed. Proceedings: Monitoring forest environment through successive sampling, IUFRO S4.02, Syracuse, New York.

Dawkins, H. C. 1952, Experiments in low percentage enumerations of tropical high forest with special reference to Uganda: Empire Forestry Review, Vol. 31, pp. 131-145.

Frayer, W. E. 1979, ed. Proceedings: Forest resource inventories, Vol I and II, Colorado State Univ., Fort Collins.

Freese, F. 1962, Elementary forest sampling, Agriculture Handbook No.232.

Fries, J. 1974, ed. Proceedings: Growth models for tree and stand simulation, IUFRO S4.01-4, Stockholm, Sweden.

Hagglund, B. 1983, The new national forest survey, In Proceedings: Renewable resource inventories for monitoring changes and trends, Oregon State Univ. Corvallis.

Hegyi, F. and R. V. Quenet, 1983, Integration of remote sensing and computer assisted mapping technology in forestry: Canadian Journal of Remote Sensing, Vol. 9(2), pp. 92-98.

Hegyi, F. 1983, Mapping and satellite image analysis for forest inventory, In Proceedings: Renewable resource inventories for monitoring changes and trends, Oregon State Univ. Corvallis.

Hegyi, F. 1985. Opportunity for increasing the scope and efficiency of forest planning through high technology, In Proceedings: Twelfth Commonwealth Forestry Conference, Victoria, Canada.

Hegyi, F. 1988, Key factors in an operational GIS for land use planning, In Report of a Workshop on GIS: Geographic Information Systems, ESCAP/UNDP, Bangkok, Thailand.

Hegyi, F. 1989, The role of GIS in Provincial inventories, In Proceedings: GIS 89: A wider perspective, Vancouver, Canada.

Hildebrandt, G. 1983. Needs for monitoring renewable resources and national ecosystems - a global prospective, In Proceedings: Renewable resource inventories for monitoring changes and trends, Oregon State Univ. Corvallis.

Hoffer, R. M. and K. S. Lee, 1989, Forest change classification using Seasat and Sir-B satellite Sar data, In Proceedings: IGARS'89 Quantitative Remote Sensing: An Economic Tool for the Nineties, Vancouver, Canada.

Husch, B., Miller, C. I., and T. W. Beers, 1972, Forest Mensuration, The Ronald Press Co., New York.

Johannsen, C. J. and J. L. Sanders, 1982, ed. Remote sensing for forest management, Soil Conservation Society of America, Ankeny, Iowa.

Kirkland, A. 1985, Data needs and recent developments in resource management and planning, In Proceedings: Twelfth Commonwealth Forestry Conference, Victoria, Canada.

Loetsch, F. and K. E. Haller, 1973, Forest Inventory, Vol. I and II, BLV Verlagsgesellschaft, Munchen.

Lund. II. G. 1978, ed. Proceedings: Integrated inventories of renewable natural resources, Univ. Arizona, Tuscon.

Lund, H. G. 1983, Change: now you see it - now you don't, In Proceedings: Renewable resource inventories for monitoring changes and trends, Oregon State Univ. Corvallis.

McPhalen, J. 1989, ed. Proceedings: GIS 89: A wider perspective, Vancouver, Canada.

Mok, S. T., Anis, Z., and A. Ramlee, 1988, Promoting remote sensing and GIS applications in Forestry in Asean, In Proceedings: Ninth Asian Conference on Remote Sensing, Bangkok, Thailand.

Schmid-Haas, P. 1983, Swiss continuous forest inventory, twenty years experience, In Proceedings: Renewable resource inventories for monitoring changes and trends, Oregon State Univ. Corvallis.

Singh, K. D. and J. P . Lanly, 1983, A review of FAO's contributions to assessment and monitoring of tropical forest resources, In Proceedings: Renewable resource inventories for monitoring changes and trends, Oregon State Univ. Corvallis.

Snedecor, G. W. and W. G. Cochran, 1956, Statistical Methods, The Iowa State College Press, Ames.

Spurr, S. H. 1948, Aerial Photographs in Forestry, The Ronald Press Co., New York.

Spurr, S. H. 1952, Forest Inventory, The Roland Press Co., New York.

Tomlinson, R. F. 1989, Geographic information systems - challenges for the 1990s, In Proceedings: Challenges for the 1990s GIS, Ottawa, Canada.

Tveitdal, S. and O. Hesjedal, 1989, GIS in the Nordic countries, Proceedings: GIS 89: A wider perspective, Vancouver, Canada.

Ware, K.D. and T. Cunia, 1962, Continuous forest inventory with partial replacement of samples, Forest Science Monograph 3.

Weller, B. S. 1983, ed. Proceedings: Automated cartography: international perspectives on achievements and challenges, Vol. I and II, Auto-Carto Six, Ottawa, Canada.

CHAPTER THIRTEEN

Brown, R.J. 1987. Preparing for Satellite Microwave Systems for Renewable Resource Management, Geocarto International (3) pp. 31-37.

Brown, R.J. 1989. Land Applications of Radarsat, Proceedings of IGARSS '89/12th Canadian Symposium on Remote Sensing, Vancouver, B.C., 3 pages.

Cihlar, J., R.J Brown and B. Guindon. 1986. Microwave Remote Sensing of Crops in Canada, Int. Journal Remote Sensing, Vol. 7, No. 2, pp. 195-212.

Dobson, M.C. and F.T. Ulaby. 1986. Active Microwave Soil Moisture Research, IEEE Trans. Geoscience and Remote Sensing, Vol. GE-24, pp. 23-26.

Lowry, R.T., P. Van Eck and R.V. Dams. 1986. SAR Imagery for Forest Management. Proc. IGARSS'86, Zurich, pp. 901-906.

Muller, P.W. and R.M. Hoffer. 1988. Spatial Filtering of Shuttle Imagery Radar - B Data. Tech. Pap 1988 ACSM-ASPRS Ann. Con., St. Louis, Vol. 3, pp 114-127.

Simonett, D.S. (ed). 1983. The Development and Principles of Remote Sensing, Manual of Remote Sensing, American Society of Photogrammetry, Falls Church, Virginia, p. 1-31.

Rochon, G., C. Gosselin, M. Rheault, P. Vincent, K.P.B. Thomson, B. Goze, S. Porrier and F. Cavayas. 1986. Study of the Use of SAR Data for Agriculture and Forestry, ESA SP-264, Proc. SAR Application Workshop, Frascetti, Italy, pp. 81-93.

Ulaby, F.T., C.T. Allen, G. Eger III and E. Kanemasu. (1984). Relating the Microwave Backscattering Coefficient to Leaf Area Index, Remote Sensing of Environment, Vol. 14, pp. 113-133.

Werle, D., Y.J. Lee and R.J. Brown. 1986. The Use of Multispectral and Radar Remote Sensing Data for Monitoring Forest Cleancut and Regeneration Sites on Vancouver Island. Proc. 10th Can. Symposium on Remote Sensing, Edmonton, Alberta, pp. 319-330.

CHAPTER FOURTEEN

Aronoff, S. (1985), Political Implications of Full Cost Recovery for Land Remote Sensing Systems, Photogrammetric Engineering and Remote Sensing, Vol. 51, No. 1, pp 4145.

Analytic Sciences Corporation (1988), A Study of an Advanced Civil Earth Remote Sensing System, NOAA Contract No. 50MANE84002, Final Report, 12 August.

Choudhury, B. J., and C. J. Tucker (1987), Monitoring Global Vegetation using NIMBUS-7 37 GHz Data: some Empirical Relations, International Journal of Remote Sensing, Vol. 8, pp 1085-1090.

Cihlar, J., E. LeDrew, H. Edel, W. Evans, D. McKay, L. McNutt, A. Roger, 1989. Contribution of Satellite Observations to the Canadian Global Change Program, Report No. 3. Canada Centre for Remote Sensing and the Royal Society of Canada, 48 pp.

DTI Telecom-Econosult (1987), RADARSAT Economic Review and Assessment Update, Contract report to the Department of Energy, Mines, and Resources, March.

Langham, E. J., E. Shaw, and R. K. Raney (1989), RADARSAT: Canada's Microwave Satellite, IEEE Geoscience and Remote Sensing Society Newsletter, November, pp 19-21.

Luscombe, Anthony P. (1989), The RADARSAT Synthetic Aperture Radar System, Proceedings of the 1989 International Geoscience and Remote Sensing Symposium, Vancouver, B.C., Canada, 10 14 July, pp 218-221.

Mrazek, Rep. Robert (1990), Firmer Ground for Landsat Support, Space News, 22-28 January, pp 23-24.

Nagy, G., and P. H. Swain, (1987), Foreword, IEEE Transactions on Geoscience and Remote Sensing, (Special Issue on Analytical Methods in Remote Sensing for Geographic Information Systems), Vol GE-25, No. 3, May, pp 254-257.

NASA (1988), Earth System Science, a Closer View, Report of the Earth Systems Sciences Committee, NASA Advisory Council, NASA, Washington, D.C., January, 210 pages.

Office of Technology Assessment (1984), Remote Sensing and the Private Sector: Issues for Discussion - A Technical Memorandum, OTA-TM-ISC-20, U.S. Congress, Washington, D.C., March.

RADARSAT (1982), Mission Requirements Document, RADARSAT Project Office, Document No. 82-7.

Raney, R. K. and C. N. Specter (1989), From Monitoring to Action: An Operational Scenario for Tropical Forestry Management, International Union of Forestry Research Organizations International Conference, Venice, Italy, 24-30 September.

Royal Society of Canada (1989) with the Canada Centre for Remote Sensing, Contribution of Satellite Observations to the Canadian Global Change Program, Report No.3, July, 48 pages.

Townshend, J.R.G. and C.O. Justice, (1988), Selecting the spatial resolution of satellite sensors required for global monitoring of land transformations, International Journal of Remote Sensing, Vol. 9, No. 2, pp 187-236.

Werle, D. (1989), Potential application of imaging radar for monitoring depletion of tropical forests, Proceedings of the 1989 International Geoscience and Remote Sensing Symposium, Vancouver, British Columbia, Canada, pp 13831390.

World Commission on Environment and Development, (1987), Our Common Future, (Report of The Brundtland Commission), Oxford University Press, Oxford, England.

CHAPTER FIFTEEN

Ahmed, S., Warren, H.R., Symonds, M.D. and Cox, R.P. 1989, The Radarsat System: Proc. IGARSS '89, pp. 213217.

Ahern, F.J. and Leckie, D.G. 1987, Digital Remote Sensing and Forestry Requirements and Capabilities Today and Tomorrow: Geocarto, Vol. 2, No. 3, pp. 4352.

Babey, S.K. and Anger, C.D. 1989, A Compact Airborne Spectrographic Imager, CASI: Proc. IGARSS '89, pp. 10281031.

Borstad, G.A., Edel, H.R., Gower, J.F.R. and Hollinger, A.B. 1985, Analysis of Test and Flight Data from the Fluorescence Line Imager: Canadian Special Publication of Fisheries and Aquatic Sciences, No. 83, pp. 138.

Casey, M.J. and Vosburgh, J. 1986, Chart Making with LARSEN: Canadian Surveyor, Vol. 40, pp. 251260.

C.N.E.S., 1988, SPOT 1 Image Utilization Assessment, Results, pp. 11500.

Dalsa Inc., Waterloo. 1989, CCD Image Sensors.

Duchossois, G. 1986, Overview and Status of the ERS1 Programme: Proc. IGARSS '86, ESA S 254, pp. 155159.

Gibson, J.R., Park, W.M., Hollinger, A.B., Dunlop, J.D. and O'Neil, N.T. 1987, Geometric Correction of Airborne Line Scanner Data: Proc. 11th Canadian Symposium on Remote Sensing.

Livingstone, C.E., Gray, A.L., Hawkins, R.K., Olsen, R.B., Halbertsma, J.G and Deane, R.A., 1987, CCRS CBand Airborne Radar: Systems Description and Test Results, Proc. 11th Canadian Symposium on Remote Sensing, pp. 503518.

Mercer, J.B. and Kirby, M.E. 1987, Topographic Mapping Using STAR1 Radar Data: Geocarto, Vol. 2, No. 3, pp. 3942.

Murai, S., 1986, Earth Resources Satellite Project in Japan, Proc. ISPRS Commission I, ESA SP 255, pp. 487488.

NASA Advisory Council, 1988, Earth System Science, A Program for Global Change, pp. 1208.

Neville, R.A., McColl, W.D. and Till, S.M. 1983, Development and Evaluation of the MEIS II Multidetector Electrooptical Imaging Sensor, Proc. SPIE, Advanced Infrared Sensor Technology, Vol. 395, pp. 101108.

Neville, R.A. and Till, S.M, 1989, MEIS FM: A Multispectral Imager for Forestry and Mapping, Proc. IGARSS '89, pp. 23902393.

O'Neil, R.A., Neville, R.A. and Thomson, V. 1983, The Arctic Marine Oilspill Program Remote Sensing Study, Environmental Protection Service Report, EPS Vol. 4EC833, pp. 1257.

Shepherd, G.G., et al., 1985, WAMDII: WideAngle Micheson Doppler Imaging Interferometer for Spacelab, Applied Optics, Vol. 24, p.p. 15711584.

Till, S.M., Neville, R.A., McColl, W.D. and Gauthier, R.P. 1986, The MEIS II Pushbroom Imager Four years of Operation, Proc. ISPRS Symposium, ESA SP252, pp. 247253.

Till, S.M. 1987, Industrial Involvement in the Airborne Data Acquisition Program, Remote Sensing in Canada, Vol. 15, p. 8.

Zwick, H.H., de Villiers, J.N. and McColl, W.D. 1978, Laboratory Evaluation of the Prototype MEIS, Report 785, Canada Centre for Remote Sensing, Department of Energy, Mines and Resources.

CHAPTER SIXTEEN

ICSU (International Council of Scientific Unions), 1990. "IGBP Data and Information System - A Blueprint for the Next Decade" (preliminary draft), ICSU IGBP Working Group 1, February, 1990.

NASA, 1986. "Earth Observing System, Volumes I, II, IIa, IIb, IIc, IId, IIe, IIf, IIg, IIh", 1986 (Volume 1 - Technical Memorandum 86129).

NASA, 1989. "Earth Observing System: Initial Scientific Assessment of the Eos Data and Information System (EosDIS)", NASA report Eos-89-1, 1989.

NASA, 1990. "Earth Observing System: 1990 Reference Handbook", NASA GSFC, 1990.

Royal Society of Canada, 1989. "Global Change Program Report No. 3, Contribution of Satellite Observations to the Canadian Global Change Program", The Royal Society of Canada and the Canada Centre for Remote Sensing, July, 1989.

Shaw, E., Raney, R.K., Langham, E.J. and Strome, W.M., 1984. "The Canadian RADARSAT Programme", ISPRS Congress, Commission I Working Group 4, Rio de Janeiro Brazil, June, 1984

Strome, W.M., 1972a. "Data Handling Facility of the Canada Centre for Remote Sensing", Proc. 1st Canadian Symposium on Remote

Strome, W.M., 1972b. "Canada Centre for Remote Sensing ERTS Program", 8th International Symposium on Remote Sensing of Environment, ERIM, Ann Arbor Michigan, October, 1972. Sensing, Ottawa, February 1972.

Strome, W.M., 1972c. "Canadian ERTS Data Handling System", National Telecommunications Conference, I.E.E.E. 1972 NIC Record, Houston Texas, December 4-6, 1972.

Strome, W.M., Morley, L.W., Goodenough, D.G., Cihlar, J. and McQuillan, A.K., 1979. "Regional Environmental Monitoring Centres -a CCRS Proposal", Proc. 3rd Conference on the Economics of Remote Sensing Information Systems, N. Lake Tahoe Nevada, November 6-8, 1979.

Strome, W.M., Guertin, F.E., Collins, A.B. and Goodenough, D.G., 1983. "Canadian Plans for Thematic Mapper Data", Proc. of the Early Results from LANDSAT-4", NASA, Greenbelt Md., February 1983.

Strome, W.M., Shaw, E., Raney, R.K. and Langham, E.J., 1984. " Radarsat - Canada's Remote Sensing Satellite Programme", Proc. 9th Canadian Symposium on Remote Sensing, CCRS, St. John's Nfld, August 14-17, 1984.

Strome, W.M., Langham, E.J., "Radarsat", U.S.-India Symposium: Workshop on Remote Sensing, March 11-15, 1985, Ahmedabad, India.

Strome, W.M. and Grush, Berne, 1985."The Scientific and Technical Issues in Integrating Remotely Sensed Imagery with Geocoded Data Bases", Proc. of Graphics Interface '85, Montreal Canada, 1985.

Strome, W.M. and Billingsley, F., 1986. "Attempts at Standardization of Remote Sensing and GIS Data", ISPRS Commission II Symposium, Photogrammetric and Remote Sensing Systems for Data Processing and Analysis, Baltimore Md., May 26-30, 1986.

Strome, W.M. 1986. "The Impact of Optical Storage Technology on Remote Sensing and Geographic Information Systems", ISPRS Commission II Symposium, Photogrammetric and Remote Sensing Systems for Data Processing and Analysis, Baltimore Md., May 26-30, 1986.

Strome, W.M., Leckie, D., Miller, J. and Buxton, R., 1990. "Applications of High-Resolution Remote Sensing Image Data", (in press) AIAA Progress in Astronautics and Aeronautics series: Space Commercialization: Satellite Technology, AIAA, Washington, D.C., 1990.

CHAPTER SEVENTEEN

Ahern, F. J., Brown, R.J., Thomson, K. P. B., Pearce, C. M., Fedosejevs, G. and Staenz, K., 1981a, Optical Characteristics of Alberta Rangeland as Related to Remote Sensing, Proceedings of the Seventh Canadian Symposium on Remote Sensing, Winnipeg, Manitoba, pp.159-173.

Ahern, F.J. Brown, R.J., Thomson, K.P.B. and Staenz, K., 1981b, The CCRS Visible-Infrared Spectroscopy Laboratory: Significant Results From Three Years' Operation Proceedings of the

First International Colloquium on Spectral Signatures of Objects in Remote Sensing, Avignon, France, pp.25-40.

Ahern, F.J., Gauthier, R.P., Teillet, P.M., Sirois, J., Fedosejevs, G. and Lorente, D., 1990, An Investigation of Continental Aerosols With High Spectral Resolution Solar Extinction Measurements, submitted to Applied Optics.

Begni, G., Dinguirard, M.C., Jackson, R.D. and Slater, P.N., 1986, Absolute Calibration of the SPOT-1 HRV Cameras, SPIE Volume 660, pp.66-76.

Barnsley, M.J., 1984, Effects of Off-Nadir View Angles on the Detected Spectral Response of Vegetation Canopies, International Journal of Remote Sensing, 5, pp.715-718.

Begue, A., Deschamps, P.Y., Podaire, A. and Tanre, D, 1988, Analyse des effets directionnels sur les images NOAA AVHRR, Proceedings of the Fourth International Colloquium on Spectral Signatures ofObjects in Remote Sensing, Aussois, France, ESA SP-287, pp.205-209.Björklund, G., 1989, The IGBP GBOs Become RRCs, Global Change Newsletter, No. 2, IGBP Secretariat, Royal Swedish Academy of Sciences, Stockholm, Sweden.

Bretherton, F.P., 1985, Earth System Science and Remote Sensing, Proceedings of the IEEE, 73, pp.1118-1127.

Brisco, B., Brown, R.J. and Sofko, G.J., 1988, The CCRS Ground-Based Microwave Facility, Proceedings of the IGARSS'89 Symposium, Edinburgh, Scotland, pp.575 576.

Brown, R.J., Ahern, F.J., Ryerson, R.A., Thomson, K.P.B., Goodenough, D.G., McCormick, J.A. and Teillet, P.M., 1980, Rapeseed: Guidelines for Operational Monitoring, Proceedings of the Sixth Canadian Symposium on Remote Sensing, Halifax, Nova Scotia, pp.321-330.

Brown, R.J. and Ahern, F.J., 1980, The Field Spectral Measurements Program of the Canada Centre for Remote Sensing, Canadian Journal of Remote Sensing, 6, pp.26-37.

Brown, R.J., Bernier, M. and Fedosejevs, G., 1982, Geometrical and Atmospheric Considerations of NOAA AVHRR Imagery, Proceedings of the Eighth International Symposium on Machine Processing of Remotely Sensed Data, Purdue University, West Lafayette, Indiana, p.374.

Brown, R.J., Ahern, F.J., Thomson, K.P.B., Staenz, K., Cihlar, J., Pearce, C.M. and Klumph, S.G., 1983, Alberta Rangeland Assessment Using Remotely Sensed Data, Research Report 83-1, Canada Centre for Remote Sensing, Ottawa, Ontario, 128 pages.

Cihlar, J., 1986, On the Relationship Between Agroclimatic Region, Crop Parameters, and SAR Image Tone in Western Canada, Canadian Journal of Remote Sensing, 12, pp.81-93.

Cihlar, J., Dobson, M.C., Schmugge, T., Hoogeboom, P., Janse, A.R.P., Baret, F., Guyot, G., Le Toan, T. and Pampaloni, P., 1987, Procedures for the Description of Agricultural Crops and Soils in Optical and Microwave Remote Sensing Studies, International Journal of Remote Sensing, 8, pp.427-439.

Cihlar, J., LeDrew, E., Edel, H., Evans, W., McKay, D., McNutt, L. and Royer, A., 1989, Contribution of Satellite Observations to the Canadian Global Change Program, Report No. 3, Canadian Global Change Program, The Royal Society of Canada, Ottawa, Ontario.

Cochran, W.G. and Cox, G.M., 1957, Experimental Designs, John Wiley, New York, pp.15-29.
Cochran, W.G., 1977, Sampling Techniques, Third Edition, John Wiley and Sons, New York.

Congalton, R.G., Oderwald, R.G. and Mead, R.A., 1983, Assessing Landsat Classification Accuracy Using Discrete Multivariate Analysis Statistical Techniques, Photogrammetric Engineering and Remote Sensing, 49, pp.1671-1678.

Curran, P.J. and Williamson, H.D., 1985a, The Accuracy of Ground Data Used in Remote Sensing Investigations, International Journal of Remote Sensing, 6, pp.1637-1651.

Curran, P.J. and Williamson, H.D., 1985b, How Many Ground Samples? A Question for Remote Sensing, in Remote Sensing: Data Acquisition, Management and Applications, Remote Sensing Society, Reading, U.K. and Centre for Earth Applications, Springfield, pp.163-169.

Curran, P.J. and Hay, A.M., 1986, The Importance of Measurement Error for Certain Procedures in Remote Sensing at Optical Wavelengths, Photogrammetric Engineering and Remote Sensing, 52, pp.229-241.

Curran, P.J. and Williamson, H.D., 1986, Sample Size for Ground and Remotely Sensed Data, Remote Sensing of Environment, 20, pp.31-41.

Daughtry, C.S.T., Vanderbilt, V.C. and Pollara, V.J., 1981, Variability of Reflectance Measurements with Sensor Altitude and Canopy Type, AgRISTARS Supporting Research Technical Report, SR-P1-04191, NAS9-15466, LARS 111481, Purdue University, Laboratory for Applications of Remote Sensing, West Lafayette, Indiana.

Deering, D.W. and Leone, P., 1986, A Sphere-Scanning Radiometer for Rapid Directional Measurements of Sky and Ground Radiance, Remote Sensing of Environment, 19, pp.1-24.

Deering, D.W. and Eck, T.F., 1987, Atmospheric Optical Depth Effects on Angular Anisotropy of Plant Canopy Reflectance, International Journal of Remote Sensing, 8, pp.893-916.

Deering, D.W., 1988, PARABOLA Directional Field Radiometer for Aiding in Space Sensor Data Interpretations, Proceedings of the SPIE, Volume 924, Orlando, Florida, pp.249-261.

Deering, D.W., Eck, T.F. and Otterman, J., 1989, Bidirectional Reflectances of Three Soil Surfaces and their Characterization Through Model Inversion, Proceedings of the 1989 International Geoscience and Remote Sensing Symposium (IGARSS'89), Vancouver, B.C., pp.670-673.

Diner, D.J., Bruegge, C.J., Martonchik, J.V., Ackerman, T.P., Davies, R., Gerstl, S.A.W., Gordon, H.R., Sellers, F.J., Clark, J., Daniels, J.A., Danielson, E.D., Duval, V.G., Klassen, K.P., Lilienthal, G.W., Nakamoto, D.I., Pagano, R.J. and Reilly, T.H., 1989, MISR: A Multiangle Imaging Spectroradiometer for Geophysical and Climatological Research from Eos, IEEE Transactions on Geoscience and Remote Sensing, GE-27, pp.200-214.

Dozier, J. and Strahler, A.H., 1983, Ground Investigations in Support of Remote Sensing, Chapter 23 in Manual of Remote Sensing, Second Edition, Edited by R.N. Colwel, American Society of Photogrammetry, Falls Church, Virginia (The Sheridan Press).

Duggin, M.J. and Philipson, W.R., 1982, Field Measurement of Reflectance: Some Major Considerations, Applied Optics, 21, pp.2833-2840.

Duggin, M.J., 1985, Factors Limiting the Discrimination and Quantification of Terrestrial Features Using Remotely Sensed Radiance, International Journal of Remote Sensing, 6, p.3.

Fitzpatrick, K.A., 1977, The Strategy and Methods for Determining Accuracy of Small and Intermediate Scale Land Use and Land Cover Maps, Proceedings of the Second W.T. Pecora Symposium, American Society of Photogrammetry, pp.339-361.

Forster, B.C., 1985, An Examination of Some Problems and Solutions in Monitoring Urban Areas From Satellite Platforms, International Journal of Remote Sensing, 6, pp.139-151.

Fung, K. and Lasserre, M., 1987, On the Establishment of Positional Control for Remote Sensing Sensors, Proceedings of the Eleventh Canadian Symposium on Remote Sensing, Waterloo, Ontario, pp.661-670.

Gauthier, R.P., Ahern, F.J. and Teillet, P.M., 1989, A Measurement Program for the Validation of Atmospheric Radiative Transfer Codes, Proceedings of the 1989 International Geoscience and Remote Sensing Symposium (IGARSS'89) and the Twelfth Canadian Symposium on Remote Sensing, Vancouver, B.C., pp. 877-880.

Goetz, A.F.H. and Herring, M., 1989, The High Resolution Imaging Spectrometer (HIRIS) for Eos, IEEE Transactions on Geoscience and Remote Sensing, 27, pp.136-144.

Guenther, 1989, Personal Communication.

Guindon, B., Teillet, P.M., Goodenough, D.G., Palimaka, J.J. and Sieber, A., 1984, Evaluation of the Crop Classification Performance of X,L, and C-Band SAR Imagery, Canadian Journal of Remote Sensing, 10, pp.4-16.

Guindon, B. and Neeman, S., 1986, Application of Accuracy Assessment Techniques to Image Classification, Proceedings of the Tenth Canadian Symposium on Remote Sensing, Edmonton, Alberta, pp.55-63.

Guyenne, T.D. (editor), 1985, Proceedings of the 3rd International Colloquium on Spectral Signatures of Objects in Remote Sensing, ESA SP-247, Les Arcs, France.

Guyenne, T.D. and Hunt, J.J., (editors), 1988, Proceedings of the 4th International Colloquium on Spectral Signatures of Objects in Remote Sensing, ESA SP-287, Aussois (Modane), France.

Guyot, G. and Verbrugghe, M. (editors), 1981, Proceedings of the 1st International Colloquium on Spectral Signatures of Objects in Remote Sensing, Les Colloques de l'INRA, No. 5, Avignon, France.

Guyot, G. and Verbrugghe, M. (editors), 1983, Proceedings of the 2nd International Colloquium on Spectral Signatures of Objects in Remote Sensing, Les Colloques de l'INRA, No. 23, Bordeaux, France.

Holben, B. and Fraser, R.S., 1984, Red and Near-Infrared Sensor Response to Off-Nadir Viewing, International Journal of Remote Sensing, 5, pp.145-160.

Holmes, R.A., 1970, Field Spectroscopy, in Remote Sensing, With Special Reference to Agriculture and Forestry, National Academy of Sciences, Washington, D.C.

Horler, D.N.H., Bernier, M., Thomson, K.P.B., Teillet, P.M., Staenz, K., Fedosejevs, G. and Wallace, K., 1983, Field Spectroradiometry in the Development of a Corn Area Estimation Method in Canada, Proc. of the Eighth Canadian Symposium on Remote Sensing, Montréal, Québec, pp. 375-386.

IGBP, 1988, Geosphere-Biosphere Observatories, Chapter 6 in The International Geosphere-Biosphere Programme: A Study of Global Change - IGBP - A Plan for Action, IGBP Report No.4, Royal Swedish Academy of Sciences, Stockholm, Sweden.

Irons, J.R. and Labovitz, M.L., 1982, A Data Analytic Approach to Look-Angle Radiance Adjustment, Journal of Applied Photogrammetric Engineering, 8, p.128.

Irons, J.R and Irish, R.R., 1988, Sensor Calibration for Multiple Direction Reflectance Observations, Proceedings of the SPIE, Volume 924, Orlando, Florida, pp.109-119.

Jackson, R.D. and Slater, P.N., 1986, Absolute Calibration of Field Reflectance Radiometers, Photogrammetric Engineering and Remote Sensing, 52, pp.189-196.

Jackson, R.D., Teillet, P.M., Slater, P.N., Fedosejevs, G., Jasinski, M.F., Aase, J.K. and Moran, M.S., 1990, Bidirectional Measurements of Surface Reflectance for View Angle Corrections of Oblique Imagery, submitted to Remote Sensing of Environment.

John, J.A. and Quenouille, M.H., 1977, Experiments: Design and Analysis, Second Edition, MacMillan Publ. Co., pp.19-24.

Kastner, C.J. and Slater, P.N., 1982, In-flight Radiometric Calibration of Advanced Remote Sensing Systems, Field Measurement and Calibration Using Electro-Optical Equipment: Issues and Requirements, Proc. SPIE 356, p.158.

King, G.J. and Mack, A.R., 1984, A Manual for Recording Significant Agricultural Ground Information in Remote Sensing Programs, Agriculture Canada, Ottawa, Ontario.

Labsphere, Inc., 1990, "Reflectance Technologies" brochure, P.O. Box 70, North Sutton, New Hampshire, 03260.

Lasserre, M., 1989, Personal Communication

Leckie, D.G., Teillet, P.M., Ostaff, D.P. and Fedosejevs, G., 1988a, Sensor Band Selection for Detecting Current Defoliation Caused by the Spruce Budworm, Remote Sensing of Environment, 26, pp. 31-50.

Leckie, D.G., Teillet, P.M., Fedosejevs, G. and Ostaff, D.P., 1988b, Reflectance Characteristics of Cumulative Defoliation of Balsam Fir, Canadian Journal of Forest Research, 18, pp. 1008-1016.

Leckie, D.G., Ostaff, D.P., Teillet, P.M. and Fedosejevs, G., 1988c, Spectral Characteristics of Tree Components of Balsam Fir and Spruce Damaged by Spruce Budworm, Forest Science, 35, pp. 582-600.

Milton, E.J., 1987, Principles of Field Spectroscopy, International Journal of Remote Sensing, 8, pp.1807-1827.

Moran, M.S., Jackson, R.D., Hart, G.F., Slater, P.N., Bartell, R.J., Biggar, S.F. and Santer, R.P., 1988, Surface Reflectance Factors Derived From SPOT-1 HRV Data at Two View Angles, Proceedings of the Symposium on SPOT-1 Image Utilization, Assessment, Results, Toulouse, France, pp.1365-1370.

NASA, 1980, Enumerator's Manual. 1980 Ground Data Survey, Report JSC-13774, NASA, Houston, Texas.

Nisbet, E.G., 1989, A Network of Geosphere-Biosphere Research Centres, unpublished discussion paper, Department of Geological Sciences, University of Saskatchewan, Saskatoon, Saskatchewan, 93 pages.

Pinter, P.J., Jr., Jackson, R.D. and Moran, M.S., 1990, Bidirectional Reflectance Factors of Agricultural Targets: A Comparison of Ground-Aircraft- and Satellite-Based Observations, submitted to Remote Sensing of Environment.

Robertson, B.C., Sharpe, B. and Teillet, P.M., 1989, Integrated Atmospheric Correction of Multispectral Satellite Imagery, Proceedings of the 1989 International Geoscience and Remote Sensing Symposium (IGARSS'89) and the Twelfth Canadian Symposium on Remote Sensing, Vancouver, B.C., pp. 893-896.

Royer, A., Vincent, P. and Bonn, F., 1985, Evaluation and Correction of Viewing Angle Effects on Satellite Measurements of Bidirectional Reflectance, Photogrammetric Engineering and Remote Sensing, 51, pp.1899-1914.
Salomonson, V.V., Barnes, W.L., Maymon, P.W., Montgomery, H.E. and Ostrow, H., 1989, MODIS: Advanced Facility Instrument for Studies of the Earth as a System, IEEE Transactions on Geoscience and Remote Sensing, 27, pp.145-153.

Slater, P.N., 1980, Remote Sensing, Optics and Optical Systems, (Addison-Wesley Publishing Co.).

Slater, P.N., 1983, A Review of Some Radiometric Calibration Problems and Methods, Proceedings of the 2nd International Colloquium on Spectral Signatures of Objects in Remote Sensing, Les Colloques de l'INRA No. 23, Bordeaux, France, p.391.

Slater, P.N., 1985, Radiometric Considerations in Remote Sensing, Proc. Soc. Photo-optical Engrs., 73, p.997.

Slater, P.N., Biggar, S.F., Holm, R.G., Jackson, R.D., Mao, Y., Moran, M.S., Palmer, J.M. and Yuan, B., 1987, Reflectance- and Radiance-Based Methods for the In-Flight Absolute Calibration of Multispectral Sensors, Remote Sensing of Environment, 22, pp.11-37.

Slater, P.N., 1988, Radiometric Calibration Requirements and Atmospheric Correction, SPIE Volume 924, Recent Advances in Sensors, Radiometry, and Data Processing for Remote Sensing, Orlando, Florida, pp.144-150.

Smith, J.A., 1982, Reflectance Models and Field Measurements: Some Issues, Field Measurement and Calibration Using Electro-Optical Equipment: Issues and Requirements, Proc. SPIE 356, p.131.

Sofko, G.J., Koehler, J.A., McKibben, M.J., Wacker, A.G., Hinds, M.R., Brown, R.J. and Brisco, B., 1989, Ground Microwave Operations, Canadian Journal of Remote Sensing, 15, pp.14-27.

SPOT Newsletter, 1989, SPOT IMAGE, 16 bis, avenue Edouard-Belin, F31030 Toulouse-Cedex, France, No. 12, December.

Staenz, K., Ahern F.J. and Brown, R.J., 1981, The Influence of Illumination and Viewing Geometry on the Reflectance Factor of Agricultural Targets, Proceedings of the Fifteenth International Symposium on Remote Sensing of Environment, Ann Arbor, Michigan, pp.867-882.

Teilhard de Chardin, P., 1956, La place de l'homme dans la nature, No. 33, Série "le monde en 10-18", Union générale d'éditions, Paris, France.

Teillet, P.M., Brown, R.J., Guindon, B. and Fedosejevs, G., 1984, Relating Synthetic Aperture Radar Imagery to Biophysical Factors, Proceedings of the Ninth Canadian Symposium on Remote Sensing, St. John's, Newfoundland, pp.693-701.

Teillet, P.M., Leckie, D.G., Ostaff, D., Fedosejevs, G. and Ahern, F.J., 1985, Spectral Measurements of Tree Defoliation, Proc. of the Third International Colloquium on Spectral Signatures of Objects in Remote Sensing, Les Arcs, France, pp. 511-516.

Teillet, P.M., Lasserre, M. and Vigneault, C.G., 1986, An Evaluation of Sun Angle Computation Algorithms, Proceedings of the Tenth Canadian Symposium on Remote Sensing, Edmonton, Alberta, pp.91-100.

Teillet, P.M., 1986, Image Correction for Radiometric Effects in Remote Sensing, International Journal of Remote Sensing, 7, pp.1637-1651.

Teillet, P.M., Slater, P.N., Jackson, R.D., Fedosejevs, G. and Moran, M.S., 1987, Reflectance Measurements at White Sands, New Mexico, Using a Mobile Spectroscopy Laboratory, Proc. of the Eleventh Canadian Symposium on Remote Sensing, Waterloo, Ontario, pp. 441-450.

Teillet, P.M., Slater, P.N., Mao, Y., Ding, Y., Yuan, B., Bartell, R.J., Biggar, S.F., Santer, R.P., Jackson, R.D. and Moran, M.S., 1988, Absolute Radiometric Calibration of the NOAA AVHRR Sensors, SPI Volume 924, Recent Advances in Sensors, Radiometry, and Data Processing for Remote Sensing, Orlando, Florida, pp. 196-207.

Teillet, P.M., 1989, Surface Reflectance Retrieval Using Atmospheric Correction Algorithms, Proceedings of the 1989 International Geoscience and Remote Sensing Symposium (IGARSS'89) and the Twelfth Canadian Symposium on Remote Sensing, Vancouver, B.C., pp. 864-867.

Teillet, P.M., 1990, Rayleigh Optical Depth Comparisons from Various Sources, Applied Optics, in press.

Teillet, P.M., Slater, P.M., Ding, Y., Santer, R.P., Jackson, R.D. and Moran, M.S., 1990, Three Methods for the Absolute Calibration of the NOAA AVHRR Sensors In-Flight, Remote Sensing of Environment, in press.

Wood, J.A., Lasserre, M., Fedosejevs, G., van der Grient, C. and Teillet, P.M., 1987, Investigation of Inertial and Thermal and Mid-Infrared Spectral Properties of Rock Outcrops, Proc. of the Eleventh Canadian Symposium on Remote Sensing, Waterloo, Ontario, pp. 345-355.

Wood, J., Lasserre, M. and Fedosejevs, G., 1990, Analysis of Mid-Infrared Spectral Characteristics of Rock Outcrops and Evaluation of the Kahle Model in Predicting Outcrop Thermal Inertias, Remote Sensing of Environment, in press.

CHAPTER EIGHTEEN

Council of State Governments. 1974. A legislator's guide to land management. Counc. of State Gov., Washington, D.C.

Larsen, B.,et al. 1978, Land Records; the cost to the citizen, a Wisconsin case study. Univ. of Wisconsin, Madison, Wis.

Bie, S. W. and Lamp, J. (1981) Criteria, Hardware and Software for a Global Land and Soil Monitoring System, GRID Information Series No. 1, UNEP, Nairobi, pp, 46.

(1986) Data sources, standards and quality control for a GEMS-GRID Kenyan case study. GRID Information Series No. 4.

Gwynne, M. D. (1982) The Global Environment Monitoring System (GEMS) of UNEP, Environmental Conservation, vol. 9, No. 1, pp. 35-41.

Mooneyhan, D. W. (1988) Applications of Geographic Information Systems within the United Nations Environment Program, in Building Databases for Global Science. H. Mounsey and R. Tomlinson (eds), Taylor and Francis, London, p. 315-329.

UNEP (1986) GRID Status Report March 1985 - April 1985, GRID Information Series No. 3, United Nations Environment Program. Nairobi, Kenya, May 1986.

REVIEWED MATERIALS

Our Common Future, World Commission on Environment and Development, Oxford Universities Press 1987, Oxford, New York.

Remote Sensing for Development, Experiences with and Requirements for User Assistance and Training, Proceedings of the International Conference in Berlin (West), 1 to 6 September 1986, Parts 1 and 2, Edited by Jorg Albertz and Rudiger Tauch, Berlin 1989.

GLOSSARY

ABLE: Amazon Boundary Layer Experiment. A 1985 NASA project which used a series of airborne lidar measurements to document the sources, transport processes and regional impacts of biomass burning in Amazonia.

ADEOS: Advanced Earth Observation Satellite. A Japanese satellite scheduled for launch in February 1995, ADEOS will carry a number of instruments for Earth science research.

acid rain: A colloquial term used to describe precipitation in a polluted environment, where the raindrops become contaminated with sulfur dioxide and nitrogen oxide from coal combustion or vehicle exhaust.

adiabatic: Applied to changes in air temperature that occur as a consequence of vertical movement without heat exchange with the surrounding environment.

Advanced Microwave Scanning Radiometer (AMSR): A multifrequency microwave radiometer to be carried on board the Japanese Advanced Earth Observation Satellite (ADEOS).

advection: The transport of air and its properties in a predominantly horizontal motion.

AFOS: Agriculture Forestry and Other Human Activities; a subgroup of the Intergovernmental Panel on Climate Change (IPCC), concerned with the policy dimension and strategies to control or reduce emissions and other human activities that may have an impact on climate (e.g. deforestation, changing land use).

albedo: The fraction of incident radiation reflected by a surface; a measure of reflectivity.
AMI: Active Microwave Instrument carried aboard the European Space Agency's ERS-1 satellite, launched in July, 1991.. The AMI senses in the C-band, and is capable of operating as either a SAR (image mode) or scatterometer (wind mode).

anthropogenic: Caused by humans, or a result of human activity.

APAR: Absorbed Photosynthetically Active Radiation

artificial intelligence (AI): computer methods designed to emulate the intelligent behaviour of humans.

ATSR: Along Track Scanning Radiometer, carried aboard the European Space Agency's ERS-1 satellite, launched in July, 1991. The ATSR is an infrared radiometer with four spectral bands between 1.6 and 12 mm. Spatial resolution is 50 km.

AVHRR: Advanced Very High Resolution Radiometer. The imaging sensors carried aboard the NOAA series of polar orbiting satellites, of which NOAA 10 and 11 are currently operational. The AVHRR has five channels in the visible, near IR and thermal IR portions of the electromagnetic spectrum, with a spatial resolution of about one km.

backscatter: The component of microwave radiation which has been reflected back to the radar unit by a target.

biomass: The weight of all living organisms forming a given population, or inhabiting a given region.

biome: A major regional ecological community of plants and animals, extending over large natural areas.

biosphere: The part of the earth and its atmosphere which is inhabited by living organisms.

boreal forest: The vast biome covering northern Europe, Asia and North America dominated by evergreen coniferous forests punctuated with numerous lakes and bogs. The winters are long, dry and cold while the summers are short and cool.

BOREAS: Boreal Ecosystems-Atmosphere Study. An international, interdisciplinary study designed to improve our understanding of the interactions between the boreal forest biome and the atmosphere, in order to clarify their roles in global change. BOREAS will run from 1993 to 1995 or 1996, with the bulk of field activities taking place throughout 1994, across large study areas in Saskatchewan and Manitoba.

BRDF: Bidirectional Reflectance Distribution Function; the mathematical function describing the geometric reflectance behaviour of a scene element.

Canada Centre for Remote Sensing (CCRS): A branch of Energy, Mines and Resources Canada, CCRS is the central agency in Canada's nationwide remote sensing program.

CASI: Compact Airborne Spectrographic Imager. An along-track imaging spectrometer produced commercially by Itres Ltd. of Calgary, Alberta. The CASI can collect up to 288 spectral bands in the 400 - 900 nm range at a spectral resolution of 1.8 nm.

CGCP: Canadian Global Change Program

CGIS: Canada Geographic Information System

chlorofluorcarbons (CFCs): Compounds containing only chlorine, fluorine and carbon commonly used as a refrigerant, a cleaning agent, and a blowing agent for plastic foams. CFCs decompose to release chlorine, which can catalyze ozone destruction.

CIDA: Canadian International Development Agency

CIRAC: Canadian Institute for Research in Atmospheric Chemistry

cryosphere: The portion of the climate system consisting of the world's ice masses and snow deposits, including continental ice sheets, mountain glaciers, sea ice, surface snow cover, and lake and river ice.

CRYSYS: Cryospheric System to Monitor Global Change in Canada. The main objective of the CRYSYS project is to improve our understanding of the interactions between the cryosphere, atmosphere and oceans, and to enable the monitoring and prediction of physical environmental changes in northern regions using remote sensing observations.

CWS: Canadian Wildlife Service

CZCS: Coastal Zone Colour Scanner.   Carried on board the Nimbus 7 satellite and launched into a sun-synchronous, near-polar 955 km orbit on October 23, 1978.   The CZSZ has six channels in the visible and infrared portion of the electromagnetic spectrum, with a spatial resolution of 825 m.

Defense Meteorological Satellite Program (DMSP): A program designed primarily to provide operational weather data for the United States Department of Defense (DoD), the latest DMSP satellites are the three in the 502-4 series, launched in February 1988.

DEM: Digital Elevation Model; a digital raster of elevations forming a continuous representation of ground topography.

Earth Observations System (EOS): The next major NASA-led remote sensing program, EOS is being planned as a multi-platform system extending over 15 years, with instruments designed to observe and study numerous aspects of the whole 'Earth system', including terrestrial areas, the oceans, ice and atmosphere.   The first American platform is scheduled for deployment in 1998.

EDC: EROS Data Center

EESI: Earth Environment Space Initiative - proposed Canadian satellite

El Nino: Periods of warm surface ocean currents and heavy rainfall off the coasts of Peru and Ecuador that coincide with relaxed trade winds over the Pacific.   El Nino events occur about twice every ten years, although the interval between two events is irregular.

Electrically Scanning Microwave Radiometer (ESMR): A passive microwave instrument operating on board the Nimbus-5 satellite from 1973-1976

EM: Electromagnetic.

EMDI: Environmental Management Development Initiative (CIDA)

ENSO: El Nino/Southern Oscillation.   A combination (teleconnection) of El Nino and Southern Oscillation events.   The Southern Oscillation is an out-of-phase relationship between atmospheric pressure over the southeast Pacific and the Indian Ocean   When the pressure is higher than usual over the Indian Ocean, it is lower than normal in the south Pacific; rainfall varies in the opposite direction.

EOSDIS: Earth Observing System Data and Information System.

EROS: Earth Resources Observation System (U.S. Dept. of Interior).

ERTS: Earth Resources Technology Satellite.   The original name for the series of satellites renamed Landsat in 1975.   The first ERTS/Landsat platform was launched in 1972.

ESA: European Space Agency.

EUMETSAT: European meteorological satellite organization.

FAO: Food and Agriculture Organization. A specialized agency of the United Nations (UN) whose main goal is to increase food production and availability throughout the world.

FIFE: The First ISLSCP Field Experiment conducted in the Konza Prairie, Kansas in 1987. The underlying objectives of FIFE were to verify the use of remote sensing data for estimation of land surface properties over a relatively uniform vegetation cover, and to study approaches of obtaining aerial averages of radiation, moisture and heat fluxes.

estuarine: Relating to, or formed in the mouth of a river where it broadens into a sea, within which the tide ebbs and flows

gaschromatograph: An instrumental procedure used for separating components from a mixture of chemical substances, based on physical absorption principles.

GCM: General Circulation Model, used for climate analysis and prediction. GCMs account for many of the physical processes in the Earth-atmosphere system using very detailed, complex mathematical formulations.

GCNet: Global Change Network; a computer network to be part of EOS.

GCNode: A computer workstation in the GCNet.

GEMS: Global Environmental Monitoring System; a system administered by the United Nations Environment Programme (UNEP) designed to monitor many aspects of the global environment, including climate and the atmosphere, long-range transport of airborne pollutants, environmental pollutants of significance to ecosystem and human health, terrestrial renewable resources, oceans and coastal areas.

geomatics: The combined disciplines of remote sensing, GIS and mapping

Geosat: A U.S. Navy satellite carrying a radar altimeter which operated between 1985 and 1989.

GEWEX: Global Energy and Water Cycle Experiment; a core programme of World Climate Research Programme (WCRP) designed to observe, understand and model the hydrological cycle and energy fluxes in the climate system.

GIAC: Geomatics Industry Association of Canada.

GISS model: An atmospheric circulation model developed by NASA's Goddard Institute for Space Sciences (GISS).

Global Change: A general term referring to past, present and future changes in the global environment.

GLOWDAT: global water quality database maintained by Environment Canada

GOES: Geostationary Operational Environmental Satellite. A series of geosynchronous satellites, only one of which remains operational, launched under NOAA's operational weather satellite program. The satellites serve as platforms for a wide range of measurement sensors, including an imaging sensor known as the Visible Infrared Spin-Scan Radiometer (VISSR).

GPS: Global Positioning System, a satellite-based navigation system which, in differential mode, is capable of locating the position of portable ground receivers with an accuracy of up to 5 m.

greenhouse gases: Atmospheric gases which are mostly transparent to incoming solar radiation, but have absorption bands in the wavelengths coinciding to the Earth's outgoing thermal radiation.

GRID: Global Resource Information Database; part of the Global Environment Monitoring System (GEMS).

gyre: A large circular, surface ocean current pattern.

halon: A compound containing carbon, bromine and one or more other halogens (chlorine, flourine). Halons are commonly used as fire extinguishers.

HIRIS: High Resolution Imaging Spectrometer to be deployed on EOS. The pointable HIRIS will have a 30 metre spatial resolution, and will acquire 192 continuous 10 nm-wide spectral bands between 400 and 2500 nm.

hydrological cycle: The cycle of water through the earth-atmosphere system, initiated through the acquisition of water vapour by evaporation and transpiration from water and land surfaces, released into the atmosphere by condensation, and deposited on land and water surfaces by precipitation.

hydrology: The scientific study of the distribution and properties of water in the earth-atmosphere system.

HRV: High Resolution Visible imager carried aboard France's SPOT series of satellites. The HRV is a pointable instrument which operates in two modes: multispectral, with three VIR bands and 20 metre ground resolution, and panchromatic, with a single 10-metre band.

ICSU: International Council of Scientific Unions; created in 1931 to promote international scientific activity in the different branches of science and their applications for the benefit of humanity.

Image Analysis System (IAS): A computer hardware and software system used to analyze digital image data.

IGBP: International Geosphere-Biosphere Programme; an interdisciplinary research endeavor carried out within the framework of the ICSU to study the biogeochemical aspects of the global change phenomenon, on Earth System modelling, and the recovery and interpretation of data dealing with global changes of the past. The IGBP is complementary to efforts in the World Climate Research Programme (WCRP).

IHP: International Hydrological Programme; a UNESCO-based programme concerned with advancing our understanding of the processes occurring in the water cycle, and integrating this knowledge into water resources management.

interferometer: A passive remote sensing instrument used in the study of optical interference. Used in applications which require high spectral resolution and small wavelength coverage, such as upper atmosphere observation.

IRIS: Infrared Interferometer Spectrometer. A nadir-looking Michelson interferometer carried on board the Nimbus-3 satellite.

IRS: Indian Remote Sensing Satellite, an operational satellite launched in 1988 carrying the Linear Imaging Self Scanner (LISS), with four visible and near-infrared bands and a 73 metre spatial resolution.

ISLCSP: The International Satellite Land Surface Climatology Project is an internationally-sponsored research program for the study of the complex and closely coupled land surface-atmosphere interactions. The major objective is to develop methodologies for deriving quantitative land surface climatological information from satellite observations.

ISPRS: International Society of Photogrammetry and Remote Sensing.

ISO: International Standards Organization.

ISY: The International Space Year (1992) was a concept intended to enhance international collaboration among space agencies and scientists on the global phenomena of the Earth's environment, and to enhance public awareness of the benefits arising from space activities.

IUCN: International Union for Conservation of Nature and Natural Resources; an independent international body formed in 1948 to initiate and promote scientifically-based conservation measures. Sister organization to the World Wildlife Fund (WWF).

JERS: Japanese Earth Resources Satellite. JERS-1, carrying and L-band SAR and four-band optical sensor, was launched into a sun-synchronous orbit in February, 1992.

JGOFS: Joint Global Ocean Flux Study; a core project of the International Geosphere-Biosphere Program (IGBP) to be carried out during the period 1990-2000. The objective of JGOFS is to understand the global biochemical and geochemical cycling of carbon and other biologically important elements which play a major role in the global environment.

katabatic: A downhill wind, usually cold, which blows down valleys at night and outwards from large ice caps. It is caused by surface cooling, which cools the lower air masses and increases air density.

LAI: Leaf Area Index; the projected leaf surface per unit ground area (m2/m2).

lambertian: Perfectly diffuse; reflects energy equally in all directions.

LANDSAT: A series of American satellites carrying Multispectral Scanners and, more recently, the Thematic Mapper. They are primarily designed for studying and mapping land surfaces, and are complementary to Seasat.

LIDAR: Light Detection and Ranging system. LIDARs operate using the same principle as radars, with a pulsed light source (usually a laser) to sound the upper atmosphere. The characteristics of the scattered signal are used to infer atmospheric parameters; backscatter intensity is proportional to the density of the scattering medium, and height can be inferred from the time delay between signal and echo.

limb viewing: A viewing geometry wherein the orbiting instrument scans up and down in positions beneath the horizon, in order to see the earth's atmosphere in horizontal paths at different altitudes.

limnology: The scientific study of physical, chemical and biological conditions in lakes, ponds and streams.

LSC: Land Surface Climatology; the scientific discipline concerned with land surface interactions with the atmosphere.

MAB: Man and Biosphere Programme of UNESCO.

mass spectrometer: An instrument designed to permit the precise measurement of the relative abundance of gaseous ions.

Meteosat: An operational weather satellite operated by the European Space Agency. Meteosat-3 was launched into a geostationary (0°) orbit in June, 1988.

MEIS: Multispectral Electro-optical Imaging Scanner; a linear array multispectral airborne imager developed and operated by the Canada Centre for Remote Sensing. MEIS records 8 spectral channels between 390 and 1100 nm.

MERIS: Medium Resolution Imaging Spectrometer designed to operate in very narrow bands (5-20 nm) in the visible and near-infrared portions of the electromagnetic spectrum, with 250/1000m spatial resolution. MERIS is scheduled for launch aboard the ESA's polar orbiting Earth observation mission (EPOP) in 1997.

MIMICS: Michigan Microwave Canopy Scattering Model; a radiative transfer model designed to simulate radar backscatter from forest targets.

MISR: The Multiangle Imaging SpectroRadiometer is part of NASA's EOS program, and is designed to provide multiangle data at the top of atmosphere and surface albedos. MISR is scheduled for launch aboard EOS AM-1 in June, 1998.

MODIS: Moderate Resolution Imaging Spectrometer designed to provide global observations of land, atmosphere and ocean properties from EOS AM-1, scheduled for launch in June 1998.

MOMS: The Modular Optoelectronic Multispectral Scanner is a pushbroom imager developed in Germany which is scheduled for operation aboard satellite platforms by the end of the century.

MOPITT: gas correlation spectrometer for monitoring pollution in troposphere from space.

MOS: Marine Observation Satellites carrying sensors for monitoring sea surface color and temperature. Satellites from the MOS program have been launched by Japan into sun-synchronous orbits in 1987 and 1989.

Multispectral Scanner (MSS): An imaging sensor carried aboard the LANDSAT series of satellites; the MSS has five bands, four in the visible and near infrared portion of the electromagnetic spectrum with spatial resolutions of 79 metres, and one in the thermal infrared with a spatial resolution of 240 metres.
nadir: The point on the ground directly beneath the instrument.

NASA: National Aeronautics and Space Administration (USA).

NDVI: The Normalized Difference Vegetation Index is the normalized ratio of (IR - Red)/(IR + Red). NDVI has been shown to have a close relationship to photosynthetic capacity of specific vegetation types, and has become widely used as a remotely sensed measure of vegetation activity.

NIMBUS: A series of seven US research satellites operating during the period 1964-1978. The Nimbus satellites carried more than 40 instruments, including cameras, scanning radiometers, atmospheric sounders, ozone mappers and ocean color sensors.

NOAA: The National Oceanic and Atmospheric Administration, the US agency responsible for the launch of over a dozen operational weather satellites.

NPP: Net Primary Productivity.

NSCAT: A NASA Scatterometer to be carried on board the Japanese Advanced Earth Observation Satellite (ADEOS) satellite, scheduled for launch in February 1995.

NSERC: Canada's Natural Science and Engineering Research Council.

OCTS: Ocean Color and Temperature Scanner; to be carried aboard the Japanese Advanced Earth Observation Satellite (ADEOS) in February, 1995. The OCTS will have 12 channels from 0.41 - 12.0 mm, and a spatial resolution of 700 metres.

OECD: Organization for Economic Cooperation and Development. An international organization dedicated to promoting policies designed to achieve the highest sustainable economic growth and standard of living in member countries, promote sound economic expansion, and contribute to multilateral, non-discriminatory world trade.

ozone hole: Extraordinary springtime destruction of atmospheric ozone over polar regions, occurring primarily over Antarctica. First reported in 1985.

PARABOLA: NASA's Portable Apparatus for Rapid Acquisition of Bidirectional Observations of the Land and Atmosphere was designed to overcome important limitations of previous field instruments for obtaining adequate samples for analyzing BRDFs. The PARABOLA has three spectral channels in the visible, near infrared and middle infrared, and facilitates rapid acquisition of directional measurements for nearly the complete sky- and ground-looking hemispheres.

photometer: An instrument which measures the intensity of light over a wavelength band within the sensor's instantaneous field of view. Unlike imaging devices, photometers cannot distinguish between photons arriving from different parts of the field of view.

phytoplankton: Tiny, sometimes microscopic plants of sea or lake which float or drift almost passively.

playa: A level or nearly level area in the central portion of an enclosed basin, in which a temporary lake forms periodically.

polynya: Any non-linear shaped opening enclosed by sea ice. A recurring polynya is found in the same position every year.

principle components analysis (PCA): A data reduction technique which minimizes data redundancy, PCA involves finding and extracting the eigenvectors of a variance-covariance matrix.

RADARSAT: Canadian satellite using Synthetic Aperture Radar (SAR)

radiation balance: The net effect of the difference between incoming and outgoing radiation at a given point on the surface of the earth.

radiometer: An instrument which measures visible, infrared or microwave radiation at one or more frequencies.

Rayleigh scattering: Atmospheric scattering of electromagnetic radiation by molecules (primarily oxygen and nitrogen) whose effective diameters are at least 0.1 times smaller than the affected wavelength.

RCM: Regional Climate Model

remote sensing: The scientific acquisition of mass data relating to objects or phenomena by a recording device which is not in physical or intimate contact with the objects or phenomena under study.

RESORS: An on line bibliographic search system for remote sensing literature maintained at the Canadian Centre for Remote Sensing (CCRS).

SAGE: The Stratospheric Aeorosol and Gas Experiment used a series of limb-viewing instruments to continuously monitor the Earth's stratosphere. Current measurements of aerosols, O3, NO2 and H2O are provided by SAGE II, launched in October 1984.

Scanning Multichannel Microwave Radiometer (SMMR): Carried aboard the Nimbus-7 satellite, launched in 1978, the SMMR provided all-weather data related to precipitation, water vapour, soil moisture, ocean wind speed, ocean temperature and sea ice morphology. Observations for the SMMR were terminated in August, 1987.

scatterometer: An instrument that measures radar backscattering coefficient as a function of angle.

SEASAT: A short-lived SAR system placed in orbit on June, 1978, SEASAT provided L-band, HH polarized data for oceanographic studies before a massive failure on October 9, 1978.

SeaWIFS: Sea Wide-Field Sensor. Ocean color scanner planned for launch in the mid-1990s. SeaWIFS is anticipated to provide real-time monitoring of sediment and river-water dispersal.

SIR: Shuttle Imaging Radar consisting of two instruments which have recently been flown on space shuttles: SIR-C, a multi-polarized SAR operating in the L- and C-bands, and X-SAR, a VV-polarized X-band instrument. These two radiometers form the core of NASA's radar preparation for EOS, capable of yielding pointable, multifrequency data for a variety of terrestrial and oceanographic applications.

SLAR: Side Looking Airborne Radar, a viewing geometry used in synthetic and real aperture radar systems where the radar looks out the side of the viewing platform.

spectrometer: An optical instrument which measures the intensity of light at various wavelengths, by dispersing the radiation incident on the instrument into it's spectral components.

SPOT: France's Système Pour l'Observation de la Terre program; responsible for the launch of the SPOT series of satellites carrying the Hugh Resolution Visible (HRV) imaging spectrometer.

SSM/I: The Special Sensor Microwave/Imager offers multichannel, dual-polarized microwave data useful for precipitation, water vapour, soil moisture, ocean wind speed and sea ice morphology. Two SSM/I instruments have been launched in 1987 and 1989.

STAR/IRIS: A commercial airborne SAR system owned and operated by Intera Technologies of Calgary, Alberta.

stratosphere: The atmospheric layer above the troposphere, extending from an altitude of 12 km to approximately 50 km.

SURSAT: Canada's Surveillance Satellite program; a precursor to RADARSAT.

Synthetic Aperture Radar (SAR): A radar system for which the antenna length is artificially increased with the forward motion of the platform.

TDRSS: Tracking and Data Relay Satellite System.

TE: Terrestrial Ecology; the scientific discipline concerned with the study of

teleconnections: The linkage of weather phenomena in one part of the globe to those in another part.

Thematic Mapper (TM): Carried by the last three satellites in the LANDSAT series, the TM has six channels in the visible and near-infrared with 30 metre resolution and a seventh in the thermal infrared with 120 metre spatial resolution. Landsat 6, carrying the Enhanced Thematic Mapper with a new, 15 metre resolution panchromatic channel, was lost soon after launch in 1994.

thermohaline: Arising from changes in the density of sea water caused by a combination of temperature (thermo) and salinity (haline) differences.

TIROS: Television and Infrared Observation Satellite, an early series of US weather satellites launched in the 1960s.

TOGA: Tropical Ocean Global Atmosphere study: a ten year study led by the Joint Scientific Community of the WMO/ICSU. The objective is to achieve a description of the large-scale transient variations of tropical ocean basins and the global atmosphere, in order to determine the extent to which this system is predictable, to understand the mechanisms underlying this predictability, and to develop the means to achieve effective predictions.

TOPEX/Poseidon: Ocean Topography Experiment, a joint US and French satellite launched in 1992 with instruments designed to study ocean topography and ocean-current signatures.

Total Ozone Mapping Spectrometer (TOMS): A six-band ultraviolet spectrometer used to produce daily global maps of the total ozone column. Originally carried on board the Nimbus-7 satellite, plans are now being made to deploy additional TOMS on future American, Russian and Japanese satellites.

tropopause: The upper boundary of the troposphere, separating it from the stratosphere.

troposphere: The atmospheric layer extending from the earth's surface to the stratosphere, an altitude of approximately 8 to 10 km in polar regions and 16 to 17 km in lower latitudes. Temperature in the troposphere normally decreases with height.

UARS: Upper Atmosphere Research Satellite; a US research satellite launched in September 1991 to perform coordinated measurements of major upper-atmospheric parameters.

UNEP: The United Nations Environment Programme, concerned with the coordination of intergovernmental measures for environmental monitoring and protection.

UNESCO: United Nations Educational, Scientific and Cultural Organization. Founded in 1945 to support and complement efforts of United Nations (UN) members to promote scientific research, education, the arts, and to develop the cultural aspects of world relations.

USGS: United States Geological Survey (part of the Department of Interior).

VIR: Visible and near infrared.

WCRP: The World Climate Research Program, a component of the World Climate Program, is jointly sponsored by the International Council of Scientific Unions (ICSU) and the World Meteorological Organization (WMO) to determine to what extent climate can be predicted, and the extent of man's influence on climate.

WHO: World Health Organization. Founded in 1946 to raise the health standards of all peoples to as high a level as possible.

WINDII: Wind Imaging Interferometer, carried aboard the Upper Atmosphere Research Satellite (UARS) for measuring wind velocities above 80 km.

WMO: The World Meteorological Organization is a specialized agency of the United Nations dedicated to establishing a worldwide network of meteorological stations, facilitating the rapid exchange of standardized meteorological observations, and promoting research and training in the field of meteorology.

WOCE: World Ocean Circulation Experiment. A worldwide oceanographic program designed to clarify the global oceanographic circulation at all depths. Organized as a component of the World Climate Research Program (WCRP), the WOCE is planned to run from 1990-1997.

INDEX